THE PROFESSION OF A CIVIL ENGINEER

A Society for the general advancement of Mechanical Science and more particularly for promoting the acquisition of that species of knowledge which constitutes *the profession of a Civil Engineer*, being the art of directing the great sources of power in Nature for the use and convenience of Man.

From the ROYAL CHARTER OF THE INSTITUTION OF CIVIL ENGINEERS, 1828

JACK WILLIAM RODERICK

MA, PhD, HonDEng,

FIStructE, FICE, FASCE, FIEAust, FAA

CHALLIS PROFESSOR OF CIVIL ENGINEERING

THE UNIVERSITY OF SYDNEY

1951–78

The Profession of a Civil Engineer

Papers written for

JACK WILLIAM RODERICK

by former students

Edited by

D. CAMPBELL-ALLEN and E. H. DAVIS

SYDNEY UNIVERSITY PRESS

SYDNEY UNIVERSITY PRESS
Press Building, University of Sydney

UNITED KINGDOM, EUROPE, MIDDLE EAST, AFRICA
International Scholarly Book Services (Europe)
Letchworth, England

NORTH AND SOUTH AMERICA
International Scholarly Book Services, Inc.
Forest Grove, Oregon

National Library of Australia Cataloguing-in-Publication data

The profession of a civil engineer.

ISBN 0 424 00064 4

1. Civil engineering – Addresses, essays, lectures.
I. Campbell-Allen, D. ed. II. Davis, E. H., joint
author.

624

First published 1979
© Department of Civil Engineering, University of Sydney 1979

Photosetting by Thomson Press (India) Limited, New Delhi
Printed in Australia by Macarthur Press (Books) Pty Limited, Parramatta

CONTENTS

Contents

EDITORS' PREFACE

This volume is a tribute to the work of Jack William Roderick, who from 1951 to 1978 was Challis Professor and Head of the Department of Civil Engineering at the University of Sydney. We have invited from those who have graduated in the School of Civil Engineering during the long period of Professor Roderick's headship, a selection of authors who hold positions of distinction in the engineering profession. We have asked each one to write on what he regards as a subject of major interest to himself. The result is a varied collection of papers which demonstrates the breadth of activity of civil engineers and the skill and versatility of those who obtained their first engineering qualification under Roderick's guidance. As the two of his colleagues who are now most closely associated with him we have added a paper which outlines some of the significant developments in the School during this period.

The central figure in this development, Jack William Roderick, was born in Edmonton, Canada in 1913 and was educated at Newport High School in Wales where he was a Scholar and at Bristol University as a Kitchener Memorial Scholar. At Bristol he was awarded the degrees of BSc (1935), MSc(1937) and PhD(1941). He was awarded the degree of MA at the University of Cambridge in 1945 and the honorary degree of Doctor of Engineering by the University of Newcastle in 1969. He was Miller Prizeman, James Forrest Medallist and recipient of a Telford Premium of the Institution of Civil Engineers and was subsequently elected a Fellow and was a Member of Council in 1969–70. In the Institution of Engineers, Australia, of which he is a Fellow, he was Chairman of Sydney Division in 1962, a Member of Council from 1959 to 1977 and in 1969 was President. In 1976 he was awarded the Peter Nicol Russell Memorial Medal. He is a Fellow of the Institution of Structural Engineers and a Fellow of the American Society of Civil Engineers. He has been a member of the Council of the Standards Association of Australia since 1957 and was Chairman of the Provisional Council and is currently a member of the Council of the Australian Welding Research Association.

Within the University he was a Fellow of the Senate in 1966 and 1967 and was Dean of the Faculty of Engineering from 1959 to 1961 and from 1966 to 1974. At various times he held positions on the Buildings and Grounds Committee, the Research Committee, the Advisory Committee on

Establishment, the Proctorial Board, the Library Committee, the Patents Committee and was Chairman of the Appointments Board. As Challis Professor he was Director of the Postgraduate Civil Engineering Foundation.

He was one of the first engineers elected to the Australian Academy of Science where he was a Member of Council for two terms and from 1962 to 1964 was Secretary. He served on the Advisory Council for CSIRO (1957–63), on the Martin Committee on the Future of Tertiary Education in Australia, on the Defence Research and Development Policy Committee (1964–70) and on the Australian Research Grants Committee (1965–7). From 1970 to 1976 he was a member of the National Capital Planning Committee. In 1973 he was appointed a Commissioner of the Electricity Commission of N.S.W. and in 1976 he became a member of the National Energy Advisory Committee. He was a member of the N.S.W. Rhodes Scholarship Selection Committee (1967–9) and has long been a member of the Sydney Rotary Club.

We have been delighted by the enthusiastic response of all those we have asked to help in this venture and acknowledge gratefully the assistance provided by staff of the University and of the Sydney University Press.

D. C. A.
E. H. D.

THE FIRST COUNCIL OF THE POST-GRADUATE CIVIL ENGINEER-ING FOUNDATION, 1968

Left to right: Mr W. G. J. Ryan, Mr R. M. Little, Mr A. F. Schmidt, Mr L. S. Hudson, Mr A. Dance, Mr K. C. Fraser, Prof. D. Campbell-Allen, Mr O. S. Potter (Tech. Secretary), Mr P. R. Pettit, Mr R. H. Whitecross (Assist. Registrar), Mr B. N. Kelman (Chairman), Prof. J. W. Roderick (Director), Mr C. A. Hawkins (Hon. Consultant), Mr V. J. Sheary

OPENING OF THE C. A. HAWKINS COMPUTING LABORATORY BY
THE CHANCELLOR, SIR HERMANN BLACK, 3 DECEMBER 1975

On left: Mr C. A. Hawkins

D. CAMPBELL-ALLEN and E. H. DAVIS

Jack Roderick, Challis Professor of Civil Engineering, 1951–78

A Man for the Time

What sort of department did Dr Jack William Roderick find when he took up his appointment as Challis Professor of Civil Engineering at the end of 1951? The man whom the Senate appointed to this position on 24 September 1951 was a graduate of the University of Bristol with the degrees of MSc and PhD and a Master of Arts of Cambridge University. After obtaining his first degree from Bristol he worked as a structural engineer, on constructional steel work and then on aircraft design. He returned to Bristol University to engage in research under Professor J. F. Baker (now Lord Baker of Windrush) on the plastic behaviour of steel structures, a field which was to continue to be one of his major interests throughout his career. In 1939 he was appointed Lecturer in Civil and Mechanical Engineering in Leeds University. In 1943 he rejoined Baker, who moved to Cambridge in that year, to continue his work on the plastic behaviour of metal structures with an appointment as Assistant Director of Research in the University Engineering School.

Civil engineering had been taught in Sydney since 1883 when W. H. Warren gave his first lecture as Lecturer in Engineering to three undergraduates and seven unmatriculated students. Yet in that long period from 1883 to 1951 only Warren, who held the position of Professor of Engineering from 1884 to 1925, and W. A. Miller who was Professor of Civil Engineering from 1926 until his retirement in 1951, had occupied chairs as civil engineers. Warren had played a leading part in the development of engineering in Australia and his achievements were recognized by his election to be the first President of the Institution of Engineers, Australia in 1919. Miller, who before his appointment to the Chair had been a colleague and admirer of Warren, continued to develop and improve the department and the courses that it taught. These two men had established over the many years of their stewardships a remarkable admiration and devotion among their staff and their many students. These bonds, which were particularly strong in the two post-war graduating groups of 1924 and 1950, enabled Roderick, in his turn, to harness with great effect the support of the graduates as his plans developed.

In 1951 there were only four full-time members of staff, of whom in 1978 three were still living. Miller and these four (R. L. Aston, C. A. M. Gray, O. S.

1

Potter and H. J. Vogan) between them accomplished the almost impossible task of training the eighty graduates of 1950 (a number which was not reached again until 1976 when the full-time staff numbered twenty-four). The Department had very limited teaching space, only a small (but nonetheless devoted) amount of technical help and hardly any funds. Both Warren and Miller had always recognized the need for laboratory work in an engineering course and the Warren Testing Laboratory, at this time under the loving care of Vogan, had an established reputation for materials testing. Miller's particular interest in mechanical stress analysis as an aid to design continued to be nurtured by Potter. Experimental hydraulics had been the love of T. D. J. Leech before he went to the Chair at Auckland in 1940 and Gray continued this responsibility. Aston had a reputation in the field of surveying and geodesy which he had established on the continental European pattern as a significant intellectual study for civil engineers.

In selecting Roderick to lead this team, the Senate was proved to have made an excellent choice. To a department with an established reputation for sound engineering teaching he brought his own teaching experience from three of the leading university engineering schools of England. Beside these three, only London could have been said at the time to have been of equal standing. He brought an established reputation for sound theoretical study allied to a skill and enthusiasm for experimental work. The standards that he set himself and his colleagues for meticulous attention to precision were found to match even the remarkably high standards of Potter and Vogan. In a department of astonishingly hard working staff he was certainly going to prove as hard working as any. Above all he brought to a department and a university, in which research had been very much a minor activity, a determination that effective university teaching would in the future have to be accompanied by effective research and he set about at once, in spite of the many difficulties, to accomplish this aim. This volume is a measure of the extent to which all these things have been achieved.

Setting the Course

Comparatively low numbers in the final year from 1952 onwards provided the opportunity to make some rearrangement to the undergraduate course. Important features already existing were the thesis in final year, the survey camp (which had had to be deferred in the post-war boom years) and the six-months practical experience. Roderick introduced a pattern of work for honours students in which they were able to choose to carry out more extensive study in some subjects (at that time structural subjects), a pattern which has been essentially maintained up to now. The substantial thesis project required of honours students, involving in all cases a considerable amount of experimental work, became possible with the development of new laboratories and with the increase in the provision for technical staff. The department acquired small amounts of additional floor area and modified parts of the basement of the PNR building to provide for new laboratories for work on concrete, soil mechanics, surveying and structures. The centrepiece of the small structures laboratory was an exact copy of the ingenious dead-weight testing frame in which Roderick had done so much of his experimental work at Cambridge.

University funds were flowing a little more freely than they had and a modest addition to the academic staff became possible. Roderick went out hunting for his staff and most of those whom he got to join are still with the department. He looked not only for people with experience in the field of civil engineering but aimed especially for people with some background in research so as to build up this very important aspect of the department's work. The introduction by the faculty of higher degrees for research provided the opportunity for post-graduate students in the department. The first PhD in the University was awarded to W. H. Wittrick in 1951 but he was at the time a member of the academic staff (in aeronautical engineering). It was not until the degree of Master of Engineering Science was introduced, and at the same time the Commonwealth government made some provision for research studentships, that the full-time post-graduate students could start to make their contribution to the research output of the department. In 1957 H. B. Harrison and B. Rawlings both were awarded degrees of MEngSc for work done in the previous years on the plastic behaviour of steel structures. Both were members of the academic staff at the time, but research students were active as well and a steady stream of research work had begun. The first PhD in civil engineering was awarded to C. J. Bellamy (an Auckland BE) in 1961. He had been supported by a scholarship from the Australian Atomic Energy Commission. The pattern of support for students and for research from outside the university had been launched. Bellamy and P. G. Lowe, who gained his MEngSc in 1959, were the first two of many post-graduate students who have been attracted to the department from other universities, an achievement which the provision of funding and the level of research activity has made possible.

Roderick's own research interests and the success of his staffing policy in widening the research activity are shown in the subjects studied for higher degrees awarded up to 1961. Six worked in topics related to steel structures, one worked in soil mechanics and two in concrete technology. At this stage he put his print on the work of the department by demanding at all times a very high standard of presentation both in the quality of the writing and in the final form of production. Many research students at that time (and since) writhed under his determined requirements but have later blessed the opportunity they were given to acquire the habit of writing with clarity, precision and even in some cases elegance.

The department had throughout its long history worked very closely with industry. The lion's share of materials testing for the State was done in the

Warren Laboratories and all the testing machine calibrations were in the hands of staff of the department. Roderick recognized the importance both to the department and to the country of maintaining such links and early in the 1950s had engineers from the Sydney Water Board conducting tests on a strain-gauged slice model of the proposed Warragamba Dam to examine the influence of the low elastic modulus of the foundation material. By the end of 1977 over 200 investigation reports had been prepared and issued on subjects covering the whole range of civil engineering activity in Australia and elsewhere.

A Chance Seized

The expansions and changes which provided additional laboratory space, some modest provision for research students and offices for the newly recruited staff could only be regarded as a temporary alleviation of a serious problem of space. It was becoming apparent that student numbers must rise substantially and makeshift teaching and research facilities could not be used for ever. The library was still only a small collection of textbooks, officially recorded as on long-term loan from the Fisher Library to a member of staff. The computing facilities had recently been increased one hundred per cent by the purchase of an electric desk calculator. Of greatest significance was the complete absence of space with either head-room or floor area where anything approaching a full-scale engineering structure could be tested.

By pressure and argument, Roderick managed to get the university to agree that the most satisfactory way to relieve the pressure on the engineering facilities as a whole was to provide a new building for civil engineering, based especially around the need for readily accessible testing laboratories. It was envisaged that a multi-storey building providing accommodation for both civil engineering and architecture, who were also severely pressed for space, should be erected on a site which could be cleared alongside the Peter Nicol Russell Building. All the staff of the department took an active part in the planning exercise and appropriate floor space arrangements were agreed for about fifty final year students and an expanding research activity. The production of sketch plans was given as a design task to Professor Ashworth's final-year architectural class and an exhibition of the resulting sketches was opened by the Deputy Vice-Chancellor, Professor C. R. McRae.

While all this was going on there occurred in 1957 what was probably the most important event in the history of Australian universities since the foundation of the first university in the very early days of the colony of New South Wales. The Commonwealth government, following the firm lead of Prime Minister R. G. Menzies, established the Murray Committee to report on the future of the universities. That committee made recommendations for much increased funding to raise universities to a recognized world standard, and further proposed the establishment of a permanent Australian Universities

Commission. At about the same time, the University Senate prepared a comprehensive plan for the future expansion of the whole university and decided in particular that the engineering departments should be relocated in an entirely new precinct in Darlington on land which had been scheduled for some years under the County of Cumberland Plan for university development.

The good work that had already been done by the department and the university did not pass unnoticed by the Murray Committee, who made a specific recommendation that funds should be provided immediately for a start on new buildings for civil engineering. The government eventually approved and, with the appointment of Messrs Ancher Mortlock and Murray as architects, serious planning work started. At first, funds were only available for part of the needs but sketch plans were to be prepared for the whole of civil engineering with provision for stage construction. It became apparent very early that the proper first stage of this great new venture should be the provision of a laboratory for the testing of structures and materials on a scale appropriate to modern engineering activity.

The buildings were planned on the basis of large laboratory areas with ground floor access. An area of about 6,000 square feet was chosen as being appropriate for each of the major activities envisaged with two such units combined for structures and materials. The open plan for each laboratory adopted at this stage has proved to be able to be adapted to changing needs, and the department is still, nearly twenty years after the initial plans were drawn up, able to accommodate just about all its laboratory needs. In that time only one major change of use has occurred. The area that was planned to be associated with the drawing offices as a structural models laboratory, under the guidance of Potter with the strongest support from Roderick, has now been converted into the C. A. Hawkins computing laboratory. The analogue aids to design have been replaced by the far more generally powerful digital aids that the modern computer can provide.

While the plans and the construction went ahead with the active participation of all the staff, the staff itself, both academic and support, was changing and expanding. New positions were added to the establishment, enabling active groups to be formed in the major areas of teaching and research activity and a much larger technical and supporting staff began to be built up. In a department of increasing size, the need for more senior positions was becoming apparent. Vogan continued as Reader until his retirement in 1959, and a new position of Associate Professor of Geodesy and Surveying was filled by Aston. There were promises of more Associate Professorships to come. One in Concrete Technology was created in 1962 and one in Soil Mechanics in 1963.

Roderick recognized fully the pool of goodwill that existed among the graduates, and took an active part in encouraging the formation of a Civil Engineering Graduates Association. Appropriately enough the President, C. A. Hawkins, was drawn from the '24 graduates and the Secretary was P. R.

Pettit from the '50 graduates. Pettit's early death in 1977 was a blow to the profession and to the department as he was by that time himself President of the Graduates Association and Chairman of the Civil Engineering Post Graduate Foundation.

In 1957, when research activity was beginning to germinate in the department, the first of many subsequent Open Days was held and graduates turned up in large numbers to be taken in conducted tours round the old laboratories, and to be given brief talks on the surprisingly large number of research and investigation projects then in progress.

In 1960 the Graduates Association undertook to raise funds from among its own members to provide equipment for the new buildings, realizing that this would provide an opportunity to ensure that not only was the department housed with adequate space but that modern methods and techniques and recent advances could be incorporated in the laboratory teaching programme. The Association Committee, with Roderick working closely with them, undertook the seemingly impossible task of raising £25,000 ($50,000) from among some nine hundred graduates. A five year plan for contributions was developed and in a concentrated one month's campaign promises of $68,000 were received. G. I. Davey was General Chairman, and F. W. Laws the Campaign Chairman of the Appeal. Many other graduates joined with enthusiasm in the task to ensure, as Laws put it, that the Department of Civil Engineering would be at the centre of the profession. 'We want it to be a better place so that your son and your grandson will be a better engineer than you are', was his comment to the 150 graduates who attended the dinner to launch the appeal. The appeal set the graduates a most challenging task and by its great success forged even stronger links between the department and its graduates, links which were to form the basis of two further great developments. Roderick, who had himself worked very hard in the background to help the appeal towards its success, recognized this future significance when he wrote to the Graduates in 1961:

> I know I speak for every one of my colleagues in the Department when I say how sincerely grateful we are, not only for your generosity to the school, but also for the manner and spirit in which you so readily responded to this opportunity to play a leading part in creating the much needed facilities required in the future for teaching and research.
> As I think you will all agree the future for the Department of Civil Engineering is indeed set fair. The enthusiasm and financial support of our graduates has certainly not gone unnoticed by those who have the responsibility of making the decisions. This example of graduate support has been remarked upon throughout the University and will undoubtedly have its effect when we come to seek additional funds from other sources.

Regular open days and the distribution of the news sheet 'Acta Structorum' continued to be ways in which graduate interest and enthusiasm was maintained, and each annual open day included a brief and informal comment on the state of play from the head of the department.

Construction of the materials and structures laboratory was completed in 1961 and equipment was transferred and new plant installed in the following months. Fortunately there was no major delay in the second stage construction and the whole department was moved and ready for business in 1963. The chance offered by the Murray Committee had in a short few years been seized and complete new facilities developed.

The Flowering of the Plan

Never one to stay still, Roderick was not content to have established a viable and increasingly recognized department, well housed and equipped and with an expanding staff. With a keen sense of political reality, helped by the many extramural contacts described later, he appreciated that the great expansion of government support for universities, in the Murray honeymoon period, could not go on. The only way to maintain the pace of development was to tap resources separate from the government grants to the university.

On 7 February 1968, after many years of painstaking work by the Civil Engineering Graduates Association, a public meeting was called by Mr Vernon H. Treat, the Chief Commissioner of the City of Sydney, to inaugurate the Post-Graduate Civil Engineering Foundation in the University of Sydney. In the university there already existed some such foundations, of which the best known was the Nuclear Science Foundation (later to become the Science Foundation for Physics), which channelled money to support research and teaching activity in various quarters. But this Foundation in Civil Engineering was to be different because the Council and members were joining not just as a public spirited gesture of support to the university but because they were all vitally interested in the work being done in the Civil Engineering Department and knew and respected the professional standing of the director and his staff. C. A. Hawkins, still president of the Graduates Association, and Roderick were largely instrumental in persuading firms and instrumentalities to take up governorships in the Foundation and once again the sound preparatory groundwork, which Roderick always insisted upon before launching any project, paid off. One of the features of all his ventures, which his colleagues have cause to remember with gratitude, was this insistence on necessary preparation and the choice of the right time. As a result almost all of his proposals, particularly in such matters as staff appointments and promotions, met with success, even though at the time others less realistic and patient complained of unnecessary delays.

The Foundation became an integral part of the work of the School and provided some welcome additional opportunities to expand and manoeuvre in what would otherwise have been straitened times. Support staff could be hired. It became possible to make appointments to lectureships and research fellowships when young qualified people were available, rather than having to wait for the chance of a vacancy on establishment. Funds were provided to

7

enable an appointment in structural dynamics to be made at Associate Professor level. Visitors were brought to the School so that they could contribute their own special expertise to the teaching and research in progress. The research work of the School, already known in international publications, could now more easily be presented personally by staff on overseas visits. It became possible to expand the already established programme of post-graduate short courses and to produce lecture notes for these courses more rapidly and with a higher quality of presentation. Above all, additional valuable links had been formed between the department and the civil engineering industry by the establishment of this first line of contact through the Foundation Council and members.

Research activity, already firmly established and supported by grants from the University Research Grant, the Australian Research Grants Committee and many other public and private sources, was able to advance further as a result of the back-up staff provided by the Foundation. The Director deftly steered the Council to agreeing that the most valuable backing they could provide was in the nature of general support for departmental activities, rather than by embarking on special research projects. When such projects were proposed, additional funds were always sought from the organizations especially interested. The steady expansion of research output was recorded in a series of Research Reports which by the end of 1978 had reached Number 338. The great majority of these research papers were subsequently published in the technical literature both in Australia and overseas. The figures for published papers appear in the table. The steady expansion after a slow beginning has since 1968 reached a remarkably high level of output, at a time when undergraduate class sizes have also been high.

In all this activity and amidst the many other demands on his time, both inside and outside the university, Roderick was himself active in structural research and guided a group of co-workers. His major interest, which was the natural consequence of his earlier work in steel framed structures, was in composite steel and concrete structures and in this field his group have made significant contributions. He himself was invited to present reports on the work of his group in Amsterdam and Lehigh.

Publications by members of staff of the
SCHOOL OF CIVIL ENGINEERING

	Total	Average number per year
1952–9	18	2.2
1960–8	110	12.2
1969–76	242	30.2

As already mentioned the department had a firmly established reputation of help to industry and government and in the period after the formation of the Foundation this activity continued to expand, partly because Foundation members naturally thought of the department when they needed help. There was less routine testing, as many newly-established commercial laboratories entered this field, but more often the members of the department were asked to advise in areas where they possessed special expertise. Roderick himself was engaged as a consultant on a number of important tasks and it was not unnatural that when the Westgate collapse occurred in 1970, the Chairman of the Lower Yarra Crossing Authority was on the phone the next day.

Roderick was insistent, and in this he had the full support of the staff, that all these activities should be undertaken on behalf of the department and should result in the issue of Departmental Investigation Reports. A fair distribution of work and reward and equally importantly the collection of some readily available funds in departmental accounts resulted. The procedures had early been established with the blessing of the Vice-Chancellor and were recognized by him as activities which not only contributed to material needs but at the same time improved the quality of teaching in civil engineering.

Roderick's aim at this time, and throughout his career in the School, was to make it the outstanding institution for advanced study in civil engineering. Though he built on traditional foundations, his view was always that of the full breadth of civil engineering activity and he has always maintained a major capacity to see the broad vision but to appreciate the practical and political restrictions within which it must be realized. A further major step in the development of the School was the appointment of two additional professors at the end of 1968. Roderick remained firmly in control as Head of the Department but he readily adapted his methods to accommodate the new expanded situation which he had himself largely created.

The graduates continued their positive and enthusiastic support, not content to rest on the success of the equipment appeal and the launching of the Foundation. In 1971, Pettit, by then President of the Graduates Association, suggested that they should be again assisting the School in a major way. By this time, computing had come to play a very major part in the research work of the department, but facilities for providing extensive teaching opportunities to undergraduates were limited. Roderick put to the graduates the challenging possibility of providing perhaps $100,000 for an in-house computer for teaching in civil engineering. The graduates agreed but the general financial climate deteriorated and it was agreed that it would not be a good time to launch the second appeal. There were doubts too among the staff (many of whom were of course graduates themselves) about the wisdom of again approaching graduates for a school already well equipped and some had reservations about the need for the computer itself. By 1973 quiet work by Roderick had silenced most of the doubts and with the situation judged to be

9

more auspicious a concentrated campaign was launched in mid-1973 with W. M. Leavey, Managing Director of Lend Lease Pty Ltd and a 1948 graduate, as Campaign Chairman. Leavey's early death in 1977 was a further reminder of the great pressures under which senior civil engineers are now operating. Many of the leaders in the campaign had been active in the earlier appeal and now again their efforts were crowned with success. At the end of 1975 the chosen computer was already installed and contributing to the work of the School. This rapid consummation was made possible by the enormous effort of the appeal committee with Leavey and Pettit in the lead, by the fortunate state of the computer market in which much more powerful computers became available for less money and by the persuasiveness of Roderick in convincing the university to advance funds against the promised contributions from the five-year appeal which still had three years to run. Once again sound advance planning and the selection of the right time to do things had paid off.

Outside the Ivory Tower

When seeking the definition of the complete engineer, it is inevitable that service to the community and to the profession be included. It is tempting to state that there has been particular emphasis in recent years on the responsibilities of the professional engineer towards society, but a longer, historical view of the work of prominent engineers reveals that this broader outlook has been rather more common than the recent phenomenon it is assumed to be.

In the training of engineers, it is often not an easy task to encourage wider horizons than soil cohesion or moment-distribution in which there is a tendency to take refuge. Fortunately the University of Sydney has provided excellent examples of engineers who have achieved eminence not only for their technical skills in the narrower sense but also for their contribution to the world outside the campus railing which so often tends to be the demarcation of a separate community. The name of Professor Warren must inevitably come to mind in this context and indeed it appears in many public documents and reports throughout the duration of his tenure of the Chair of Engineering. Ultimately Professor Warren was one of the activists in the establishment of the Institution of Engineers, Australia, and became its first president.

It was therefore fitting that Professor Roderick should be the President of the Institution during its golden jubilee year, 1969–70, the least reason being that he was in line of succession to Professor Warren at the University. This election to office was the culmination — though by no means the end — of diligent service to the professional body virtually since Roderick's arrival in Sydney. He was a member of the Council of the Institution from 1959 to 1976 and Chairman of Sydney Division in 1962 in addition to serving on numerous branch and other committees.

Two other bodies, closely related to the engineering profession in which Roderick has served as a member of Council are the Australian Welding Research Association and the Standards Association of Australia — in the latter since 1957. As a Fellow of the Australian Academy of Science, he was a member of its Council on two occasions: from 1957 to 1959 and as a Secretary from 1962 to 1964. It was also over this span of time that he was a member of the Advisory Council of the Commonwealth Scientific and Industrial Research Organization.

As already noted, in the latter years of the Menzies era, there was an increasing public awareness of the problems of the Australian tertiary education system, including specifically the large disparity between the financial resources and the task demanded of the universities by the community. More important, the concept of greater government involvement permeated more widely at the political level and few people were not convinced, at that time, of the excellence of the cause.

The work of the Murray Committee, reporting to the Commonwealth government, has been referred to earlier in relation to the advantage taken by the School of Civil Engineering of the resulting benefits to the universities. A great deal had been achieved as far as increasing government interest in the existing university system. The next task logically was to attempt to plan for the future on a national basis.

It was therefore in 1962 that a committee was formed, under the chairmanship of Emeritus Professor L. H. Martin, to advise the government on the future of tertiary education in Australia and this was its formal title. For such a momentous task, it was to be expected that the membership of this committee would, of necessity, include the highest level of academic staff experienced and capable of working in the environment of a constructive committee of this type. There were no surprises when the membership of the committee was announced. On the list was the name of Professor J. W. Roderick of the University of Sydney.

The nation's system of universities, institutes of technology and colleges of advanced education has perhaps evolved a little differently from the vision of the Martin Committee but, at the end of its main work in 1965, its recommendations were indisputably an excellent blueprint for future development.

One result was the establishment of the Australian Research Grants Committee in 1968 by which direct funding by the national government was made to specified research projects. Whilst the total funds allocated were generous in relation to the times, applications for assistance were equivalent to many times the availability. The committee, on which Roderick served for the first two years, was therefore another one of which the decisions were of considerable importance. The ARGC grants system has become an unqualified success, not only from the point of view of the research encouraged but also, incidentally, with regard to public relations in that since the earliest

11

days a full list of recipients has been published in major newspapers each year. This is one of the rarer occasions when the public has a direct and easily accessible account in detail of how its money is being used.

Since the time of Warren, there have been many instances of co-operation between the School of Civil Engineering and the government of the State of New South Wales. Roderick served on the Technical Advisory Committee of the Sydney Opera House Executive Committee and, in 1973, he was appointed Commissioner on the Electricity Commission of New South Wales. This appointment must be particularly gratifying to civil engineers because the amount and range of civil engineering work in the large-scale production of electricity is regrettably not fully appreciated outside the profession.

The onset of the so-called energy crisis — though the noun seems inappropriate for a developing predicament — caused considerable concern in government circles, both states and federal. In 1976, the Minister of National Resources established the National Energy Advisory Committee to advise 'on matters relating to national energy policy'. Although it is not easy to make comparisons between the merits of the various committees on which Roderick has served, it requires little imagination to appreciate that the advice of the NEAC and its degree of acceptance by governments will be of very great and direct consequence to the lives of all Australians. We are indeed fortunate that, towards the end of a distinguished career, Professor Roderick is able to serve on this committee.

Strength for the Future

The last twenty-seven years have seen great changes. The Department of Civil Engineering has participated in these changes but has at the same time retained its essential purpose. When Miller had been some time in the Chair he travelled to Britain to obtain a measure of his stewardship by making a comparison with standards overseas. He came back reassured that the course here was probably above the average standard and in many fields well ahead of the best he had seen overseas. The graduates from the Miller era hold senior positions in many New South Wales and Australian organizations and their background training has stood them in good stead.

The maintenance and improvement of teaching standards has remained as the foremost objective of the department. The course has changed slowly with changing needs and changing facilities but it has remained as an essentially broad-based civil engineering training appropriate to the broad scope of civil engineering work to be done in Australia. Emphasis has been placed on the need for sound scientific background to enable analytical skill to be developed. Temptations to reduce experimental work have been avoided and the new computational facility has added a further dimension to practical teaching aids. A well-rounded and challenging design course has been made an integral part of every student's education. The thesis still remains a valued component of the final year course. Above all the emphasis by Roderick on the need to acquire the essential 'feel' of structure and structural behaviour has spread to all other branches of a very widely-ranging course.

The graduates of this era also have established themselves firmly in Australian engineering but they have also spread themselves into many other parts of the world. The authors of three of the papers in this volume hold chairs in North America and a fourth has returned to Australia after being a professor in the United Kingdom. The quality of students and the standard of the course can still be described as 'well ahead' in a number of ways, not least in the strength of the research groups and their contribution to the teaching process. Research has never been treated as an activity to be done in a closed room away from the disconcerting eyes of students. Rather students by their thesis contributions and their laboratory work have been expected to be concerned and involved in the research and investigation work of the department.

The links between research groups in the School and corresponding groups overseas have been formed as a result not only of the quality of the work involved but from the early established policy of promoting the distribution of research material and of sponsoring visits to and from Australia. The work at Sydney is now on the world map. The position of the School in Australia is also strong. There is a steady demand for the post-graduate short courses which are regularly presented and this support comes from all over the country. Thirty-two of the eighty-six participants in such a course recently came from outside Sydney and included engineers from all states and the Northern Territory.

It is a common phenomenon in universities that departments that have been for a long time under the control of one strong head lose their way when that head finally retires. The very breadth and versatility of the group of staff that Roderick has brought together is sufficient to ensure that no such pheno-menon will occur in this School. He has built an organic structure which has a significant future ahead, a future based on sound principles of demanding always the highest standards of performance and of hard work and of careful and meticulous preparation of ground work. Most importantly he has continued the tradition in this university that only sound, well-conceived ideas come from the Department and that the proposals from the Department can be treated as reliable and responsible.

The story of civil engineering at Sydney is an astonishing one. William Henry Warren, William Aitken Miller and Jack William Roderick have between them developed that story for only five years short of a century from 1883 to 1978. The third chapter, which we have tried to outline in this paper, is in many ways the most spectacular. Its success is the result of the skill with which the third of these men, as a sound and imaginative engineer, used the foundations and materials so skilfully and well provided by his predecessors to build his own design.

B. G. HUTCHINSON

Advances in Urban
Transport Systems Analysis

THE URBAN TRANSPORT PLANNING PROCESS

Comprehensive transport planning studies have been conducted in hundreds of urban areas throughout the world during the past twenty years. Rapidly growing urban areas and sharp increases in private car ownership required that capital investment plans for primary road and public transport facilities be developed in a comprehensive and objective manner. The broad sequence of steps involved in a typical urban transport planning study is illustrated in Fig. 1, which process had its origins in the metropolitan transport studies conducted in Detroit, Chicago, Toronto and Pittsburgh during the late 1950s and 1960s. While there have been significant improvements in the analytical techniques imbedded in the process illustrated the broad sequence of planning activities remains much the same as that developed in the earlier studies.

Fig. 1 illustrates that data on existing land use and travel are used to construct and calibrate computer models of the transport system. These models are then used to estimate the transport demands created by future land development patterns and equilibrium flows in alternative transport networks. Major considerations in the formulation of alternative transport strategies are the objectives set for the transport system, the urban development goals of a community and the available transport technologies.

The final phase of the process illustrated in Fig. 1 is concerned with the probable impacts of alternative strategies on the community. The impacts of concern in the typical study include noise and air pollution effects, energy consumption, changes in the mobility of the various socio-economic groups in a community and the economic efficiency of the proposed investments. Fig. 1 suggests that the choice of a particular transport strategy is not part of the technical process of transport planning but is the prerogative of governments. Technical information on the probable impacts of alternative strategies allows informed debate and the necessary arbitration by politicians to take place.

The urban transport planning process that has emerged represents one of the first civilian applications of modern systems analysis techniques. An important principle of systems analysis is that the technical components of the process are directed towards explicitly defined objectives. Fig. 1 suggests that the objectives established for a system have an important influence on the alternative strategies proposed as well as on the way in which these

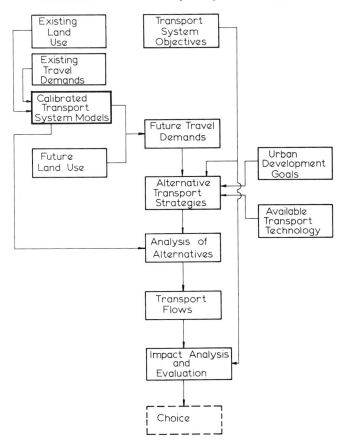

FIG. 1   The urban transport planning process

alternatives are analysed and evaluated. Changes in the objectives set for transport systems will stimulate changes in the technical process used to achieve the new objectives.

CHANGING OBJECTIVES OF URBAN TRANSPORT PLANNING

The changing character of urban transport system objectives over the past twenty years is best illustrated by quoting from representative transport planning studies. Martin [1] in commenting on the first London Transport Study observed:

> In the 1950s the problem was defined in the rather restricted terms of congestion on city streets. How can this congestion be removed and provision be made for future growth of traffic? This was certainly a major consideration in defining the initial objectives of the London studies in 1960. Car ownership was expected to increase rapidly, but there was no basis to estimate how large the increase in road traffic would be and how the nature and pattern of travel would be influenced.

Martin's observations apply to most of the studies conducted throughout the United Kingdom, North America and Australia during the 1960s. Urban transport planning was concerned primarily with the development of long-range capital investment programs for primary road and public transport facilities. The planning objective was one of reducing road congestion given the conditions of sustained urban growth and rapidly increasing car ownership.

The preoccupation of urban transport planning with the development of long-range capital investment programs began to change during the late 1960s. Many communities throughout the world abandoned plans for freeways and fixed route public transport systems that had been developed in studies performed in the late 1950s and early 1960s. The extent of this change in urban transport planning may be gauged from the following comments by Lockwood [2] about the Boston Transportation Plan Review conducted in 1973:

> Transportation planning is a technical/political process concerned with trade-offs among conflicting values of different groups in society. Transportation service decisions are a form of allocation of scarce resources to different groups in society and require political ratification aided by technical information. All decisions about the desirability of a particular public action must be understood as policy choices that involve the trading of increases in transportation service for community and environmental disruption as well as dollar costs. There is no single public interest or 'best' solution short of a planner imposing his own values. Objectives are multiple and conflicting and alternatives are infinite. There are as many best answers as there are personal value systems.

The transport systems analysis techniques used in the transport planning studies of the 1960s were rather cumbersome and time consuming. A period of about two years was required for data collection, model development and network analysis. While these techniques were found to be appropriate for estimating probable car traffic volumes on the primary road system, they were found to be unsatisfactory for testing the probable impacts of shorter run policy changes such as price changes, traffic restraint and levels of service changes.

The primary purpose of this paper is to examine the major advances in transport systems analysis techniques that have occurred during the past two decades and to examine these against the changing requirements of transport planning. It has been emphasized in Fig. 1 that transport systems models represent just one part of the planning process and because of this the techniques must change as other components of the process change.

URBAN SYSTEM BEHAVIOUR

The spatial patterns of human activities that exist and which are likely to emerge in urban areas must provide the backdrop against which urban transport policy must be formulated and evaluated. Fig. 2 provides a simple

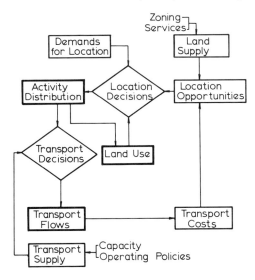

FIG. 2   A view of growth and change in the urban system

view of the urban system in terms of the spatial distributions of human activities, land use and the transport flows.

This diagram suggests that the basic driving force of growth and change in the urban system is the demand for new locations within an urban area. These location demands might consist of new locators or re-locators within the system. New households may be formed from within an urban area or by migrants to a community. Demands for new job locations may be created by the expansion or re-location of existing institutions or by the creation of completely new job opportunities.

Fig. 2 suggests that location decisions will be made in response to the existing distribution of human activities and to the supply of new location opportunities. The supply of opportunities and their desirabilities are a function of the land available for each of the major activity types (residential, industrial, commercial) and the accessibilities to these areas provided by the transport system. The supply of land for various purposes is influenced by planning constraints and servicing decisions.

The spatial distribution of human activities which result from these location decisions creates a spatial pattern of demand for transport services. Decisions regarding the choice of a transport mode and network path within a transport mode are made in response to the supply of transport services and the operating policies applied to these services. A pattern of transport flows will emerge which represents an equilibrium between the demand for and the supply of transport services. Associated with these transport flows is a set of transport costs where the term cost is used in a very general sense and reflects not only the monetary costs of travel but also travel time and the general convenience of travel.

The processes illustrated in Fig. 2 will clearly operate with respect to very different time scales. For example, changes in transport system operating policies, such as the creation of reserved bus lands or fare changes, may be implemented quickly and will have almost immediate impacts on traffic flow patterns and may have longer-run impacts on human activity patterns. The construction of a new transport facility may have immediate impacts on transport modal choice and location decisions. Finally, decisions affecting land use such as zoning and servicing may have little immediate impact on transport demands but may elicit profound changes in the patterns of transport demand over the long run.

CHANGING CHARACTER OF TRANSPORT PLANNING

The mechanisms of urban growth and change illustrated in Fig. 2 provide a useful framework for reviewing briefly the changing character of urban transport planning. It has been mentioned earlier that during the 1960s transport planning was concerned with estimating the probable traffic flows on alternative regional-scale transport networks with varying amounts of transport capacity. The optimum level of investment in transport capacity was normally determined from an evaluation of the travel benefits to users and the resource costs of constructing and maintaining the proposed systems. The planning studies of the 1960s were directed principally by members of the engineering profession and the outputs of these studies formed the basis of more detailed engineering design studies. This was a natural evolution of the traditional responsibilities of the civil engineering profession for road and bridge design.

During the past decade the perception of the range of potential public policy responses to urban transport problems has broadened. The emphasis in many recent urban transport planning studies has changed to shorter-run transport management type responses. Resource constraints, greater sensitivity to the mixed blessings of capital-intensive additions to the transport system and uncertainties about the future of current forms of urban transport technology have combined to re-orient the thinking of transport planners and policy makers. The transport systems analysis tools required to support this type of policy environment are quite different from those used in the earlier studies.

While much of the current transport planning emphasis is on the shorter-run tactical policies there is also an increasing recognition of the need for longer-run strategic studies which focus on the potential for manipulating travel demands through better land development planning. Studies of this type attempt to focus on the mechanisms of urban growth and change of the type illustrated in Fig. 2 where transport is simply one of the sectors of interest. Clearly studies of this type must be supported by analytical capabilities with a very different character from those used in the shorter-run management studies and the medium-run transport systems studies.

UNDERSTANDING TRANSPORT BEHAVIOUR

The fundamental requirement of transport systems modelling is to develop a modelling framework which captures the transport decision making behaviour of individuals within a community and the way in which this behaviour is influenced by changes in the transport policy environment. The transport decision making behaviour of urban residents has been represented traditionally by a sequence of sub-models of the following type:

1. trip generation which is concerned with the frequency with which individuals make trips;

2. trip distribution which is concerned with determining the joint locations of trip origins and destinations such as places of residence and places of employment;

3. modal split which is concerned with the choice of transport modes by urban residents;

4. route assignment which is concerned with the choice of a route within a mode between specific origins and destinations.

Most of the transport systems models which have been developed have incorporated each of these four sub-models but there have been differences in the sequence in which the sub-models have been used. These differences have resulted from differences in the assumptions about the way in which trip decisions are actually made.

Transport systems models which are constructed from the four sub-models mentioned previously have the following form:

$$t_{ij}^{mr} = p_i s_{ij} s_{ij}^m s_{ij}^{mr} \qquad (1)$$

where t_{ij}^{mr} = the number of trips from zone i to zone j by mode m and route r

p_i = the number of trips produced in zone i

s_{ij} = the proportion of trips produced in zone i that travel to destinations in zone j

s_{ij}^m = the proportion of the trips between i and j that travel by mode m

s_{ij}^{mr} = the proportion of the trips between zones i and j by mode m that travel by route r.

Trip matrices estimated by equation (1) are conditional in the sense that they are for a particular activity distribution and transport system.

Many studies of urban residential location and transport behaviour have shown that it is important to recognize explicitly the different socio-economic groups in urban society in the development of transport systems models. The most obvious example is the classification of urban residents into car-owners and non-car owners. Equation (1) may be re-written in the following way:

$$t_{ij}^{kmr} = p_i^k s_{ij}^k s_{ij}^{km} s_{ij}^{kmr} \tag{2}$$

$$= t_{ij}^k s_{ij}^{km} s_{ij}^{kmr}$$

where t_{ij}^{kmr} = the number of trips by person type k from zone i to zone j by mode m and by path r.

Two basic sub-model sequences have been used in the urban transport planning studies performed to date where the differences are in the location of the modal choice sub-model in the sequence. In equation (2) the modal split analysis follows the trip distribution analysis but in some studies the modal split analysis precedes the trip distribution analysis in the following way:

$$t_{ij}^{kmr} = p_i^k s_i^{km} s_{ij}^{km} s_{ij}^{kmr} \tag{3}$$

With this sub-model sequence modal transport choice is assumed to be determined exclusively by the socio-economic characteristics of trip makers. In contrast the model sequence of equation (2) assumes that modal choice is influenced by both the socio-economic characteristics of individuals and the transport system properties.

A fundamental issue that arises in estimating the parameters of the sub-models of equations (2) and (3) is the extent to which travel decisions may be treated as a series of separate choices or as a set of simultaneous decisions. Most of the operational forms of equations (2) and (3) that have been developed rely on the assumption that the choice decisions are separable. Equations (1), (2) and (3) may be viewed as being built up from a sequence of conditional probabilities which reflect the chains of decisions made by urban trip makers. For example, in equation (2) s_{ij}^k may be interpreted as the conditional probability that a trip maker will select zone j as a destination given that i is the zone of origin and that the trip maker is of person type k; s_{ij}^{km} may be interpreted as the conditional probability that a trip maker will choose transport mode m given that the trip is between zones i and j and that the trip maker is of person type k. At each level of decision, choice is viewed as being made conditioned on fixed preceding decisions and on optimal succeeding decisions. If the utility derived from each level of decision is additive then decisions may be treated as being separable. If utility is not separable then the decisions must be treated in a simultaneous way. This is a very critical issue since it governs the way in which model structures are specified and their parameters estimated. The following sections of this paper outline the current knowledge on the major sub-models and some of the major deficiencies.

TRIP GENERATION

The first sub-model in the model sequences described in equations (2) and (3) is trip generation. Trip generation has been largely a matter of empirical investigation in which observed rates of trip generation for some system of basic spatial units have been related to measures of the amount of human activity in those spatial units through regression analysis or category analysis techniques [3]. Traditionally these trip generation magnitudes have been assumed to be inelastic to transport supply. However, with the emerging emphasis on traffic restraint in many countries there is a need to develop trip generation models which have elastic properties [4].

URBAN SPATIAL INTERACTION

Perhaps the most important and intractable problem in transport systems modelling is in understanding human activity interactions. This understanding not only embraces existing spatial interaction linkages but how these linkages might change and develop in response to changes in the transport system and land development patterns.

The set of spatial linkages that exist in an urban area have been built up over many years and reflect a myriad of individual location decisions made by households and institutions. Most of the spatial interactions models that have been calibrated are of the comparative static type in that they are based on cross-sectional data at one point in time. Some of the models require fully specified activity distributions at both the origin and destination ends while other models require only partially specified activity distributions with the models estimating the locations of the remaining linkages along with the spatial linkages. Some of the spatial interaction models have their origins in the gravity and potential concepts of social science while others are based on certain principles of mathematical programming.

Gravity Type Models

There are two basic components of the spatial interaction problem and these are the number of trips between any zonal pair, t_{ij}, and the corresponding travel costs, c_{ij}. The term travel cost is used in the generalized sense and includes monetary costs, time costs and the general comfort and convenience of travel. The row and column totals of any trip interchange matrix may be determined to produce the so-called trip-end constraint equations:

$$\sum_j t_{ij} = p_i \qquad (4)$$

= the total number of trips with origins in zone i, the so-called trip productions,

$$\sum_i t_{ij} = d_j \tag{5}$$

= the total number of trips with destinations in zone j, the so-called trip attractions.

Additional constraint equations may be introduced which deal with the travel cost matrix such as the total amount of effort spent on travel:

$$C = \sum_i \sum_j c_{ij} \tag{6}$$

The constraint equations contain the information normally known about the horizon year trip matrix.

Most of the spatial interaction models that have been used in transport planning studies throughout the world had their origins in the pioneering work of Voorhees [5]. Voorhees adapted some of the earlier work of social scientists who had applied simple gravity and potential concepts to model human interactions of various types including trade, migration and communications flows. The gravity model is based on the hypothesis that the amount of interaction between any two concentrations of human activities varies directly with the product of the sizes of the two concentrations of human activities and inversely with some measure of the spatial separation or travel costs between the two activity concentrations.

The basic form of the gravity model which emerged from the earlier transport studies had the following form:

$$t_{ij} = p_i s_{ij} \tag{7}$$

$$s_{ij} = a_j f_{ij} / \sum_j a_j f_{ij} \tag{8}$$

where f_{ij} = some function of the generalized travel costs, c_{ij}, where the parameters of this function are estimated from observed travel behaviour; the function is usually referred to as the deterrence function.

Several functional forms of f_{ij} have been used and the parameters of these functions are normally estimated by searching for parameter magnitudes which when used in equations (7) and (8) reproduce the observed travel patterns. The normal criterion used to compare the observed and estimated travel patterns is the mean trip length of each trip linkage distribution.

The gravity type trip distribution models used in most transport planning studies have been of the heuristically derived form given in equations (7) and (8). In 1967 Wilson [6] made a major contribution to spatial interaction modelling by proposing a formal procedure for deriving spatial interaction models. Using some entropy maximizing methods from statistical mechanics and information theory he showed that a family of spatial interaction models could be derived in a consistent manner from the constraints associated with a particular problem. The Wilson version of the production-attraction constrained gravity model specified in equations (7) and (8) is:

$$t_{ij} = b_i b_j p_i a_j e^{-\beta c_{ij}} \qquad (9)$$

$$b_i = 1/\sum_j k_j a_j e^{-\beta c_{ij}} \qquad (10)$$

$$b_j = 1/\sum_i k_i p_i e^{-\beta c_{ij}} \qquad (11)$$

The terms b_i and b_j are usually referred to as balancing factors which ensure that the constraint equations (4) and (5) are satisfied. β is a parameter calculated to ensure that constraint equation (6) is satisfied. The other members of this family of spatial interaction models have the same form as equation (9) with the variations between the models being reflected in differences in the balancing factors. While each of the spatial interaction models proposed by Wilson may be derived heuristically the major contribution of Wilson's method has been to ensure that they are also derived consistently. Much of the theoretical and empirical work on spatial interaction modelling that has been performed over the last decade is summarized in references [7, 8, 9, 10].

Mathematical Programming Approaches

While most of the work on urban spatial interaction has been with gravity-type models a number of alternative approaches have been proposed [9]. One of the most interesting alternative approaches is derived from linear programming. Blunden and his co-workers [11, 12, 13] have formulated the trip distribution problem in the following way:

minimize $\qquad\qquad Z = \sum_i \sum_j t_{ij} c_{ij} \qquad\qquad (12)$

subject to $\qquad\qquad \sum_i t_{ij} = p_i \qquad\qquad (13)$

$$\sum_j t_{ij} = a_j \qquad\qquad (14)$$

$$t_{ij} \geq 0, p_i \geq 0, a_j \geq 0 \qquad\qquad (15)$$

The assumption of this approach is that the equilibrium trip distribution state for a given land use allocation and a particular transport network is given by the set of trip distributions which minimizes the total travel costs of all trip makers. Blunden and others have shown how this formulation may be solved using the classical transportation problem solution of linear programming. Others have shown the trip matrices estimated by the linear programming solution are approached by those estimated by a gravity model with β tending to infinity [14].

The validity of the linear programming approach to spatial interaction rests on the assumption that residential and workplace locations, for example, are selected jointly by all locators so as to minimize collectively the total travel costs. Comparisons of the trip matrices estimated by linear programming and those observed show that the estimated mean trip lengths are shorter than the observed. Trip matrices estimated by linear programming method assume implicitly that location decisions will be made on the basis of the marginal social costs of travel. However, locators perceive the average costs of travel in making location decisions and this encourages the longer trip lengths observed.

While the linear programming approach suffers from these types of deficiencies it does provide some important insights into the interactions between land use and transport through the dual formulation of the problem stated in equations (12) through (15). The dual formulation may be stated in the following way:

maximize $$Y = \sum_i x_i p_i + \sum_j y_j a_j \tag{16}$$

subject to $$x_i + y_j \le c_{ij} \tag{17}$$

$$p_i \ge 0 \quad a_j \ge 0 \tag{18}$$

and x_i and y_j are known as the dual variables.

At the optimum $Y = Z$ and the magnitudes of the dual variables provide some interesting information about the travel cost implications of unit changes in the trip ends brought about by the relocation of residences and workplaces. The marginal increases or decreases in travel time brought about by shifts in the locations of residences and jobs between zones may be estimated from the dual variable magnitudes. Information of this type is particularly useful for strategic planning where the transport implications of alternative arrangements of land use are being explored. Blunden and Black [13] provide an interesting application of these concepts to the Sydney region. Others have suggested that the balancing factors of the gravity model may be interpreted in an analogous way.

Urban Systems Models

Many have argued that spatial interaction patterns estimated by the methods described previously are essentially arbitrary since they simply reflect the constraints specified exogenously to the trip distribution models. While the exogenous specification of trip ends may be tolerable for the shorter-run studies, modelling capabilities are required in the longer-run studies which capture the joint character of the mechanisms of growth and change illustrated in Fig. 2. Lowry [15] was the first to suggest linking gravity-type allocation models together in order to reduce the extent of the exogenously specified constraints imposed on the allocations of future urban activities. Wilson [7] and Batty [16] have reviewed much of the work on urban activity systems models conducted over the past two decades.

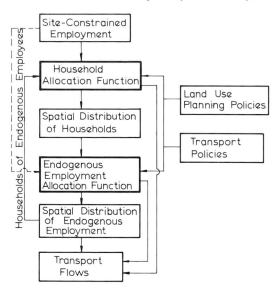

FIG. 3   Structure of urban activity systems models

Most of the approaches which have been developed specify part of the employment distribution exogenously to the model and the model allocates endogenously the spatial distributions of the remaining employment and households in response to specified land development and transport policies. Fig. 3 illustrates the structure of spatial interaction models of this type. The allocation functions imbedded in the model framework have been of the gravity type such as the following household allocation function:

$$s_{ij}^{wk} = l_j^{hk} e^{-\beta^k c_{ij}} / \sum_j l_j^{hk} e^{-\beta^k c_{ij}} \tag{19}$$

where s_{ij}^{wk} = the probability of an employee of person type k working in zone i and living in zone j

l_j^{hk} = the amount of land available in zone j for residential development that is compatible with person type k housing preferences

and β^k and c_{ij} reflect the effects of the transport system properties on the residential location choice behaviour of person type k.

Urban systems models of the type illustrated in Fig. 3 have been developed and used which recognize a number of separate transport modes and endogenously allocated employment types which are not simply dependent upon the spatial distribution of households. In addition, dynamic versions have been developed which allow time-staged paths of urban development to be estimated. Wilson [7] and Batty [16] describe many of these more complex versions of urban systems models.

Normative urban systems models have also been developed which search

25

for urban development patterns that optimize a particular objective function. These models are usually formulated in the following way [17, 18]:

$$\text{maximize} \qquad V(a_{ki}) = \sum_k \sum_i \sum_l \sum_j t_{kilj} b_{kilj} + \sum_k \sum_i a_{ki} u_{ki} \qquad (20)$$

where $V(a_{ki})$ = the net benefit of the set of allocations of urban activities k to zone i

t_{kilj} = the amount of interaction between activities of type k in zone i and activities of type l in zone j

b_{kilj} = the benefits minus the costs of the interaction t_{kilj}

a_{ki} = the amount of activity k allocated in zone i

u_{ki} = the benefits minus the costs of activity k allocated in zone i.

In some normative models the benefit components are omitted and the objective function becomes one of minimizing the sum of the interaction and location costs. Since the objective function is usually non-linear, some form of non-linear optimization technique must be used to search for optimal solutions such as iterative linear programming and geometric programming.

Urban systems models of both types have been used in strategic land use-transport studies. Hutchinson [19] has described an application of the gravity-type spatial interaction models to the analysis of the regional development impacts of alternative programs in water supply, sewerage and transport in the Toronto region. Sharpe and Brotchie [20] have demonstrated the use of models of the type described in equation (20) to regional planning problems in Australia.

UNDERSTANDING TRANSPORT MODE CHOICE

In the earlier transport studies empirically derived relationships were used for estimating the modal transport choice decisions of trip makers. Relationships were developed between the modal split probabilities of different person types and some very coarse indicators of transport system properties. These methods of analysis were not found to be sufficiently sensitive to significant changes in the transport policy environment. It has been pointed out earlier in this paper that the analysis needs of contemporary transport studies has changed from one of estimating future traffic volumes to one of understanding the impacts on trip maker decisions of changes in the transport policy environment. Transport planners and policy makers are becoming increasingly concerned with the impacts of more immediate policies such as pricing, traffic restraint schemes and the provision of more specialized transport services.

Two of the principal contributions to the better understanding of modal choice decisions during the past decade have been the development of the so-called disaggregate models of transport demand and the concept of generalized transport cost. Disaggregate models of transport demand began to emerge in the early 1960s [21] and became quite well developed in applications to modal choice during the late 1960s and early 1970s [22, 23, 24]. The term disaggregate was used to reflect the fact that the analytical techniques focused on the behaviour of individuals rather than on large groups of people. The basic form of disaggregate modal split models is:

$$s_{ij}^{km} = f(w^k, x_{ij}^m) \Big/ \sum_m f(w^k, x_{ij}^m) \tag{21}$$

where $\qquad s_{ij}^{km} =$ the probability of an individual of type k choosing a transport mode m for a trip between zones i and j

$f(w^k, x_{ij}^m) =$ a function of a set of variables w^k which describe the characteristics of an individual and variables x_{ij}^m which describe the characteristics of a transport mode m between zones i and j.

A number of mechanisms of choice have been postulated in order to derive the character of the function used in equation (21). These mechanisms have been derived from theories of choice in economics and psychology and a typical functional form is the so-called logit model of the following form [25]:

$$s_{ij}^{km} = \frac{e^{-\lambda^k c_{ij}^m}}{\sum_m e^{-\lambda^k c_{ij}^m}} \tag{22}$$

in which $\qquad \lambda^k =$ a person-type specific parameter which reflects the impact that transport mode attributes have on the modal choice behaviour of person type k

$c_{ij}^m =$ the generalized costs of using mode m between zones i and j.

A critical component of the modal choice model specified in equation (22) is the generalized travel cost variable which typically has the following structure:

$$c_{ij}^m = a_1 x_{ij}^{1m} + a_2 x_{ij}^{2m} + x_{ij}^{3m} + x_j^{4m} \tag{23}$$

where $\qquad x_{ij}^{1m} =$ the in-vehicle travel time between zones i and j by mode m

$x_{ij}^{2m} =$ the out-of-vehicle travel time between zones i and j by mode m

$x_{ij}^{3m} =$ the fare or other monetary costs of travel between zones i and j by mode m

$x_{ij}^{4m} =$ the parking charges or other terminal costs at zone j for travel by mode m.

A number of investigators have shown that the λ parameter magnitude of equation (22) is sensitive to the estimation method used. Typically the λ parameter magnitude is also subject to a great deal of uncertainty because the data available for parameter estimation are severely limited. In addition the calibrated model is influenced by the choice of the particular generalized travel cost function used.

27

The general form of the logit model specified in equation (22) has been used to analyse other types of transport choice situations such as decisions about car ownership, time and frequency of travel and destination choice [26]. Disaggregate choice models have been used recently to explore the probable impacts of a range of transport systems management policies.

ROUTE CHOICE MECHANISMS

The final transport systems sub-model identified in equations (2) and (3) is the route assignment sub-model. In many of the earlier transport studies demands were assigned to the minimum travel time path between each zonal pair on the assumption that this represented the demand for road capacity and that adequate road capacity would be provided. However, many of the transport studies performed during the 1960s used traffic assignment methods which recognized the traffic capacity constraints of the individual links within a road network. Most of these traffic assignment procedures are based on the assignment principles enunciated by Wardrop [27] in 1952. The basic principle proposed by Wardrop is that traffic on a network distributes itself in such a way that the travel costs on all routes used from any origin to any destination are equal while all unused routes have equal or greater travel costs.

Route assignment methods which are based on Wardrop's principle and which employ some form of capacity restraint seem to give adequate representations of total traffic patterns [28, 29]. However the earlier sub-models in the urban transport systems model chain derive their travel cost components from the route characteristics. With most of the existing assignment methods there is some uncertainty about the extent to which these travel costs can reasonably be extracted from the traffic assignment models.

CONSISTENCY WITHIN AND BETWEEN SUB-MODELS

One of the primary problems with current transport systems models is the lack of consistency both within and between the sub-models. At the broadest level there is the concern about the order in which the modal split and trip distribution models should occur and whether the choice mechanisms may be treated sequentially or must be examined simultaneously. While both of the sub-model sequences identified in equations (2) and (3) have been shown to capture the macroscopic characteristics of travel in urban areas there is concern about the consistency with which behaviour is really captured by the model sequences. Each of the sub-models incorporates some measure of generalized travel costs and in most transport systems models these travel costs are not consistent between each of the sub-models. Travel times between zones are typically used in trip distribution models whereas generalized travel costs of the type specified in equation (23) have been used in many modal split models. The difficulties of interfacing the cost functions for the distribution and modal split models have been noted by a number of analysts.

Perhaps the major difficulty with all of the sub-models is that while they are capable of reproducing travel behaviour observed in the base year there is no guarantee that these cross-sectional type models are useful for estimating future behaviour. For example, gravity-type trip distribution models calibrated to cross-sectional data from one particular year simulate in some average way the spatial interaction patterns that have formed over many years and stages of development. However, there is real concern about their ability to capture the spatial interaction patterns at future time horizons. Similar concerns exist about each of the other sub-models.

CONCLUSIONS

Urban transport planning studies conducted during the 1960s were concerned primarily with establishing road and public transport network plans that would be capable of supporting rapidly growing urban areas and accommodating an increasing number of private cars. Robust transport systems models were developed in these studies which allowed objective estimates of future travel demands to be made.

The character of urban transport planning began to change during the late 1960s and early 1970s. Resources constraints, greater sensitivity to the mixed blessings of capital-intensive additions to the transport system and uncertainties about the future of current forms of urban transport technology have resulted in a greater emphasis on shorter run tactical studies geared to improving the efficiencies of existing transport facilities. Pricing policies, traffic restraint schemes and other types of management policies are the primary concern rather than the provision of new transport capacity. The transport systems models required to support this type of policy environment must be more behaviourally oriented and capable of estimating the responses of urban trip makers to changes in transport policy. Current urban transport systems models are not capable of servicing fully this new policy environment.

As the costs of transport begin to increase sharply during the 1980s and new forms of transport technology begin to emerge much greater attention will have to be paid to new forms of urban spatial structure and the role of transport within that structure. New analytical techniques will be required which focus on the transport requirements of individuals and institutions rather than the transport demand focus of the 1960s or the transport response focus of the 1970s. A greater interest in normative models might be expected in the 1980s in order to support the concern with transport requirements.

References

1. Martin, B. V., 'Transport Planning Models: The London Experience', Research Record No. 309, Highway Research Board, Washington, D. C. 1970.
2. Lockwood, S., 'Transportation Planning in a Changing Environment', *Traffic Quarterly*, Vol. XXVIII, No. 4, October 1974.

3. Wootton, H. J., and Pick, G. W., 'A Model of Trips Generated by Households', *Journal of Transport Economics and Policy*, Vol. 1, pp. 137–53, 1967.
4. Wilson, A. G., 'Further Development of Entropy Maximizing Transport Models', *Transportation Planning and Technology*, Vol. 1, pp. 183–93, 1973.
5. Voorhees, A. M., 'A General Theory of Traffic Movement', *Proceedings*, Institute of Traffic Engineering, Vol. 1, pp. 46–56, 1955.
6. Wilson, A. G., 'A Statistical Theory of Spatial Distribution Models', *Transportation Research*, Vol. 1, pp. 253–69, 1967.
7. Wilson, A. G., *Urban and Regional Models in Geography and Planning*, John Wiley and Sons Limited, London 1974.
8. Stopher, P. R., and Meyburg, A. H., *Urban Transportation Modeling and Planning*, D. C. Heath and Company, Lexington, Mass. 1975.
9. Hutchinson, B. G., *Principles of Urban Transport Systems Planning*, Scripta Book Company — McGraw Hill Book Company, 1974.
10. Senior, M. L., and Williams, H. C. W. L., 'Model Based Transport Policy Assessment I: The Use of Alternative Forecasting Models', Working Paper 195, School of Geography, University of Leeds, July 1977.
11. Blunden, W. R., *The Land Use-Transport System*, Pergamon Press, Oxford 1971.
12. Colston, M., and Blunden, W. R., 'On the Duality of Desire Line and Land Use Models', *Proceedings*, Australian Road Research Board, pp. 170–83, 1970.
13. Black, J., and Blunden, W. R., 'Mathematical Programming Constraints for Strategic Land Use-Transport Planning', *Proceedings*, 7th International Symposium on Traffic and Transportation, Kyoto 1977.
14. Evans, S. P., 'A Relationship Between the Gravity Model for Trip Distribution and the Transportation Problem of Linear Programming', *Transportation Research*, Vol. 7, pp. 39–61, 1973.
15. Lowry, I. S., 'A Model of Metropolis', RM-4035-RC, Rand Corporation, Santa Monica, California 1964.
16. Batty, M., *Urban Modelling: Algorithms, Calibrations, Predictions*, Cambridge University Press, Cambridge 1976.
17. Sharpe, R., Brotchie, J. F., Ahern, P. A., and Dickey, J. W., 'Evaluation of Alternative Growth Patterns in Urban Systems', *Comput. and Ops. Research*, Vol. 1, pp. 345–62, 1974.
18. Hopkins, L. D., 'Land Use Plan Design: Quadratic Assignment and Central Facility Models', Environment and Planning A, Vol. 9, pp. 625–42, 1977.
19. Hutchinson, B. G., 'Land Use-Transport Models in Regional Development Planning', *Socio-Economic Plan. Sci.*, Vol. 10, pp. 47–55, 1976.
20. Sharpe, R., and Brotchie, J. F., 'An Urban Systems Study', *Roy. Aust. Planning Institute, Jl.*, Vol. 10, p. 105, 1972.
21. Warner, S. L., *Stochastic Choice of Mode in Urban Travel: A Study in Binary Choice*, Northwestern University Press, Evanston, Illinois 1962.
22. Stopher, P. R., 'A Probability Model of Travel Mode Choice for the Work Journey', Research Record No. 283, Highway Research Board, 1969.
23. de Donnea, F. X., *The Determinants of Transport Mode Choice in Dutch Cities*, Rotterdam University Press, 1971.
24. Charles River Associates, *A Disaggregated Behavioural Model of Urban Travel Demand*, U.S. Department of Transportation, Washington, D.C. 1972.
25. Domencich, T. A., and McFadden, D., *Urban Travel Demand: A Behavioural Analysis*, North-Holland Publishing Company, Amsterdam 1975.
26. Stopher, P. R., and Meyburg, A., (eds), *Behavioural Travel-Demand Models*, Lexington Books, D. C. Heath and Company, Lexington, Mass. 1976.

27. Wardrop, J. G., 'Some Theoretical Aspects of Road Traffic Research', *Proceedings Inst. of Civil Engineering*, Part II, Vol. 1, pp. 325–78, 1952.
28. Burrell, J. E., 'Multiple Route Assignment and Its Application to Capacity Restraint', 4*th International Symposium, Theory of Traffic Flow*, Karlsruhe 1968.
29. Van Vliet, D., 'Road Assignment — I: Principles and Parameters of Model Formulation', *Transportation Research*, Vol. 10, pp. 137–43, 1975.

Concrete Technology — Yesterday, Today and Tomorrow

Introduction

At the time of John Roderick's arrival the concrete materials technology in the undergraduate course was in the hands of the inimitable H. J. Jimmy Vogan. The emphasis was on the basic mix design philosophies expounded by Duff Abrams, Fuller and others, mainly concentrating on the concepts of water-cement ratio and maximum density. There was much emphasis on the concept of grading curves and the blending together of materials, come what may, to fulfil the requirements of those grading curves. Those were the days of 4 : 2 : 1, stone, sand, cement combinations. The acceptance criteria for materials and concrete were based on Standards Association of Australia Codes and Specifications typically drafted prior to World War II. For example, the Concrete Code (of only 69 pages) was CA2-1937, and the Ready Mixed Concrete Specification was one of the wartime emergency documents, (E) A502-1941, prepared with the advent of ready-mixed concrete during the early years of the war.

Since that time, concrete technology, its basic principles and applications have progressed rapidly both here in Australia and elsewhere throughout the world. It is interesting to note that much of the development in the technology of ready-mixed concrete in other parts of the world had its origins in Australia in the 1950s, when several of the companies based in this country took the concept of ready-mixed concrete to the United Kingdom and Europe, for example, to invade the previously site-mixed dominated construction in-dustries in those countries.

Progress

The development of the ready-mixed concrete industry in Australia is highlighted by the graph shown in Fig. 1 in which the production volumes of ready-mixed concrete and cement are shown. Fig. 2 shows the proportion of cement produced in Australia used in ready-mixed concrete. The latter proportion is, at best, an estimate because of the changing technology within the industry in terms of the amount of portland cement used per cubic metre steadily decreasing in the last fifteen years in particular, for reasons which will be discussed later.

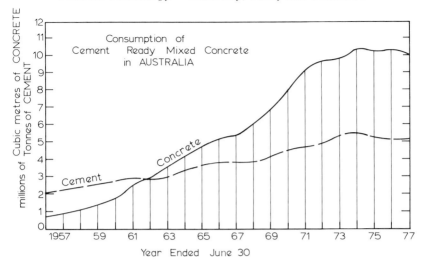

FIG. 1

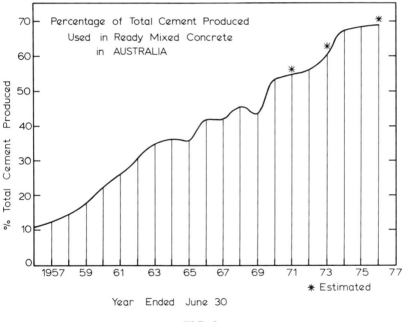

FIG. 2

The development of concrete technology in Australia is closely tied in many ways to the ready-mixed concrete industry. The latter in turn gathered its initial impetus with the development of the equipment used within it. In its earliest days in the 1940s and early 1950s it was dependent upon mixing concrete within a plant, discharging from plant mixers into rotating drums mounted on trucks and then carried to the site. In effect, these truck-mounted drums were agitators only. Early in the 1950s the design of the truck-mounted units was advanced to the stage where they became mixers, and it was thus possible to charge them with the dry materials in the plant and rely on the truck-mounted mixer for all the mixing effort.

In the early days this was very much a trial-and-error operation, but the advent of the Snowy Mountains Scheme, with advisors present from the United States Bureau of Reclamation, introduced the concept of mixer efficiency testing and at this stage the design of the Australian truck-mounted mixers took a major step forward as they strove for compliance with the mixer performance requirements in the Snowy Mountains Authority.

At the same time, the Standards Association of Australia was very actively engaged in bringing up to date the various codes and specifications with which the industry, and concrete construction and design in general, had to comply. A new Aggregate Specification AS A77 was published in 1957, as was a comprehensive volume the AS A100 to 110 series on Methods of Testing Concrete. In 1958 CA2, a new Code for Concrete in Buildings, was published (volume increased to 109 pages). While it introduced quite new concepts in terms of structural design requirements, it made a spectacular advance in terms of the acceptance criteria for concrete used in buildings. For the first time anywhere in the world, the concept of statistical evaluation of concrete test data was introduced as the basis for the acceptance criterion in a national standard. This was alternately greeted with alarm, mystification and joy. Most of all, it introduced the performance concept in terms of compressive strength. as being the major means of assessing the compliance of concrete with the specification. The idea of supply of concrete by proportions was being phased out. In 1960 a new Standard Specification for Ready-Mixed Concrete AS A64 was published and this again represented quite an advance on previous developments in this segment of the concrete industry. For example, it introduced the concept of measurement by plastic volume of concrete as discharged from the truck, a most controversial issue with contractors at the time.

At approximately this stage, the first steps were being taken by the American origin chemical companies to launch water-reducing admixtures in Australia. Most usually based on calcium lignosulphonates, by-products of the manufacture of paper, in the United States and Canada, these admixtures were gaining increasing acceptance particularly during periods of extreme high temperature in the west coast areas of the United States. They were initially produced as water-reducing set-retarding admixtures but subsequently were modified with small doses of accelerators to off-set the retardation effects so that they could be used all the year round. With a performance specification for compressive strength, the way was open with the advent of water-reducing admixtures to reduce the cement content of the mixes, thus allowing the water-cement ratios to be maintained constant to maintain a constant level of compressive strength. This process was immediately surrounded with controversy on the part of both specifying authorities and producers. Not all of the products being marketed were of appropriate quality and varied in their reactions with the chemical composition of cements. Cement composition was varying to some extent at this time, as was the fineness, as the cement industry entered a period of extreme competitiveness and ready-mixed concrete producers pushed for maximum pounds per square inch of compressive strength for minimum pounds of cement per cubic yard of concrete. At the same time, attempts were being made by some backyard admixture manufacturers to market materials with very limited quality control and technology.

Thus the early 1960s, particularly in N.S.W., saw a concrete construction industry in great turmoil, and this was the situation prevailing at the time the Association of Consulting Structural Engineers of N.S.W. introduced their own Concrete Specification in March 1964. At the same time, the Standards Association of Australia had initiated further action to review the CA2 document and thus early 1964 the next edition CA2-1963 was issued. This further advanced in particular the concepts of statistical acceptance criteria for concrete supplied to a job site.

The early 1960s was a period of great activity in the Standards Association of Australia with regard to documents relating to concrete. The Methods of Test underwent extensive revision, to be followed later with a major update of the Aggregates Specification and the initiation of work on documents for Chemical Admixtures for concrete and a Code of Practice for the use of these materials.

During this period there was also intense activity in another aspect of concrete technology, the use of fly ash as a partial replacement for cement. This technology had been explored in the 1950s in Australia but ash quality had prevented the wide acceptance here that development in the United States and in Europe had enjoyed. Fly ash from the United States and Japan was being utilized in some aspects of the Snowy Mountains Scheme, in particular 'intrusion prepakt' lining of penstock tunnels into the underground power stations Tumut 1 and Tumut 2. Investigation into local sources of fly ash resulted in the commencement of production of concrete with Wangi, and later Vales Point Power Station, ashes in 1964. The utilization of such materials has now advanced to the stage where most concrete in Brisbane, Sydney and Adelaide contains at least a proportion of fly ash. It has made a most significant contribution to the production of pumpable concrete to which reference is made later.

In 1966, this particular area of technology was advanced further with the introduction of fine ground granulated blast furnace slag from Port Kembla Steelworks. This material enabled far greater levels of cement replacement but had associated with it some shortcomings, particularly when the concrete was not cured. Subsequently, the two technologies of fly ash and slag have come together in production of significant volumes of concrete in N.S.W. with blends of fly ash, slag, and cement in the proportions 20:40:40, for use, for example, in the steelworks in Newcastle and Wollongong. In Western Australia, a blend of 70 per cent to 30 per cent slag is now finding increasing acceptance.

While this aspect of materials technology was receiving great attention, designers and specifiers were expressing alarm about the increasing incidence of deflection and cracking particularly in concrete structures in the Sydney metropolitan area. This matter was aired at the Newport Symposium on Drying Shrinkage and Creep, sponsored by the Association of Consulting Structural Engineers, held in November 1963. This was the beginning of a further period of controversy in the field of concrete technology. The first really definitive statements on one aspect of the problem, namely the contribution of aggregates, appeared in mid 1966, originating in the CSIRO Division of Applied Mineralogy. The team from CSIRO working in this particular field subsequently took up residence within the School of Civil Engineering and actively pursued many aspects of the materials technology of drying shrinkage and creep. They were particularly concerned with the contributions which cement and aggregates made to these properties of concrete. A major project to evaluate the aggregate contribution was carried out by this team, under sponsorship from the principal quarrying companies in Sydney, at that time involved in the marketing of crushed volcanic breccia as a concrete aggregate in this area.

This was typical of the increasing level of communication between designers and specifiers, researchers and concrete producers in the Sydney area. While relations between the various parties were not always harmonious, there was much investigation and accumulation of data to provide a better design base. However, the ACSE introduced an amendment to their concrete specification, placing constraints on the chemical composition of the cements in use with the intention of further restraining and confining the drying shrinkage problem being encountered. While many aspects of this controversy continue to this day, much of the comment is far better informed than was the case in the mid 1960s.

On the equipment side in concrete construction, there were major steps occurring at this time associated with the introduction of truly portable concrete pumps. While the first concrete pump patent was taken out in the 1920s it was not until the 1960s that these erstwhile mechanical monsters were reduced to a size and efficiency and portability whereby they could be quickly moved from site to site and around the job site and yet handle the discharge of ready-mixed concrete trucks. The pumps at this time were many and diverse in mechanical design, some more effective than others. However, as the better units came into wider acceptance, increasing demands were placed on the ready-mixed concrete industry in terms of the rate at which supply was required to a particular site. This in turn prompted the introduction of the larger truck-mounted mixers up to 9 cubic yards (7 cubic metres) in capacity, mounted on 8-wheel trucks, the first introduced into Australia specifically for the mounting of truck-mounted mixers. Initially, concrete pumps were confined in their use to large volume placements, but subsequently as competition became keener between the operators and prices were reduced, the average size of job progressively reduced to the stage where it was typically around the 40 to 50 cubic yard mark. At this time also, there was increasing interest in the use of automatic batching equipment in the concrete plants. However, automation has not been widely adopted in the Australian ready-mixed concrete industry. Quite apart from the capital costs involved, the general practice of requiring the delivery of concrete to, by world standards, a very tight tolerance of slump or consistency, and the ability to measure moisture content of aggregates to the necessary precision, has mitigated against the use of automatics. Most concrete batching plants in Australia today are still manually operated with a visual (sometimes mechanical) assessment of slump to ensure the delivery of a uniform product on site.

Throughout the 1960s the manufacture and use of lightweight aggregates and concretes therefrom, was going through great trauma. A series of investors came and went with different processes for expanding shale or clay, or importing naturally occurring scoria from outside Geelong in Victoria. Despite the success enjoyed by each of them as evidenced by some outstanding structures constructed with them, none have proved viable long term, with the new very demanding requirements for pollution control proving to be the 'last straw' for the most recent operator. Indeed, pollution control has introduced many 'new rules' by which materials suppliers and the building industry generally must 'play the game' now, never contemplated twenty-five years ago. Any industry such as this, traditionally noisy and dirty as it is, has had to become very conscious of its responsibilities in this regard. Unfortunately, the community has in turn been in many situations reluctant to recognize and to accept the increased costs resulting.

The early 1970s saw a continuing boom in the building industry and the ready-mixed concrete industry generally, in Australia. However, the subsequent recession has seen a marked turn-down in the activities of the industry and very little development has taken place in terms of plant or equipment other than for miscellaneous labour-saving devices whereby the numbers employed in the industry have been significantly reduced.

During this period the construction industry went metric with its strange new words, e.g. megapascals and different orders of numbers. This proved to be an excellent opportunity to update specifications and rationalize some traditional requirements. Typical of this activity was the introduction of standard strength grades of concrete in AS 1480, the first metric version of the old CA2.

The early 1970s also saw the advent of a demand by designers for concretes having higher compressive strengths. Prestressed concrete designers had in the

1960s progressively increased strengths to where producers were generally able to readily supply 6000 p.s.i. (say 40 MPa) concrete. Then came the push to go to 7000 p.s.i., then 8000 p.s.i. (55 MPa). This concrete was most demanding of aggregate and cement characteristics — stone shape and surface texture were most critical, test results were found to be acutely sensitive to testing procedures. On the job site, the contractor found the handling characteristics vastly changed and had to change his placing techniques, most importantly his overall organization and speed. After overcoming these difficulties, the supply and placing of such high strength concrete soon became a routine operation. However the availability of suitable raw materials must always be a constraint on proposed supply and use of such concrete.

Future

A major factor in years to come will undoubtedly be energy conservation. In other countries in the world not as well endowed with energy as is the case with Australia, tremendous research effort has been generated in the last three years into the many and diverse aspects of energy conservation in construction generally, and in materials technology in particular. Concrete generally appears to be widely accepted as a relatively energy minimizing construction medium particularly in terms of its insulating properties and the manner in which operating costs in terms of heating and cooling in buildings primarily of concrete are generally lower than those associated with other construction materials. At the same time the utilization of waste products such as fly ash and fine ground granulated blast furnace slag as partial replacements for high energy cost cement provide further opportunities for reducing the energy cost of concrete. Government instrumentalities in many countries in the world are now actively engaged in pursuing these opportunities for energy conservation and quantification of the various factors. There is increasing interest in the introduction of energy conservation and means of achieving it as part of tertiary education courses in concrete design, construction and materials technology in countries such as the U.S.A.

Included in the concrete technology of the future, there will be increasing interest in the use of fibre reinforcement. In most countries the technologies, now fairly intensively developed to a research stage, have yet to find large-scale commercial application. The coated glass fibres developed in the United Kingdom and the United States are still not being used for structural applications pending further long-term assessment of their durability. Steam curing for precast articles made with them is still discouraged and yet there appear to be significant opportunities for their utilization, for example, in architectural façades. Steel fibres are being used particularly in pavement overlays where abrasion resistance and/or flexural strength are required. Similarly, there appear to be great opportunities in shotcreting. The development in Australia of an end modification of the short fibre, as originally patented in the United States, has represented a significant step forward in terms of the handling and production of steel fibre reinforced concrete, and the properties of the hardened concrete.

Another more exotic technology, well advanced in research but yet to find significant commercial application, is polymer concrete. The cost of the chemicals involved in these processes, whether polymer impregnated or polymer substitute for cement, or polymer mixed in with the plastic concrete, are such as to provide, at this stage, serious limitations on their commercial viability. However, they do produce very significant increases in properties such as chemical resistance, tensile strength and compressive strength, and there will undoubtedly be applications where these particular properties are of such enormous benefit as to justify the cost involved.

Of more mundane, but almost certainly of more immediate consequence has been the introduction of the superplasticizing admixture into concrete technology. So far, only the melamine formaldehyde resin concentrate based product has been used in Australia but several others are being utilized in other parts of the world. These admixtures produce, for a period of up to about one hour, a most significant increase in slump or consistency immediately upon addition. They are fluidizing admixtures of great potency. Alternately, they can be used as very high powered water-reducing admixtures. Whatever the use, they do represent most significant advances in basic concrete technology. The façade panels for the MLC Tower in Sydney, for example, presented very serious difficulties to the precast concrete manufacturer with their relatively thin sections very heavily reinforced. By use of one of these superplasticizers it was possible to produce concrete with very high flowing characteristics for the necessary time required without increasing water and cement contents significantly to maintain the strength, with all the inherent shrinkage and cracking tendencies which such a traditional move would have developed. These chemicals are very expensive but again this additional cost can more than offset the cost which would have been involved in the achievement of concrete of this workability by more conventional means.

Conclusion

For those of us who have worked through the last twenty-five years of concrete technology, we can look back on some remarkable advances. This progress has not been without its trauma and controversy. However, when we look at the quality of the finished article in terms of the concrete structures which abound throughout this great country, we can say with more than a fair degree of confidence that very high standards have been achieved and maintained. A review of the Awards of Excellence of the Concrete Institute of Australia highlights both the quality of design and construction and overall technology involved, as well as the ability of the professions involved, to conceive and execute concrete structures of the highest order and on a par with those anywhere else in the world.

Interim 350 to AS1170: Developments in the Prediction of Wind Loads

INTRODUCTION

In the twenty-five years since the appearance of the design code, SAA Interim 350 [1], there has been a rapid development of methods of evaluating wind loads. This development is reflected in the growth of wind codes generally and the Australian code in particular. In a quantitative sense, the code has grown from some 8000 words or word equivalents to a formidable 30 000. That this growth met with some resistance from the profession is evident in the reluctance to include the code in building ordinances. This resistance was not peculiar to Australia and the British code met with similar opposition [2]. Much of the resistance was centred on the increased complexity and upon the observation that existing codes had resulted in satisfactory performance. The latter point is questionable but it is true that major structural failures due to wind action are comparatively rare, however failures in a serviceability sense are not uncommon.

It is the intent of this paper to review the major changes that occurred with the appearance of AS1170 [3] and the developments in wind engineering on which these were founded. Attention is concentrated on a few of the more significant changes, particularly those which caused some concern within the profession. Among these were the reformulation of and increase in the design speeds and the marked increase in the uplift forces on roofs. Also discussed is the increasing use of wind tunnels as a means of evaluating wind loads. In the latter part of the paper attention is focused on the accuracy of loads determined from the application of the code rules.

WIND TUNNEL TESTS

Prior to 1950 or thereabouts most aerodynamic data was obtained using aeronautical wind tunnels designed to model the passage of a vehicle through still air. The recognition of the importance of the chief features of atmospheric flows, namely turbulence and a velocity gradient, came remarkably slowly. A clear statement of the need to model both the structure and the flow was made by Jensen [4] (1958) in his formulation of the 'model law' although Jensen placed more emphasis on the velocity gradient rather than the presence of

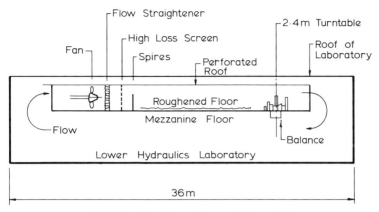

Working Section 2·4m x 2·0m x 20m
Maximum Speed 15m/sec.

FIG. 1 Boundary layer wind tunnel, School of Civil Engineering, The University of Sydney

turbulence. It would appear that the first major investigation conducted in a wind tunnel designed specifically to model atmospheric flows was that conducted by Davenport [5] in 1964 for the twin towers of the World Trade Centre, New York. Since this time numerous facilities have been constructed; the boundary layer tunnel in the School of Civil Engineering (Fig. 1) at the University of Sydney [5] was operational in 1972 and has been used in numerous investigations including studies for the National Art Gallery, the High Court, the MLC building and Centrepoint Tower. Similar facilites exist at Monash and at James Cook Universities.

AS1170 is the only wind code which specifies minimum requirements for wind tunnel tests. The code permits tests in comparatively smooth flow provided that a velocity gradient is present and provided that dynamic effects are not important. The determination of load fluctuations requires that turbulence be correctly scaled although in the context of AS1170 peak loads may be estimated from mean pressure or load coefficients used in conjunction with a peak gust speed. If dynamic effects are considered to be of significance then AS1170 requires that the flow be scaled correctly in regard to the velocity profile and the turbulence level and that the model be correctly scaled in regard to mass stiffness and damping.

The requirements for wind tunnel modelling have been discussed in some detail by Whitbread [7], Cermak [8], Melbourne [9], Vickery [10] and Nemoto [11] among others. Whitbread's contribution was prepared prior to the acceptance of the need for correctly modelled flow characteristics and is concerned primarily with aeroelastic models. Cermak and Nemoto discuss the flow modelling in some detail while Melbourne and Vickery are concerned primarily with the models and the latter author includes a discussion of the simplifications that can be employed in the construction of an aeroelastic model. A useful discussion of the expectations of a designer who is commissioning a wind tunnel investigation has been given by Melbourne [12] while Davenport [13] has discussed the incorporation of wind tunnel data into the design process.

Along with the increased use of the boundary layer wind tunnel the past decade has seen numerous full-scale investigations [14] which have provided benchmarks for the calibration of tunnel data. In general it can be stated that the comparison between full scale and model results is favourable and there has been no suggestion that correctly modelled wind tunnel tests do not provide the most reliable method of evaluating wind loads. An assessment of the accuracy level that can be anticipated from model studies is difficult since the approaches adopted vary from the simple evaluation of load coefficients to comprehensive studies involving not only wind tunnel tests but an evaluation of the wind climate and the synthesis of these two phases to produce a complete probabilistic description of the predicted behaviour. Based upon full scale/model comparisons it appears that, for comprehensive studies, an accuracy of better than 20 per cent can be anticipated with a high level of confidence or a coefficient of variation of less than 10 per cent. As is shown later in this paper this level of accuracy constitutes an improvement by a factor of 3 or 4 over that associated with loads determined solely from code rules.

DESIGN WIND SPEEDS

The basis of the specified speeds in both Int.350 and AS1170 is the maximum gust speed recorded by the Dines anenometer which has a response time of the order of 2 seconds. The adoption of this reference value is a direct result of the recording instrument commonly employed rather than any merit intrinsic to such a measure. In the U.S.A. the reference speed is the 'fastest-mile' which again stems from the recording instruments employed. In assessing the most desirable form for the specification of wind speed Davenport has argued for the adoption of a mean hourly value at gradient height. While this definition offers two distinct advantages, namely stability and freedom from local topographic effects, it is not necessarily the most convenient for the estimation of wind loads on the majority of structures. The mean hourly speed must be supplemented by information concerning turbulence levels and, while this division of the wind speed into two components is highly desirable for tall buildings, bridges and structures likely to have a significant dynamic component in their response, it is an unnecessary complication for the myriad of comparatively small structures designed in accordance with a wind code. Most structures of this type respond in an essentially quasi-static mode and the maximum load is closely related to the maximum gust speed averaged over a few seconds. While Int.350 presented gust speeds only, AS1170 offers a two level approach; most structures would be designed in accordance with a peak gust speed but provision (Clauses 11.3.3 & 11.3.4) is made for the determination of a mean hourly speed and a turbulence component. It should be recognized however that the mean speeds so determined are derived solely from observations of peak gusts rather than direct observations of mean hourly values. Mean hourly data are available in Australia but not in a computer compatible form and the analysis would be most time consuming.

The design speeds of Int.350 were extremely simple in specification. Geographically, there were only two subdivisions, namely (i) areas subject to tropical cyclones and (ii) the remainder of the country. For each region there were three levels corresponding to sheltered exposure, average exposure and extreme exposure. No provision was made for any increase in speed with height above ground. The actual speeds recommended were not at all unreasonable for low rise structures in a built-up environment and this of course covers the majority of structures. In the above situation the design speeds of Int.350 were 65 mph and 95 mph for normal and cyclonic areas respectively. The corresponding values in AS1170 would be from 60 to 75 mph normally and from 100 to 105 mph in cyclonic areas. In terms of risk, the speeds of Int.350 corresponded to a return period of typically twenty years rather than the fifty years for AS1170.

For tall structures, particularly those located in a comparatively exposed location, there is no doubt that the speeds specified in Int. 350 were well below the speeds which could be expected during a typical structure lifetime of say, thirty years. That there were no failures of major structures designed in accordance with Int.350 cannot be attributed to the adequacy of the wind design loads and one must look elsewhere for an explanation. The most probable explanation is that the designs were dominated by dead loads and live loads other than wind and that, as a result, the safety factor against failure by wind was considerably in excess of the prescribed minimum.

The design speeds specified in AS1170 are the result of a careful study of the data available through the Bureau of Meteorology. The first comprehensive investigation of the Australian wind climate was that by Whittingham [15] and it was this study which provided a working basis for AS1170. Whittingham analysed the annual maximum gust data for each station and fitted an extreme value distribution using the Gumbel approach which produces a relationship of the form:

$$V_R = V_1 + a \log_e R \qquad (1)$$

where; V_R = speed corresponding to a return period of R years

V_1 = mode

a = slope

In evaluating Whittingham's work or the similar analyses involved in preparing code speeds it is necessary to pay particular attention to

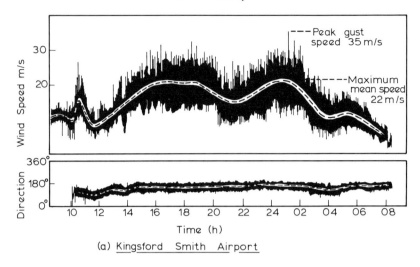

(a) Kingsford Smith Airport

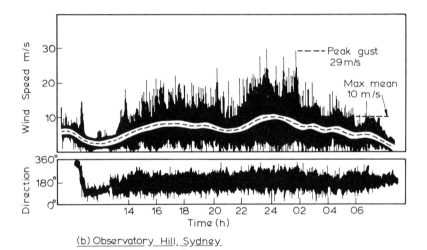

(b) Observatory Hill, Sydney

FIG. 2 Anemographs

(a) the time span of the data,

(b) the quality of the data, and

(c) the adequacy of the Gumbel approach (i.e. the validity of using an extreme
value distribution of the Fisher-Tippet Type 1).

(a) and (b) above were given considerable attention when evaluating design
speeds for AS1170. Stations with recording periods less than 10 years were
ignored as were records from stations for which topographic effects were
believed to be significant and unknown. All wind speeds presented in AS1170

have been adjusted to represent values at a standard height of 10 metres over open country.

The difficulty in adjusting data to a common datum is illustrated by the two anemographs presented in Figs. 2a and 2b which were obtained from anemometers at Kingsford Smith Airport and Observatory Hill (Sydney) respectively. The maximum mean speeds differ by a factor of 2.2 while the peak gust speeds differ by 20 per cent. The situation is further confused when it is realized that for westerly winds the situation is reversed and the Observatory Hill anemometer records speeds substantially greater than those at the airport.

Difficulties such as those illustrated in Fig. 2 arise not only in interpreting anemometer data but also in estimating design speeds at a particular site. The code gives guidance in regard to the influence of ridges but many topographic effects and interference effects from nearby structures cannot be evaluated without wind tunnel tests. Topographic models constructed at scales of about 1:3000 have been used [16] to transfer meteorological data from an anemometer site to a building site.

A significant problem which was not recognized in the preparation of the design speeds for AS1170 was the inadequacy of the Fisher-Tippet Type 1 distribution when applied to mixed wind climates. Equation (1) has been shown to be acceptable when the annual maximum gusts at a site are all associated with one particular type of disturbance but it is not suitable when the maxima comprise a mix from two or more storm types. In Australia the three major storm types giving rise to annual maxima are:

(a) large scale extra-tropical cyclones or extensive pressure systems (EPS),
(b) thunderstorms (T), and,
(c) tropical cyclones (C).

Only in a few locations is the climate dominated by a single storm type. Gomes and Vickery [17–21] have investigated the influence of a mixed climate on prediction of extreme speeds and conclude that the Gumbel method can lead to severe underestimates of the wind speeds corresponding to low probabilities of occurrence. A somewhat exaggerated example is given in Fig. 3 which shows the predicted speeds for thunderstorms and cyclones in Darwin together with the observed distribution over a twelve year period during which cyclones did not produce an annual maximum. A prediction based upon the observations would yield a speed of 33 m/s for $R = 100$ years whereas the analysis of cyclone records indicates a value of 55 m/s. The latter value is much closer to the truth and a period of twelve years or even twenty or more years is not sufficient to adequately define a design speed if only observed annual maxima are employed. Similar, but not as severe, effects may be noted in the records for Launceston (Fig. 4) where EPS storms are dominant but thunderstorms will be responsible for the extreme winds.

The technique used by Gomes and Vickery in determining the distribution

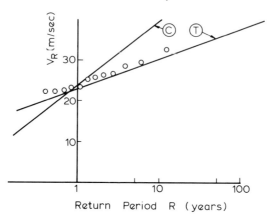

FIG. 3 Comparison of observed and predicted extreme gusts for Darwin

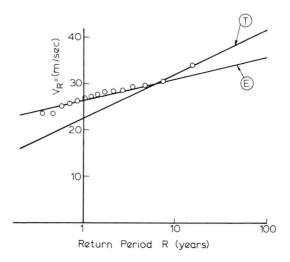

FIG. 4 Comparison of observed and predicted extreme gusts for Launceston

of extreme winds associated with tropical cyclones was developed by Russell and Schueller [22] in a study of U.S. hurricanes. The difficulties of dealing with data from stations with mixed climates has also been recognized by Thom [23] and more recently by Riera *et al.* [24].

There is little doubt that the distribution of extreme wind speeds in Australia warrants further attention but it would appear from the evidence presently at hand that such a study would not produce a reduction in design speeds.

ROOF LOADS ON LOW RISE STRUCTURES

External Pressures and Loads

It is in the pressure and load coefficients for the roofs of simple shed type structure that the variations from Int.350 to AS1170 are most apparent and it is this which prompted much of the opposition to the new code. Coupled with moderate increases in the design speed the new coefficients produced increases in roof uplift design loads in excess of 100 per cent. Local uplift, near eaves and corners was increased by 200 per cent in many instances. There is no doubt that experimental data warranted a substantial increase and further, the failure rate for roof cladding has been far from negligible.

The major deficiency of the revised coefficients is associated with large roofs, particularly those with a depth (in the direction of the wind) to height ratio less than about 0.5. For these roofs the large pressure coefficients are restricted to a region comparatively close to the leading edge and pressures over the remaining parts of the roof are very much lower than AS1170 suggests. The total uplift on such roofs is severely overestimated by the present code and a revision appears necessary. Some results obtained at Sydney illustrate the deficiency; measured pressure distributions for $h/d = 0.25$, 0.50 and roof slopes $\theta = 0, 6°, 12°$ and $22°$ are shown in Figs. 5 and 6. The total uplift on the front and rear segments of the roof are presented in Table 1 together with the code values. It is clear that Int.350 produced extremely severe underestimates

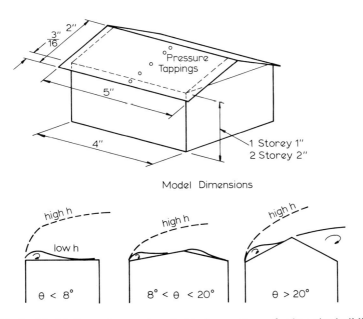

FIG. 5   Model dimensions and probable flow patterns for low rise building

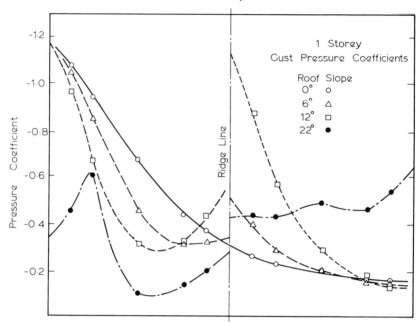

FIG. 6a   Pressure coefficients for model shown in Fig. 5; h/d = 0.25 (single storey)

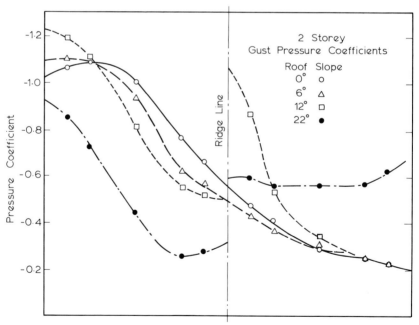

FIG. 6b   Pressure coefficients for models shown in Fig. 5; h/d = 0.50 (two storey)

TABLE 1   Spatially Averaged Pressure Coefficients for Roofs

h/d	θ	FRONT HALF			REAR HALF		
		Int. 350	AS 1170	Measured	Int. 350	AS 1170	Measured
0.25	0	− 0.40	− 0.90	− 0.70	− 0.40	− 0.70	− 0.21
	6	− 0.27	− 0.90	− 0.60	− 0.40	− 0.70	− 0.25
	12	− 0.15	− 0.90	− 0.53	− 0.40	− 0.70	− 0.41
	22	+ 0.05	+ 0.22	− 0.27	− 0.40	− 0.70	− 0.47
0.50	0	− 0.40	− 0.90	− 0.92	− 0.40	− 0.70	− 0.33
	6	− 0.27	− 0.90	− 0.86	− 0.40	− 0.70	− 0.33
	12	− 0.15	− 0.90	− 0.84	− 0.40	− 0.70	− 0.40
	22	+ 0.05	− 0.65	− 0.50	− 0.40	− 0.70	− 0.58

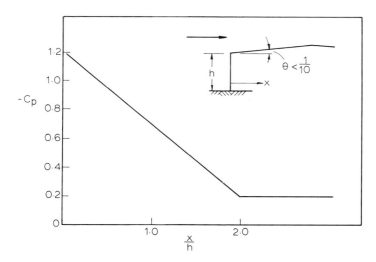

FIG. 7   Suggested pressure coefficients for flat and nearly flat roofs

of the uplift on the leading half of a roof but, for h/d < 0.5, the uplift on the rear was very reasonable. In contrast, AS1170 produces a marked overestimate for the rear half and moderate overestimates for the front when h/d < 0.25. At larger values of h/d AS1170 yields very reasonable values of the uplift force.

A more satisfactory specification of the loads on large roofs with small slopes (less than about 1 in 10) is shown in Fig. 7. For these low roof slopes the ridge has a minimal influence on pressures (except perhaps very locally) and its presence can be ignored in the determination of loads for member design.

Internal Pressures

The increased external roof loads specified in AS1170 were compounded by changes in the specification of internal pressures which in many cases doubled the uplift due to this cause. In Int.350 the internal pressures were quite mistakenly associated with the percentage of openings or potential openings on a face rather than the distribution of openings around the building. The actual size of an opening plays very little part in determining the magnitude of the internal pressure, only for very small openings which heavily restrict the flow into a building does the response time increase to the point where there is a significant reduction in the internal pressures induced by gusts. This point is illustrated by the numerical example presented in Fig. 8 which shows the internal pressure developed in a large industrial building due to a short duration change in external pressure. The internal pressure is presented as a

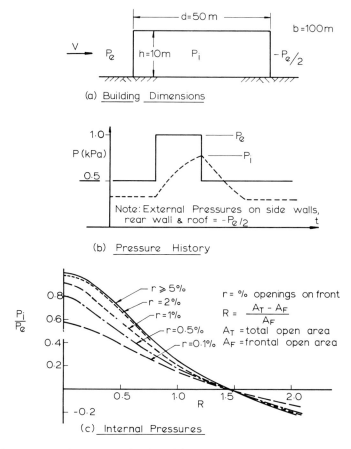

FIG. 8   Internal pressures developed by a short duration change in external pressure

function of relative porosity (front wall openings/total openings on other walls) and the percentage openings on the front face. It is clear that the relative porosity is the significant parameter and that a reduction in internal pressure due to the absolute size of the openings is only significant when these are less than about 1 per cent or 2 per cent of the front face. In terms of the building studied it can be seen that the failure of a large roller door would be quite sufficient to develop the full internal pressure specified in AS1170. Internal pressures can however be controlled by the incorporation of open vents, particularly ridge vents which are always a region of negative pressure. This solution is only possible if natural ventilation is desired; in a controlled environment the provision of such vents would place undue loads on heating and cooling systems.

There is no doubt that the uplift forces on roofs were severely under-estimated in Int.350 and that modifications were required for both the internal and external pressures. The changes introduced in AS1170 were justified in general but the loads on large roofs $\left(\dfrac{h}{d} < 0.5\right)$ are now overestimated significantly and some modification of the code is highly desirable. The study of low rise structures has been neglected over the past years but a comprehensive study by Davenport, Surry and Stathopoulos [25] is nearing completion and this work should provide a solid basis for the reappraisal of present approaches.

THE RELIABILITY OF CODE PRESCRIBED WIND LOADS

In common with most codes, neither Int.350 nor AS1170 attempt to define the accuracy or reliability of the prescribed loads. The few examples presented herein illustrate that the code is far from infallible and some indication of reliability would place the code provisions in proper perspective. Unfortunately the reliability is difficult to assess and varies markedly from case to case. Some results in this area have been obtained by Davenport, Kitchen and Vickery [26] in a study of surface pressures on eight high-rise structures that have each been the subject of extensive wind-tunnel studies. Maximum (positive) and minimum (negative) pressure coefficients were evaluated for some 1400 locations and these were compared with the coefficients derived from the application of code rules. Using the provisions of AS1170 as a basis the average maximum coefficient observed was $+0.73$ with a coefficient of variation of 26 per cent as compared to the code value of $+0.85$. The average minimum coefficient was -0.69 with a coefficient of variation of 34 per cent while the code value is -1.00 for small elements on tall buildings. Assuming a normal distribution, the above results suggest that the positive cladding pressures predicted by AS1170 are conservative in 68 per cent of all cases while the negative pressures are conservative in 82 per cent of all cases.

It should be pointed out that the variability measured in the test program includes not only variations in the coefficients but also variations in the wind speed profile from that assumed in the application of code rules. The variability is due in no small part to interference effects from nearby structures which were modelled in the tunnel. The observed variability would not occur for isolated structures but such structures are the exceptions, not the norm, although the pressure coefficients prescribed in codes are invariably determined for this situation.

Recognition of the limited reliability of the code provisions provides a rational basis for simplification. There is little point in adding or retaining clauses which add complexity without producing changes that are significant in regard to overall accuracy. There would appear to be a case for producing a two-level code which offered a simple approach for the majority of structures that are located in an environment of similarly sized structures and a detailed approach for major structures and wind sensitive structures in particular. Perhaps the move to limit-state approaches will provide a vehicle for such a major change in the code.

CONCLUSION

In this brief review of the major changes brought about by the introduction of AS1170 two points emerge clearly. One is that a move from Int.350 was essential and the second is that the new code has inadequacies and that modifications are inevitable. The major areas requiring attention are the design speeds, particularly in areas subject to tropical cyclones, and the design loads for low rise buildings. Recent research in both these areas has been referred to and this should provide a sound basis for a review of the present provisions.

References

1. Interim Code for Minimum Design Loads on Buildings, SAA Int. 350, Standards Association of Australia, 1952.
2. Taylor, R. G., 'Blow, Blow Thou Winter Wind, Th'Art Not So Unkind as Chap. V: Part 2', *The Structural Engineer*, Vol. 51, No. 12, December 1973.
3. SAA Loading Code Part 2 — Wind Forces. Australian Standard 1170, Standards Association of Australia, 1975.
4. Jensen, M., *The Model Law for Structures in the Natural Wind*, Int. Edn, Vol. 2, Ingenioren, Copenhagen 1958.
5. Davenport, A. G., 'The World Trade Centre Wind Study', unpublished Report for Skilling, Helle, Christiansen and Robertson, New York 1966.
6. Vickery, B. J., 'The Design and Performance of a Low-Cost Boundary Layer Wind Tunnel', *Wind Effects on Structures*, University of Tokyo Press, pp. 99–104, Tokyo 1976.
7. Whitbread, R. E.,'Model Simulation of Wind Effects on Structures', *NPL Int. Conf. on Wind Effects on Buildings and Structures*, HMSO, London 1964.
8. Cermak, J. E., 'Laboratory Simulation of the Atmospheric Boundary Layer', *JAIAA*, July 1971.

9. Melbourne, W. H., 'Modelling of Structures to Measure Wind Effects', *Proc. Struct. Models Conference*, School of Arch. Sc., University of Sydney, 1972.

10. Vickery, B. J., 'On the Aeroelastic Modelling of Structures in Wind', *Proc. Struct. Models Conference*, School of Arch. Sc., University of Sydney, 1972.

11. Nemoto, S., 'Similarity Between Natural Local Wind in the Atmosphere and Model Wind in a Wind Tunnel', *Met. & Geophys.*, Vol. 19, No. 2, 1968.

12. Melbourne, W. H., 'Wind Tunnel Test Expectations', *Proc. Conf. on Planning and Design of Tall Buildings*, Vol. DC, pp. 301–4, Lehigh University, Bethlehem, August 1972.

13. Davenport, A. G., 'On the Statistical Prediction of Structural Performance in the Wind Environment', ASCE Nat. Struct. Meeting, Baltimore, Md., April 1971.

14. 'Symposium on Full-scale Measurements of Wind Effects on Tall Buildings and Other Structures', Proceedings Reported in *Int. J. Ind. Aero.*, Vol. 1, Nos 1 & 2, pp. 14–219, June–October 1975.

15. Whittingham, R. E., *Extreme Wind Gusts in Australia*, Bureau of Meteorology, Bulletin No. 46, Melbourne 1964.

16. Isyumov, N. and Davenport, A. G., 'A Study of the Surface Wind Speed Climate for the Place Montreal, Montreal, Quebec', BLWT-SS4, Boundary Layer Wind Tunnel Laboratory, University of Western Ontario, June 1977.

17. Gomes, L., 'Design Wind Speeds for Australia', unpublished PhD thesis, School of Civil Engineering, University of Sydney, 1977.

18. Gomes, L. and Vickery, B. J., 'On the Prediction of Extreme Wind Speeds From the Parent Distribution', *J. Ind. Aero.*, Vol. 2, No. 1, 1977.

19. Gomes, L. and Vickery, B. J., 'On Thunderstorm Wind Gusts in Australia', *Civil Eng. Trans.*, Inst. Eng. Aust., Vol. CE18, No. 2, 1976.

20. Gomes, L. and Vickery, B. J., 'On the Prediction of Tropical Cyclone Gust Speeds Along the Northern Australian Coast', *Civil Eng. Trans.*, Inst. Eng. Aust., Vol. CE18, No. 2, 1976.

21. Gomes, L. and Vickery, B. J., 'Extreme Wind Speeds in Mixed Wind Climates', Res. Rep. No. R301, School of Civil Engineering, University of Sydney, January 1977.

22. Russell, L. and Schueller, G., 'Probabilistic Models for Texas Gulf Coast Hurricanes', *J. Petroleum Tech.*, March 1974.

23. Thom, H. C. S., 'Toward a Universal Climatological Extreme Wind Distribution', *Proc. Wind Effects on Buildings and Structures*, Vol. 1, pp. 669–84, University of Toronto Press, 1968.

24. Riera, J., Viollaz, A. and Reimundin, J., 'Some Recent Results on Probabalistic Models of Extreme Wind Speeds', *J. Ind. Aero.*, Vol. 2, No. 3, November 1977.

25. Davenport, A. G., Surry, D. and Stathopoulos, T., 'Wind Loads on Low Rise Buildings: Final Report of Phases I and II', BLWT-SS8-1977, Boundary Layer Wind Tunnel Laboratory, Univ. of Western Ontario, November 1977.

26. Davenport, A. G., Kitchen, R. and Vickery, B. J., 'The Reliability of Pressure Coefficients for the Determination of Local Pressures', Draft Report, Boundary Layer Wind Tunnel Laboratory, Univ. of Western Ontario, March 1977.

An Engineer in the World

We walked into the foyer of the AMP Building in Bourke Street, Melbourne. As was intended by the designers, we were impressed.

A very high ceiling, quietly luxurious finishes and elegant furnishings — sparse indeed in the enormous space — all combined to create an atmosphere of solid wealth. It was clear that only very successful businesses would have offices in this building.

The lift took us to the 17th floor, quietly and quickly. As we stepped out the overall impression of luxury was reinforced — but now there was a difference. Important elements in the decor were natural timber and heavy extruded aluminium sections.

The pretty young girl at the reception desk was expecting us and showed us into an office on the corner of the building. It was large, with panoramic views over Melbourne to the east and south. The River Yarra wound its way between green parks — beautiful in early summer with the trees in their new foliage, and under bridges filled with busy traffic.

Furnishings were simple but elegant. At one end were the usual executive desk and chairs with credenza. At the other was a comfortable lounge setting. Obviously important matters were discussed in comfort. As I'd expected all was immaculate. Not a thing was out of place, and the desk was completely bare. This was the office of a tidy man, with a penchant for detail. How I knew it!

The girl served us tea. We were early — but I knew our host (who'd been out of town on business) would be punctual. He was.

The door opened. The man who entered was tall and distinguished. His dark hair was slightly thinning at the front, and there were touches of grey at the temples. An immaculate dark blue pin striped business suit was complemented by a pastel shirt and a quietly correct striped tie.

Smiling, he put down his gold monogrammed leather brief case and greeted me.

Phil Spry-Bailey and I shook hands warmly. We'd seen each other only two or three times in the previous twenty-two years. But, prior to that, we'd worked in the same group of four in our third and fourth years of the civil engineering course at Sydney University.

Phil is presently the General Manager for Finance and Company Secretary of Alcoa of Australia Limited. Alcoa is one of Australia's leading companies — its 1977 profit of $65.2 million testifies to that. Its major shareholders include the Aluminium Company of America, Western Mining Corporation Ltd, B.H. South Ltd, and North Broken Hill Ltd.

To my way of thinking, Phil is a perfect example of an engineer who has been eminently successful in a field usually reserved for professionals other than engineers. The sort of position he holds is normally reserved for people with academic training in accountancy, economics or law.

No doubt Phil's Master's degree in Business Administration was of help to him — but it's interesting to contemplate the assistance and influence of his degrees in the physical sciences — particularly Engineering.

What follows is Phil's biography, which he very kindly prepared for me. I believe you will find it interesting.

As both my grandfathers were civil engineers and my father followed a career in engineering and architecture, it was not surprising that I chose to become a civil engineer when I finished school in 1950. I was selected at that time for a cadetship with a State government department and entered the portals of the Peter Nicol Russell Building as a full-time student at the University of Sydney.

During vacations I worked with the government department and spent most of my time on road design. I decided at that time to become a consulting engineer, and at the end of the second year of engineering obtained a Commonwealth scholarship to complete a science degree. I took a year off from engineering to study mathematics and physics in the science faculty.

During vacations my assignments with the government department took me to a number of country areas where I discovered the roads were already built and that my design work amounted to putting on paper designs for roads that existed! This was rather a demoralizing task.

When time came for the six-month practical experience period during my third year of engineering studies, I saw very little benefit from any of the practical work I would undertake with the government department. I therefore asked to be released for the six-month period to work on construction of the Spit Bridge, so that I could gain experience on a major project. Approval was withheld and as a result I resigned from the department. I did spend the six months working on both the Spit and Liverpool Bridges. The majority of my time was spent at Liverpool because during four of the six months work on the Spit Bridge was stopped because of industrial unrest.

This experience was the first real exposure I had to engineers, managers, workers and unionists. It was probably during this time I realized that I wanted to be a manager rather than an engineer. I found the high degree of conflict which seemed to exist between the men on the job and their supervisors frustrating — but also fascinating. Even though I was only a young student, I considered that the management position was sometimes wrong. A number of suggestions put forward by the workers appeared very practical to me, but were often rejected simply because they were suggested by the workers rather than by the management.

By the time I had completed my final year of engineering studies in 1955, I had firmly decided to be a manager rather than a consulting engineer. Both Neil Ellis (the Sub-Dean) and Professor Roderick, in commenting on careers for their students, advised that anyone wishing to follow other career paths should try and do so immediately rather than spending time in engineering and then later branching out. As a result, I sought a position that would lead to a supervisory role and joined Mobil Oil Company as a technical sales assistant.

Although the position required some engineering knowledge, it was really an entrée to marketing. However, from marketing I moved into a work-study assignment and eventually became a superintendent of a small oil terminal. I then spent several years back in the marketing department, in both selling and analysing marketing investments. I developed an interest during this period in investment analysis and accounting, and I gained further supervisory experience.

When the Business School was established at the University of N.S.W., I was one of its first students. It was while studying for the Degree of Master of Business Administration that I decided to concentrate on finance and wrote a thesis on investment. I subsequently developed the thesis into a book titled *Investment Risk and Uncertainty*, which was published in 1967.

I completed my final year of the MBA course as a full-time student in 1965, and resigned from Mobil Oil. I then joined Lend Lease Development Pty Limited as an Assistant Project Manager, as this position required many management skills, including a knowledge of financing.

A year later, the Department of Trade asked me to become a trade consultant for three years in order to develop inter-firm comparisons for Australian industry. This work involved the application of a technique aimed at improving the efficiency of industry. Industry accounting data, and, where applicable, engineering data, was compiled so that various companies in an industry could more readily assess their strengths and weaknesses by comparing their performance with industry standards. In addition to seeing much of Australian industry, I also had the opportunity during this period to review and discuss company accounting practices and to observe relationships between engineering and accounting functions, as most of the companies I dealt with were in the manufacturing sector.

At the conclusion of the Department of Trade assignment I chose to return to industry and joined Alcoa of Australia Limited as Manager of Finance and Accounting. After four years in this position, during which I was assigned for eighteen months to the International Finance Department of the Aluminium Company of America in Pittsburgh, U.S.A., I returned to Australia as Company Secretary and Manager of Corporate Services. In this position I was responsible for personnel, industrial relations, purchasing, transportation and legal functions. I assumed my current position as General Manager of Finance and Accounting, retaining the function of Company Secretary, in 1975.

In 1977 Phil spent several weeks overseas — mainly in London and New York. He was renegotiating loans in excess of $300,000,000 for his Company. He was dealing with such famous names as: Schroder Wagg; Lazards; Citibank; Chase Manhattan, and Morgan Guaranty, heady stuff for a civil engineer.

The other members of our 'Group of Four' were Nick Trahair and Don Douglas. Both earned science degrees on their way through civil engineering and both graduated with First Class Honours. For me, this august company was a bit depressing academically.

Nick is now a Professor of Civil Engineering at Sydney, and will be well known to many of you. After graduation, he completed his Master's degree in Engineering Science and then his PhD. He has taught at universities in the U.S. and U.K., and has lectured world-wide on his speciality — instability problems in steel structures — in some aspects of which he is acknowledged internationally as an expert.

Don is a Director of Frankipile Australia Pty Limited, Australia's leading specialist in Foundation Engineering. He also completed his Master's degree in Engineering Science, specializing in Soil Mechanics. Don is also Managing Director of Ground Test Pty Limited (a Frankipile subsidiary), and in this capacity his energies are devoted to foundation testing and consulting to the profession on foundation problems.

Typical of the major commercial and industrial structures for which Ground Test has provided advice are the new MLC Centre in Sydney, various power stations, and bridges such as the Lower Yarra.

After a little more than twenty years it is obvious that the careers of the four of us are quite diverse. And yet each of us has had some success in our chosen field of endeavour, even though only two of us have followed the profession.

I asked Phil Spry-Bailey to outline the principal factors which influenced his eventual career. Phil writes:

When considering possible turning points in my career I believe the first was probably in the final year of engineering. After resigning from the government department cadetship I had an obligation to repay a bond. To meet the necessary payments I took several part-time jobs as a taxi-driver and waiter. My earnings as a waiter averaged £1 per hour and taxi driving paid only ten shillings per hour, but the experiences gained in dealing with people were a very real education in human behaviour — and one I thoroughly enjoyed.

In addition, I believe the six-month practical experience on bridge construction and my taxi driving together helped me decide I wanted to be a manager rather than a consulting engineer. Of course, it was while studying for my MBA degree I discovered I had insufficient knowledge of finance and accounting and therefore increased my concentration on these areas.

Reflecting on the various studies that I completed, I believe the engineering course, apart from the engineering that was taught, was the most rigorous, in that it requied the student to:

1. Organize time under conditions of constant pressure.

2. Complete the assignment, whatever it might be.

3. Find workable and practical solutions.

4. Develop a pragmatic or empirical approach to problem solving.

The science course did not have the same time pressures. However, it presented problems which often could not be answered in an empirical way, thus forcing one to think. The post-graduate course in business built on former studies and provided an understanding of management techniques.

I also asked him for his views on the engineer in management, to which he replied:

The engineer, in considering a management position, must first of all have the desire to become a manager and be prepared to accept the numerous responsibilities that come with the job. Secondly, he should have an interest in working with people and developing the organization, for much of his time will be spent negotiating and dealing with people in situations where solutions or answers are not often expressed in numbers. Although these are management skills which might be taught in a classroom, effective management is an art which can only be mastered with experience and judgement.

There are a number of engineering graduates holding senior and middle non-engineering management positions in Alcoa of Australia. These people are in such diverse areas as marketing, planning, personnel, accounting and commercial operations.

While an engineering background assists in understanding the business of a mining and manufacturing company, an additional set of skills is required to be an effective manager. However, if Alcoa is typical — and I believe it is — training in engineering provides a sound base for the potential manager to follow in developing skills for dealing with people and solving problems.

There is a school of thought which holds that engineering degree courses should stick solidly to engineering. Presumably, the theory is that this is the best way to produce top quality professional engineers — and this *may* be the case.

The view is one with which I disagree entirely. My reason is that such a course neglects legitimate and vital needs of students.

At the time of writing I have three children aged 21, 19 and 18. All have studied (or are studying) at tertiary institutions, and the eldest is now a graduate in Economics from Sydney University.

The relevance of my family situation is that — as a parent — I've been involved for some years now in helping children decide the moves they should make which are most likely to be beneficial in the future. I've found developing the right sort of advice a very difficult task indeed — and one which is most onerous — and I'm sure many of you have had the same experience and feelings.

I've always envied people who know from a young age just what they want from life in terms of occupation — and this is so whether they choose to be a doctor, carpenter or labourer. But the fact is — or so it seems to me — that most young people just don't know. And quite a few older people have the same problem.

In this age of enlightenment, we're all aware of the countless surveys which prove conclusively that 'job satisfaction' is the most important factor in the relationship between an individual and his work. The level of satisfaction is determined by many factors — remuneration, prestige, relationship with others, future prospects, and so on. It's a highly complex thing to analyse, but one of great significance to the individual.

In my experience, there is no doubt at all that the person who is happy in his work to the extent that he thoroughly enjoys it is a highly motivated individual who is very likely to succeed — even when his basic ability (in terms of formally measured intelligence) is less than 'desirable' for the work concerned.

At a comparatively young age, all of us are faced with a choice. 'What will I be (or do)?' Academic achievements may be such that a number of professional careers can be selected, but there are enormous differences between — say — engineering and veterinary science, and there is no 'middle road' to select for those in doubt. Yet I believe these to be in the majority.

I challenge anyone to explain to a sixteen or seventeen year-old person what civil engineering is all about. Of course, we can talk about buildings, bridges, railways, wharfs, dams and so on *ad infinitum* — *but* (and it's a very important 'but') — *we* know what we're talking about. Our listener doesn't.

I've personally experienced great frustration trying to explain the profession to school leavers at 'Careers Nights'. Not once have I been remotely satisfied that I've conveyed really relevant information to my listeners, and I've seen many a perplexed look on the young eager faces of those in the audience.

Even within our profession there are so many branches and so many roles played by engineers in their proper professional capacities that it's all very confusing. For instance, there's a big difference between the functions of a researcher at a university and a construction manager on a major project in some isolated locality. Equally, there is no real similarity between the duties of a consulting structural engineer (engaged in design) and an engineer concentrating on survey work.

The differences between a 'desk' job and an 'outside' construction job are enormous. But the list of 'legitimate' careers for engineers — and by legitimate I mean those generally considered to be within the profession — is very lengthy. We can investigate, research, teach, design, construct, specify, supervise, administer and even sell!

My argument is not that there are many facets to engineering — although this is something we shouldn't overlook — but the very fact that we can carry out a variety of tasks well should make us aware as to just how good a grounding the profession can be for many other activities.

It is a fact that there are engineers who are successful in innumerable careers outside the profession — both in government and commerce. And there are many engineers whose work within the profession has nothing to do with 'pure' engineering. These are they who have advanced to senior administrative and/or marketing jobs for which they are totally unprepared except by 'on the job' experience or formal training received after graduation.

Our present approach errs in three ways. First, potential students are not made aware of the full range of activities available within the profession. Second, students are not told what an excellent base an engineering course provides for a whole range of careers *outside* the profession. Finally, there is nothing in the course content which specifically prepares students for their potential involvement in administration, finance, human and industrial relations, marketing and sales. And yet there are few of us who have not been deeply involved in one or all of these facets.

My case can be summarized as follows:

1. Young people are often confused as to their choice of career. Engineering *can* be a frightening choice.

59

2. Civil engineering is a very broad and complex field. While the results of civil engineers' work are often seen, the nature of the work of the engineer is not easily comprehended.

3. The profession and schools of engineering should adopt the view that civil engineering is an excellent grounding for many activities other than 'pure' engineering.

4. Engineering courses are deficient at present in that they do not provide even an introduction to many aspects of business life to which virtually all engineers will be exposed in their careers.

Having outlined the problems, I can now offer some possible solutions.

The profession generally and engineering schools in particular need to recognize that engineering training is an excellent basis for numerous activities outside the profession. In fact, it's my belief that engineers — *because* of their training — can make valuable contributions to society by working 'outside'.

Which of us would not agree that a larger number of engineers in politics, government and commerce, would not result in better communication between the profession and the 'outside' world? In fact, a wider understanding of capabilities of engineers would be most beneficial to the profession and, I believe, to the community at large.

Once an appropriate degree of conviction is established, schools of engineering should restructure their courses so that some of the fundamentals of business life can be taught. I can hear the complaints now — 'There just isn't time'. But I regard this matter as of such importance that we should take the view that the necessary time *must* be found.

Simultaneously, a public relations campaign with schools should be commenced. This would highlight normal professional activities — showing clearly the diversity of careers within the profession — and also emphasize the excellent grounding provided for many other careers.

The immediate result would be a substantial stimulus to interest in the profession and, logically, a higher standard of undergraduates and graduates. Finally, as a service to the community and the profession, professional appraisals of the fitness of potential undergraduates should be carried out. Determinations of intelligence, aptitudes, interests and temperament — in skilled hands — will minimize failures and heartbreak. The end result will be graduates suited to their profession who will enjoy their work.

It is clear that graduates well suited to the profession and who are well stimulated by their work will enhance the quality of engineering available to the community. This you will agree is a worthy objective.

At the same time, young people will enter the course with the objective of obtaining a worthwhile background for other careers. Their dissemination throughout the business and government communities will be, I believe, of material benefit to our country.

N. S. TRAHAIR

Elastic Lateral Buckling of Continuously Restrained Beam-Columns

Summary

The resistance to flexural-torsional buckling of an elastic beam-column may be dramatically increased by the presence of elastic restraints which are distributed continuously along the beam-column. In this paper, the types of continuous restraint which may act are categorized, and their effects on the elastic buckling of simply supported mono-symmetric beam-columns in uniform bending are studied.

A general closed-form solution is obtained, and it is shown that there may be a number of half waves in the buckled shape. The general solution is particularized to the case of a doubly-symmetric I-beam. This is then used to study the effectiveness of the various types of restraints.

INTRODUCTION

The resistance to flexural-torsional buckling of a beam-column such as that shown in Fig. 1 may be dramatically increased by the presence of continuous restraints distributed along the length of the beam-column. These restraints occur in many practical situations, as for example when wall or roof sheeting is fixed at close intervals to the structural members of a building, as shown in Fig. 2. In many cases the restraints act at some distance away from the shear centre of the beam-column, as indicated in Fig. 3. The restraints may inhibit the lateral deflection, twist, minor axis rotation, or warping of the beam-column, or combinations of these. In this paper the effects of continuous restraints on the elastic flexural-torsional buckling of beam-columns are studied.

The restraining effects of an elastic foundation on the flexural buckling of a simply supported column (see Fig. 4a) have been investigated by many researchers [4, 17]. In this case the foundation acts as a uniform continuous translational restraint which exerts restraining forces $-k_t u$ per unit length when the column deflects u. The column may buckle in n half sine waves so that

$$u = \delta \sin n\pi z/L \tag{1}$$

To each value of the integer n, there corresponds an elastic critical load

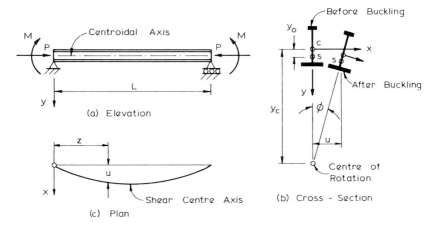

FIG. 1   Buckling of a simply supported beam-column

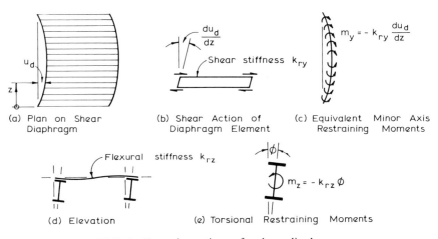

FIG. 2   Restraint actions of a shear diaphragm

$$P_n = P_y \sqrt{\frac{k_t L^2}{P_y}} \left[\frac{n^2}{\sqrt{k_t L^2 / P_y}} + \frac{\sqrt{k_t L^2 / P_y}}{n^2} \right] \tag{2}$$

in which

$$P_y = \pi^2 EI_y / L^2 \tag{3}$$

is the elastic flexural buckling load of an unrestrained column ($k_t = 0$). It can be seen that these critical loads vary with the number of half-waves, as well as with the dimensionless restraint stiffness parameter $\sqrt{k_t L^2 / P_y}$. The lowest values of P_n are shown in Fig. 4b by the solid lines.

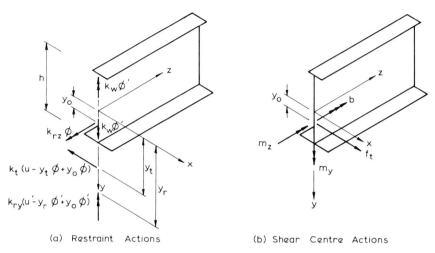

(a) Restraint Actions   (b) Shear Centre Actions

FIG. 3   Actions of continuous elastic restraints

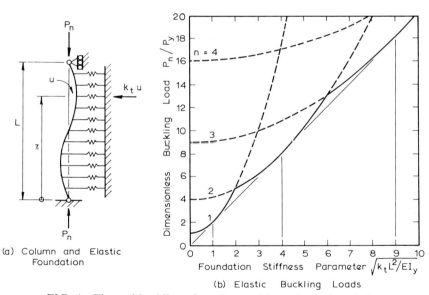

(a) Column and Elastic
    Foundation

(b) Elastic Buckling Loads

FIG. 4   Flexural buckling of a column with an elastic foundation

Closed form solutions for the corresponding elastic flexural-torsional buckling behaviour of simply-supported mono-symmetric beam-columns in uniform bending (see Fig. 1) were obtained by Vlasov [18]. These include the

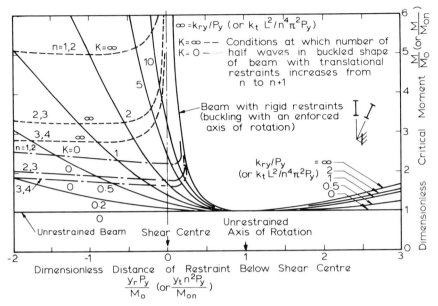

FIG. 5   Buckling of beams with minor axis rotational (or translational)
        restraints

effects of continuous elastic torsional restraints (see Fig. 3a) which oppose
twisting of the beam-column, as well as those of continuous translational
restraints at the shear centre. The solutions also allow for translational
restrains which do not act at the shear centre (see Fig. 3a), and which may
oppose both lateral deflection and twist. Vlasov also studied the case for which
the translational restraints are infinitely stiff, in which case the beam-column
buckles with an enforced axis of rotation which is the line through which the
restraint acts, as shown in Fig. 5.

Vlasov's studies have been confirmed and extended by many other
researchers [3, 5, 10, 11, 13, 15, 16, 20]. In particular, Pincus and Fisher [14]
investigated the effects of continuous diaphragm bracing (see Fig. 2) which
acts at the compression flange of a doubly symmetric I-section beam-column.
The flexural stiffness of the diaphragm provides torsional moments which
oppose twisting of the beam-column, while the shear stiffness of the diaphragm
provides moments which oppose rotation about axes parallel to the section
minor axis. These latter moments not only restrain the minor axis rotation
of the beam-column, but also restrain its warping. Thus these moments can
be replaced by statically equivalent shear centre moments and equal and opposite flange moments. These flange moments contribute to the bimoment
b [18, 19] represented by the triple headed vector shown in Fig. 3b.

This research on diaphragm bracing was extended by Errera, Pincus and
Fisher [9] to beam-columns whose ends were built-in against minor axis
rotation and warping, and by Errera and Apparao [6] to diaphragms which

acted at any distance from the shear centre. Later studies by Apparao, Errera and Fisher [1] were concerned with the effects of geometrical imperfections on the bending and twisting of continuously restrained beam-columns, while design procedures were proposed for continuously restrained beams by Nethercot and Trahair [12] and Errera and Apparao [7], and also for continuously restrained columns [8].

In this paper, the previous research on the effects of continuous restraints on elastic flexural-torsional buckling is extended to the case of simply supported mono-symmetric I-section beam-columns with general uniform restraints. The particular solution for doubly symmetric I-section beams is discussed in detail.

RESTRAINTS

A beam-column which fails by lateral buckling may be continuously restrained in the four ways shown in Fig. 3a. The translational restraint of stiffness k_t which acts at a distance y_t below the centroid exerts a restraining force per unit length of $k_t(u - y_t\phi + y_0\phi)$. The minor axis rotational restraint of stiffness k_{ry} which acts at a distance y_r below the centroid exerts a restraining minor axis moment per unit length of $k_{ry}d(u - y_r\phi + y_0\phi)/dz$, while the torsional restraint exerts a torque per unit length $k_{rz}\phi$. The warping restraint exerts two equal and opposite flange moments per unit length $k_w d\phi/dz$ which form a component

$$b_r = hk_w \frac{d\phi}{dz} \tag{4}$$

of a restraining bimoment per unit length [18, 19].

The actions exerted by these restraints can be replaced by the shear centre actions

$$\{r\} = \{f_t, m_y, m_z, b\}^T \tag{5}$$

shown in Fig. 3b, in which b is the bimoment per unit length. For this set of actions to be statically equivalent to those of the restraints, they must be related to the shear centre displacements

$$\{d\} = \left\{ u, \frac{du}{dz}, \phi, \frac{d\phi}{dz} \right\}^T \tag{6}$$

by

$$\{r\} = [k]\{d\} \tag{7}$$

in which the restraint stiffness matrix is

$$[k] = \begin{bmatrix} -k_t & 0 & k_t(y_t - y_0) & 0 \\ 0 & -k_{ry} & 0 & k_{ry}(y_r - y_0) \\ k_t(y_t - y_0) & 0 & -\{k_t(y_t - y_0)^2 + k_{rz}\} & 0 \\ 0 & k_{ry}(y_r - y_0) & 0 & -\{k_{ry}(y_r - y_0)^2 + k_w\} \end{bmatrix} \tag{8}$$

65

The strain energy per unit length stored in the restraints when the beam displaces $\{d\}$ is

$$s_r = \tfrac{1}{2}\{d\}^T\{r\} = \tfrac{1}{2}\{d\}^T[k]\{d\} \tag{9}$$

ANALYSIS OF LATERAL BUCKLING

The simply supported mono-symmetric beam-column shown in Fig. 1 has axial loads P and equal and opposite end moments M, and is continuously restrained by uniform elastic restraints of the types shown in Fig. 3a. When the end moments reach the elastic critical value, the beam-column may buckle by deflecting laterally u and twisting ϕ as shown in Fig. 1b. The minor axis distributed force equilibrium equation for the buckled beam-column can be obtained by extending equation (5–66) in [17] for an unrestrained beam-column to

$$-EI_y\frac{d^4u}{dz^4} = P\frac{d^2u}{dz^2} + (M + Py_0)\frac{d^2\phi}{dz^2} - f_t + \frac{dm_y}{dz} \tag{10}$$

in which EI_y is the minor axis flexural rigidity. The distributed torque equilibrium equation of an unrestrained beam-column can be similarly extended to

$$(GJ - Pr_1^2 + M\beta_x)\frac{d^2\phi}{dz^2} - EI_w\frac{d^4\phi}{dz^4} = (M + Py_0)\frac{d^2u}{dz^2} - m_z + \frac{db}{dz} \tag{11}$$

in which GJ and EI_w are the torsional and warping rigidities, respectively, r_1^2 is given by

$$r_1^2 = \frac{I_x + I_y}{A} + y_0^2 \tag{12}$$

and the monosymmetry parameter β_x is

$$\beta_x = \frac{\int y^3 dA + \int x^2 y dA}{I_x} - 2y_0 \tag{13}$$

in which A is the cross-sectional area and I_x is the major axis second moment of area.

The boundary conditions for the simply supported ends of the beam-column are

$$(u)_{o,L} = \left(\frac{d^2u}{dz^2}\right)_{o,L} = (\phi)_{o,L} = \left(\frac{d^2\phi}{dz^2}\right)_{o,L} = 0 \tag{14}$$

The equilibrium equations (10) and (11) and the boundary conditions (14) are satisfied by the buckled shapes

$$\frac{u}{\delta} = \frac{\phi}{\theta} = \sin\frac{n\pi z}{L} \tag{15}$$

in which n is any integer. If these and equations (5)–(8) are substituted into equation (10), then the magnitudes δ, θ of these shapes can be shown to be related by

$$\frac{\delta}{\theta} = y_c - y_0 = \frac{M + Py_0 + k_{ry}y_r + k_t y_t L^2/n^2\pi^2}{n^2 P_y - P + k_{ry} + k_t L^2/n^2\pi^2} \tag{16}$$

in which
$$P_y = \pi^2 EI_y/L^2 \tag{17}$$

and y_c defines the axis shown in Fig. 1b about which the cross-section rotates during buckling.

When equations (15), (16) and (5)–(8) are substituted into equation (11), then an equation involving the elastic critical load and moment can be obtained as

$$(M + Py_0 + k_{ry}(y_r - y_0) + k_t(y_t - y_0)L^2/n^2\pi^2)^2$$
$$= (n^2 P_y - P + k_{ry} + k_t L^2/n^2\pi^2) \times (GJ + n^2\pi^2 EI_w/L^2 - Pr_1^2 + M\beta_x$$
$$+ k_{ry}(y_r - y_0)^2 + k_w + \{k_t(y_t - y_0)^2 + k_{rz}\}L^2/n^2\pi^2) \tag{18}$$

This is a quadratic in M and P, and can be solved directly for the elastic critical values which cause the beam-column to buckle. In the particular case when all the restraints are of zero stiffness, equation (18) reduces to the well-known solution [17]

$$(M + Py_0)^2 = (P_y - P)(GJ + \frac{\pi^2 EIw}{L^2} - Pr_1^2 + M\beta_x) \tag{19}$$

An alternative method of deriving equation (18) is to use the energy equation

$$W_M + W_P = S_b + S_r \tag{20}$$

in which the work done by the end moments during buckling is [2, 17]

$$W_M = \tfrac{1}{2}M\beta_x \int_0^L \left(\frac{d\phi}{dz}\right)^2 dz - \int_0^L M\phi\frac{d^2u}{dz^2}dz \tag{21}$$

the work done by the axial loads is [17]

$$W_P = \tfrac{1}{2}P \int_0^L \left\{\left(\frac{du}{dz}\right)^2 + r_1^2\left(\frac{d\phi}{dz}\right)^2\right\}dz \tag{22}$$

the strain energy stored in the beam during buckling is (17)

$$S_b = \tfrac{1}{2}\int_0^L \left\{EI_y\left(\frac{d^2u}{dz^2}\right)^2 + GJ\left(\frac{d\phi}{dz}\right)^2 + EI_w\left(\frac{d^2\phi}{dz^2}\right)^2\right\}dz \tag{23}$$

and the strain energy stored in the restraints (see equation 9) is

$$S_r = \int_0^L s_r dz \tag{24}$$

When equations (9), (15) and (16) are substituted into equations (20)–(24), then equation (18) is obtained.

DOUBLY SYMMETRIC I-BEAMS

In the special case of doubly symmetric I-beams, $y_0 = 0$, $\beta_x = 0$, and $P = 0$, and so equation (18) reduces to

$$(M + k_{ry}y_r + k_t y_t L^2/n^2\pi^2)^2$$
$$= (n^2 P_y + k_{ry} + k_t L^2/n^2\pi^2) \times (GJ + n^2\pi^2 EI_w/L^2$$
$$+ k_{ry}y_r^2 + k_w + (k_t y_t^2 + k_{rz})L^2/n^2\pi^2) \tag{25}$$

For an unrestrained beam, this reduces to the well known solution [17]

$$M^2 = M_0^2 = P_y(GJ + \pi^2 EI_w/L^2) \tag{26}$$

Torsional and Warping Restraints

Continuous torsional and warping restraints increase the resistance to lateral buckling from the value of M_0 for unrestrained beams (equation 26) to

$$M = \sqrt{P_y(GJ + \pi^2 EI_w/L^2 + k_w + k_{rz}L^2/\pi^2}$$

It can be seen that the effects of these restraints are to increase the effective resistance to torsion by an amount $(k_w + k_{rz}L^2/\pi^2)$.

Minor Axis Rotational Restraints

For beams with continuous minor axis rotational restraints, equation (25) can be expressed as

$$\left(\frac{M}{M_0} + \frac{k_{ry}}{P_y} \cdot \frac{y_r P_y}{M_0}\right)^2 = \left(1 + \frac{k_{ry}}{P_y}\right)\left\{1 + \frac{k_{ry}}{P_y}\left(\frac{y_r P_y}{M_0}\right)^2\right\} \tag{28}$$

which enables the dimensionless critical moment M/M_0 to be found as a function of the dimensionless restraint stiffness k_{ry}/P_y and the dimensionless restraint position $y_r P_y/M_0$. Equation (28) is shown graphically in Fig. 5.

For negative values of $y_r P_y/M_0$ (i.e. when the restraint acts above the shear centre), the elastic critical moment M increases indefinitely with the restraint stiffness. In practice, therefore, the strengths of such beams with stiff restraints are likely to be governed by in-plane yielding considerations, rather than by lateral buckling.

However, this is not the case for beams with restraints which act below the shear centre ($y_r P_y/M_0$ positive). For these beams, the critical moment increases with increasing restraint stiffness towards a limiting value M_∞ which is given by

$$\frac{M_\infty}{M_0} = \frac{1}{2}\left(\frac{y_r P_y}{M_0} + \frac{M_0}{y_r P_y}\right) \tag{29}$$

These limiting values, which correspond to the case where the beam buckles with an enforced centre of rotation (at the restraint position y_r), are also shown graphically in Fig. 5. It is of interest to note that M_∞/M_0 is a minimum $(= 1.0)$ when $y_r P_y/M_0 = 1.0$. In this case, the restraint acts at the axis of cross-section rotation (see Fig. 1b) of an unrestrained beam, and has no restraining effect, so that the beam buckles at the unrestrained value M_0.

For beams with restraints which act below the unrestrained axis of rotation (i.e. when $y_r P_y/M_0 > 1.0$), the restraints are comparatively ineffective unless they act at some considerable distance below the unrestrained axis of rotation, as can be seen in Fig. 5.

Translational Restraints

For beams with continuous translational restraints, equation (25) can be expressed as

$$\left(\frac{M}{M_{on}} + \frac{k_t L^2}{n^4 \pi^2 P_y} \cdot \frac{y_t n^2 P_y}{M_{on}}\right)^2 = \left(1 + \frac{k_t L^2}{n^4 \pi^2 P_y}\right)\left\{1 + \frac{k_t L^2}{n^4 \pi^2 P_y}\left(\frac{y_t n^2 P_y}{M_{on}}\right)^2\right\} \quad (30)$$

in which
$$M_{on}^2 = n^2 P_y(GJ + n^2 \pi^2 EI_w/L^2) \quad (31)$$

Equation (30) has the same format as equation (28) for beams with minor axis rotational restraints, and so Fig. 5 can also be used for beams with translational restraints provided M/M_0, k_{ry}/P_y, and $y_r P_y/M_0$ are replaced by M/M_{on}, $k_t L^2/n^4 \pi^2 P_y$, and $y_t n^2 P_y/M_{on}$ respectively. Fig. 5 can therefore be interpreted for beams with translational restraints in the same way as for beams with rotational restraints.

However, equations (30) and (31) indicate that there are a number of different elastic critical moments whose values vary with the number n of half waves into which the beam buckles. It is the lowest of these critical moments which is of interest, and in general, this can only be determined after a number of trial calculations.

The results of some of these trials are shown by the dashed and dash-dot lines in Fig. 5. These lines represent the conditions for which buckling is equally likely to occur in n and n + 1 half waves for the two limiting cases of beams with zero torsional rigidity (in which case the torsion parameter

$$K = \sqrt{\pi^2 EI_w/GJL^2} \quad (32)$$

is infinite), or zero warping rigidity $(K = 0)$. Thus the region below the upper $(n = 1,2)$ curve represents the restraint parameters $y_t n^2 P_y/M_{on}$ and $k_t L^2/n^4 \pi^2 P_y$ (with n = 1) for which the beam buckles in a single half wave. If the restraint parameters plot outside this region, then they must be recalculated with n = 2. If they then plot within the region bounded by the second $(n = 2,3)$ curve, then the beam buckles in two half waves. If, however, the restraint parameters plot outside this region, then they must be recalculated for n = 3, and so on.

A more convenient method of determining the lowest critical moment is to use the rearranged form of equation (30)

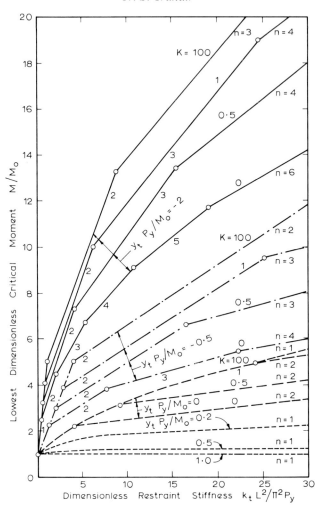

FIG. 6   Buckling of beams with translational restraints

$$\left\{\frac{M}{M_0} + \frac{1}{n^2}\left(\frac{k_t L^2}{\pi^2 P_y}\right)\left(\frac{y_t P_y}{M_0}\right)\right\}^2$$
$$= \left\{n^2 + \frac{1}{n^2}\left(\frac{k_t L^2}{\pi^2 P_y}\right)\right\} \times \left\{\left(\frac{1 + n^2 K^2}{1 + K^2}\right) + \frac{1}{n^2}\left(\frac{k_t L^2}{\pi^2 P_y}\right)\left(\frac{y_t P_y}{M_0}\right)^2\right\} \qquad (33)$$

A simple calculation procedure for determining the lowest value of M/M_0 for given values of $k_t L^2/\pi^2 P_y$ and $y_t P_y/M_0$ is to calculate successive values of M/M_0 from equation (33) for $n = 1, 2, 3 \ldots\ldots$ In general, these values will decrease at first until the minimum is reached, and then increase. Thus the successive calculations are terminated as soon as there is an increase in M/M_0.

Some solutions of equation (33) are plotted in Fig. 6. It can be seen that in general, the number n of half waves at buckling increases with the dimensionless restraint stiffness $k_t L^2/\pi^2 P_y$, but decreases as the dimensionless restraint position $y_t P_y/M_0$ and the torsion parameter K increase. Thus the number of half waves at buckling will be high in beams with low warping rigidity EI_w which are highly restrained at points high above the shear centre.

Combined Restraints

Usually, a beam will be acted on by a combination of continuous restraints, in which case the elastic critical moment can be determined from equation (25). In general, there are a series of values which correspond to increasing numbers of half waves in the buckled shape. The lowest critical moment can be found in the same way as that discussed above by calculating successive values until these start to increase.

CONCLUSIONS

Continuous elastic restraints may cause substantial increases in the resistance of an elastic beam-column to flexural-torsional buckling. These restraints may oppose minor axis translation, minor axis and torsional rotations, and warping of the beam-column. Minor axis rotational and translational restraints may act away from the shear centre, in which case they affect the warping and torsional restraints.

A general closed-form solution (equation 18) has been obtained for the effects of general uniform continuous restraints on the elastic buckling of simply supported mono-symmetric I-section beam-columns in uniform bending. In general, the critical loads and moments determined from this depend on the number of half waves into which the beam-column buckles, and the lowest values can be obtained by calculating successive solutions (for increasing numbers of half waves) until the minimum is found.

This general closed-form solution has been particularized (equation 25) for the case of a doubly symmetric I-beam. Beams with torsional and warping restraints only buckle in a single half wave, and these restraints increase the effective torsional resistances of the beams.

The effectiveness of minor axis rotational and translational restraints increases with their distance from the axis of rotation of an unrestrained beam. They are much more effective when they act above the unrestrained axis of rotation than below. When these restraints act below the shear centre, there is an upper bound to their effectiveness which corresponds to the situation in which the beam buckles with an enforced centre of rotation. There is no upper bound when these restraints act at or above the shear centre.

While beams with minor axis rotational restraints alone always buckle in a single half wave, those with translational restraints may buckle in a number of half waves. The lowest critical moment can be obtained by calculating successive solutions for increasing numbers of half waves until a minimum is found. The number of half waves in the buckled shape is high for beams with low warping rigidity which are highly restrained at points high above the unrestrained axis of rotation.

Appendix: NOTATION

A	cross-sectional area	m_y, m_z	moments per unit length acting about y, z axes
b	bimoment per unit length		
b_r	restraining bimoment per unit length	n	number of half waves in buckled shape
d	vector of shear centre displacements	P	axial load
		P_n	elastic critical loads
E	Young's modulus of elasticity	P_y	$\pi^2 EI_y/L^2$
f_t	minor axis force per unit length	r	vector of shear centre actions
G	shear modulus of elasticity	r_1	a radius of gyration defined by equation (12)
h	distance between flange centroids		
		S_b	strain energy stored in beam
I_x, I_y	major and minor axis second moments of area	S_r	strain energy stored in restraints
		s_r	strain energy per unit length stored in restraints
I_w	warping section constant		
J	torsion section constant	u	shear centre displacement parallel to x axis
K	torsion parameter $= \sqrt{\pi^2 EI_w/GJL^2}$	u_d	diaphragm displacement parallel to x axis
k	restraint stiffness matrix		
k_{ry}, k_{rz}	stiffness of rotational restraints acting about y, z axes	W_M	work done by end moments
		W_P	work done by axial loads
k_t	stiffness of minor axis translational restraints	x, y	major and minor principal axes
		y_c	co-ordinate of centre of rotation
k_w	stiffness of warping restraints	y_0	co-ordinate of shear centre
L	length of beam-column	y_r, y_t	positions of minor axis rotational and translational restraints
M	major axis end moment		
M_0	lowest elastic critical value of M for unrestrained beam		
		z	distance along beam-column
M_n	higher elastic critical moments of unrestrained beam	β_x	monosymmetry parameter defined by equation (13)
M_∞	elastic critical moment for beam with rigid minor axis rotational or translational restraints	δ	maximum deflection
		ϕ	angle of twist rotation
		θ	maximum twist rotation

References

1. Apparao, T. V. S. R., Errera, S. J. and Fisher, G. P., 'Columns Braced by Girts and a Diaphragm', *Journ. Struct. Divn.*, ASCE, Vol. 95, No. ST5, May 1969, pp. 965–90.
2. Barsoum, R. S. and Gallagher, R. H., 'Finite Element Analysis of Torsional and Torsional-Flexural Stability Problems', *Int. Journ. Num. Methods in Engg.*, Vol. 2, 1970, pp. 335–52.
3. Bleich, F. *Buckling Strength of Metal Structures*, McGraw-Hill Book Co. Inc., New York 1952.
4. Column Research Committee of Japan, *Handbook of Structural Stability*, Corona Pub. Co., Tokyo 1971.
5. Dooley, J. F., 'On the Torsional Buckling of Columns of I-Section Restrained at Finite Intervals', *Int. Journ. Mech. Sci.*, Vol. 9, 1967, pp. 1–9.
6. Errera, S. J. and Apparao, T. V. S. R., 'Beams and Columns Braced by Thin-Walled Steel Diaphragms', *Proceedings*, Eighth Congress, IABSE, New York 1968, pp. 247–59.
7. Errera, S. J. and Apparao, T. V. S. R., 'Design of I-Shaped Beams with Diaphragm Bracing', *Journ. Struct. Dvn*, ASCE, Vol. 102, No. ST4, April 1976, pp. 769–81.
8. Errera, S. J. and Apparao, T. V. S. R., 'Design of I-Shaped Columns with Diaphragm Bracing', *Journ. Struct. Dvn*, ASCE, Vol. 102, No. ST9, September 1976, pp. 1685–1701.
9. Errera, S. J., Pincus, G. and Fisher, G. P., 'Columns and Beams Braced by Diaphragms', *Journ. Struct. Dvn*, ASCE, Vol. 93, No. ST1, February 1967, pp. 295–318.
10. Horne, M. R. and Ajmani, J. L., 'Stability of Columns Supported Laterally by Side Rails', *Int. Journ. Mech. Sci.*, Vol. 11, 1969, pp. 159–74.
11. Milner, H. R., 'The Elastic Buckling of Equal Flanged Beams Torsionally Restrained by Stiff Braces', *Proceedings*, 5th Australian Conf. Mech. Struct. and Materials, Melbourne 1975.
12. Nethercot, D. A. and Trahair, N. S., 'Design of Diaphragm-Braced I-Beams', *Journ. Struct. Dvn*, ASCE, Vol. 101, No. ST10, October 1975, pp. 2045–61.
13. Pincus, G., 'Buckling of Channel Purlins with an Enforced Axis of Rotation', *Welding Journal*, Vol. 3, 1965, pp. 141s–3s.
14. Pincus, G. and Fisher, G. P., 'Behaviour of Diaphragm-Braced Columns and Beams', *Journ. Struct. Dvn*, ASCE, Vol. 92, No. ST2, April 1966, pp. 323–49.
15. Schmidt, L. C., 'A Problem of Elastic Lateral Stability', *Quart. Journ. Mech. Appl. Math.*, Vol. 18, No. 4, 1965, pp. 501–12.
16. Taylor, A. C. and Ojalvo, M., 'Torsional Restraint of Lateral Buckling', *Journ. Struct. Dvn*, ASCE, Vol. 92, No. ST2, April 1966, pp. 115–29.
17. Timoshenko, S. P. and Gere, J. M., *Theory of Elastic Stability*, 2nd edn, McGraw-Hill Book Co. Inc., New York 1961.
18. Vlasov, *Thin-Walled Elastic Beams*, 2nd ed, Israel Program for Scientific Translations, Jerusalem 1961.
19. Zbirohowski-Koscia, K., *Thin Walled Beams*, Crosby Lockwood & Son Ltd, London 1967.
20. Zuk, W., 'Lateral Bracing Forces on Beams and Columns', *Journ. Engg. Mech. Dvn*, ASCE, Vol. 82, No. EM3, July 1956, pp. 1032–1–1032–16.

A. J. W. POWELL

Canberra as a Case Study in the
Art and Science of Town Planning

'Every great town planner has been driven on to
attempt realisations that only the future can justify.'
— SIGFRIED GIEDION

Introduction

Canberra is the national capital and seat of government of Australia. It is a
planned city of 200 000 people whose physical development has reached the
stage where it is increasingly being recognized as a significant attempt to
realize the ideal city that the art and science of town planning strives to
achieve.

After almost 200 years of European settlement the Australian continent has
few if any outstanding works of architecture or civil engineering. The Snowy
Mountains hydro-electric scheme would be regarded as a major national
achievement by most Australians but it would be difficult to argue that it has
any international significance, or that it represents a landmark in the historical
evolution of civil engineering science. In a similar vein the Sydney Opera
House is probably the best known architectural work in Australia but it has
exerted no influence on the continuing practice of architecture in this country.
Canberra, on the other hand, is likely to be of great significance both within
Australia and abroad, partly because it demonstrably provides a satisfying
and efficient living environment, and partly because the way in which it has
been planned and built offers important object lessons for others.

Historical Processes of Urban Development

It is important to view Canberra in the context of the history of urban
development if its true significance is to be properly assessed. Broadly
speaking there are two typologies of urban development. One is referred to by
geographers as the 'natural city' which grows and develops, without the
intervention of princes or governments, by virtue of its favourable position
and the enterprise of its inhabitants. The other is the 'new town' which is
deliberately established on a chosen site and is fostered by royal or republican

74

governments, or sometimes by entrepreneurs. Place names such as Newton, Neustadt and Villeneuve are indicative of the many new towns which dot the historical map of Western Europe.

Planned towns appear very early in the archaeological record. There is evidence that in the period 2150 to 1950 BC the neolithic cities of Mohenjo-Daro and Harappa in the Indus Basin were planned on the basis of a gridiron street pattern and with districts allocated to specific land uses. From the early part of the fifty century BC Greek town planners made extensive use of the gridiron as part of a systematic approach to the organisation of physical space in cities. The basic elements of Greek city planning were the agora (public square), the acropolis (citadel), the enclosing wall, and defined districts for residential, commercial and religious purposes. Probably the most notable example of early classical Greek planning was the rebuilding of Miletus in 475 BC, attributed to Hippodamus who was described by Aristotle as 'the inventor of the art of planning cities', albeit incorrectly as history now shows.

The Renaissance is the first historical phase in which the evolution of architecture and town planning can be traced in a clear and unbroken line to twentieth-century urbanism. From about 1420 onwards publication of the writings of Vitruvius, an architect who worked in the Rome of Augustus, caused a widespread interest in concepts of 'the ideal city'. This particular notion continued to have a significant philosophical influence on town planning ideologies right up to the nineteenth century, and can be clearly identified in the 'garden-city' principles of Ebenezer Howard whose ideas subsequently found expression in the new towns of this century, including Canberra.

Renaissance architecture and town planning were motivated by a strong sense of order, balance and symmetry. The principal elements were the fortified city boundary, the straight street as a major axis, public spaces enclosed by formal arrangements of buildings having a mercantile rather than an ecclesiastical character, and gridiron residential districts.

Relatively high rates of population growth from the fourteenth century onwards and the growing power of princes and merchants made possible the construction of large groups of buildings arranged in accordance with a pre-determined layout or design. Buildings were placed symmetrically in relation to axially planned avenues. Particular emphasis was given to the closing of vistas by means of carefully placed monumental buildings, obelisks or statues at the ends of long, straight streets. Individual building facades were related to one another by arcades, stringcourses and parapets so as to achieve an architectural ensemble.

The application of Renaissance planning principles, especially the innovation of the straight street as a primary axis, was used during later historical periods particularly in the restructuring of Rome by Pope Sixtus V (1585–90) and the redevelopment of Paris by Napoleon III and Haussmann (1853–69).

Genesis of Canberra's Planning

Griffin's plan for Canberra has, as its two most important historical antecedents, the planning of Washington as a national capital in a federal system of government and the re-planning of Central Paris during the reign of the Emperor Napoleon III.

Georges-Eugene Haussmann, Prefect of the Seine under Napoleon III during the period 1853–69, transformed the physical layout of Central Paris to the form in which we largely see it today. He organized the construction of an extensive road system by demolishing many of the old and worn-out districts of the inner city. The Rue de Rivoli and the Boulevarde Sebastapol were typical of the many major avenues constructed by Haussmann ostensibly to facilitate the movement of troops, also to give better access to railway stations and centres of commerce, and to bring light and air to the redeveloped parts of the city made possible by these large scale engineering works and their associated land resumptions and demolitions.

The Champs-Elysees exemplified his system of wide avenues punctuated by formal squares, each with a central park for strollers but capable of allowing the free circulation of vehicular traffic around and through. According to Giedion 'no innovation in urban planning was more generally imitated in the years immediately following than this arrangement of squares filled with greenery in the midst of traffic'.

Haussmann planned a series of metropolitan parks and proposed that they be linked by a belt of open space along the line of the old city fortifications. Although his green belt idea was not accepted, the Bois de Boulogne, the Bois de Vincennes and the Longchamps racecourse were established as extensive areas of public leisure and recreation on a scale not seen before in European cities. Haussmann's true historical significance lay not only in his material achievements but also because of the particular way in which his planning and development was implemented. In essence he saw the city as a 'technical problem' and marshalled his technical and financial resources accordingly.

To solve the problems of congestion and overcrowding, and the lack of public recreation space and adequate light and air, he brought together a co-ordinated group of technicians. His closest collaborators were the engineers of water, sewerage and roads. There were no architects or town planners with the skills needed. The plan of Paris was prepared by Deschamps who was a roads surveyor, the parks were planned and constructed by Alphand who was a bridge and highway engineer. Haussmann's achievements have been summarized by Giedion who states that 'Louis XIV spent a lifetime in building Versailles despite the fact that he had all the resources of France at his disposal. In seventeen years Haussmann, by a mixture of determination and foresight, created the great nineteenth century city'.

As a contrast, and as an exercise in a more formal style of town planning, Washington was planned in 1791 by a French military engineer, Major Pierre

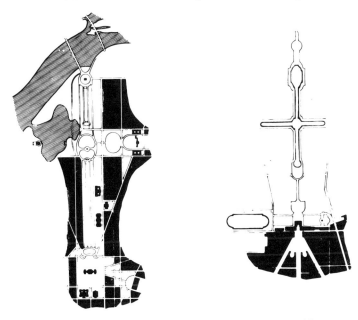

Washington   Versailles

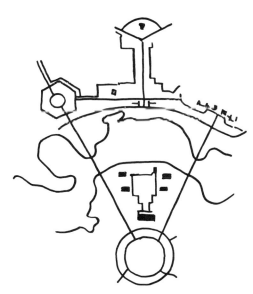

Canberra

FIG. 1

Charles L'Enfant, his plan being submitted roughly 100 years after the building of Versailles and to a marked degree influenced by it. He had lived for a time as a child at Versailles and later acknowledged that he had been inspired by its triangular geometry of tree-lined walks, round-points and symmetrical stretches of water when he came to prepare his design for Washington. His plan required six times more space for roads (3600 acres) than for public buildings (540 acres). He allocated only 2000 acres for building lots which later proved to be grossly inadequate and led to the breakdown of his plan in terms of metropolitan-wide development. He placed the major civic buildings and squares on the most prominent natural sites and designed long, wide avenues to link them visually and functionally in a basic triangular pattern.

L'Enfant's plan embodied many of the classical elements of Renaissance and Baroque town planning. John Reps summarizes an urban design concept which by virtue of its scale and comprehensiveness was unique to America:

> All the baroque design motifs of European planning developed over the years in the Old World suddenly and splendidly found application on this virgin site for the capital of the newest of the world's nations. It was a supreme irony that the plan forms originally conceived to magnify the glories of despotic kings and emperors came to be applied as a national symbol of a country whose philosophical basis was so firmly rooted in democratic equality.

Central Washington as it now appears, however, is largely the result of major town planning improvements and changes contained in the report of the Senate Park Commission of 1902. The Commission was appointed at the time of the city's centenary, ostensibly to prepare a plan for the District's parks but in the minds of its proponents the real intention was to prepare a comprehensive development plan for all of Central Washington.

As part of its investigations the Commission toured the historic centres of Western Europe and was greatly impressed by the Rome of Sixtus and Haussmann's Paris. It concluded that the plazas and fountains of Rome and the grand axial avenues of Paris were appropriate models to follow. Reps observes that in Paris the monumental central axis of the city stretching from the Louvre through the Gardens of the Place de la Concorde, and up the Champs-Elysees to the Arc de Triomphe, constituted a monumental and formal composition similar in concept and scale to what the Commission members envisaged for the centre of Washington.

Although not everything recommended by the Commission has been realized in practice, nevertheless, most of what has been built has been done in accordance with its proposals. The Senate Park Commission's plan for Washington had an enormous influence on the planning of other American cities. This and Haussmann's work in Paris were commonly held up as examples of what could be achieved in pursuit of the ideal of the 'city beautiful'.

The Griffin Plan

The establishment of Canberra as a national capital was a duty imposed upon

Parliament by the Constitution of 1900. Section 125 provides that the Commonwealth Seat of Government should be in Commonwealth territory, not less than 100 square miles in area, situated in the State of New South Wales not less than 100 miles from Sydney. The Seat of Government Acceptance Act 1909 ratified the site in the Yass-Canberra district and made provision for 910 square miles to be ceded to the Commonwealth.

In 1911 an international competition was launched for the design of the new capital. The conditions specified that the city was to be the permanent seat of government, likely to grow at a rate similar to that of Washington in the nineteenth century and to accommodate a population 25 000. Particular consideration was to be given to the siting of major buildings, such as the Parliament, which should become the dominating feature of the city. Provision was generally to be made for the Houses of Parliament, residences for the Governor-General and for the Prime Minister, a National Art Gallery, National Library, the State House, government offices, mint, museum, university, national theatre, stadium, courts, military barracks and city hall.

The first prize was awarded in 1912 to Walter Burley Griffin, a Chicago architect, whose plan was not finally adopted until 1916 because of attempts by officials radically to alter its proposals, and because changes of government, divided administrative responsibility and lack of money inhibited the initial growth of the city.

Griffin approached the problem of Canberra's planning more as a landscape designer than as an architect. He continued the traditions of Renaissance urban design in his adoption of a central triangle, processional ways and circular street patterns in the Baroque manner. These elements are similarly expressed in L'Enfant's plan for Washington and were later amplified and extended in the designs of the 1902 Senate Park Commission. In his suburban planning Griffin also adopted 'garden-city' principles based on the ideas of Ebenezer Howard (1898) which at the time were attracting growing interest in the United States and subsequently formed the basis of the so-called 'greenbelt' cities and the British new towns.

Griffin foresaw that it might be several generations before there would be sufficient public buildings to establish an architectural fabric which would visibly delineate the axial elements and formal spaces of his plan. He accordingly designed a grand formal landscape using avenues, lakes, the immediate hills and distant mountains in order to obtain maximum visual advantage from every natural feature that the site had to offer. The few principal buildings were intended to create an impression not so much by virtue of their architecture and scale but by their siting in the landscape.

The central triangle of Griffin's plan is similar in scale to that of Washington. It comprises a land axis, which is in the main a visual rather than a movement axis, spanning between Red Hill, Capital Hill and Mount Ainslie. There are two parallel transverse axes, one a water axis subsequently expressed in the form of Lake Burley Griffin, the other along the line of Constitution Avenue

FIG. 2   Griffin's central triangle seen from Capital Hill looking along the land
axis to Mount Ainslie

spanning between City Hill and Mount Pleasant.

On Capital Hill Griffin proposed a Capitol building as a place of popular assembly and the most visually prominent piece of architecture. The Hill itself was the focus of nine avenues, of which Commonwealth and Kings Avenues serve as arms of a movement triangle having Constitution Avenue as its base.

Griffin remained in control of national capital works until his departure from Canberra in 1921. By this time the framework of principal streets was established on the ground. In 1924 his plan, slightly amended, was gazetted and accordingly confirmed as the official plan to be used as the basis for future development control by Parliament. Peter Harrison has commented that 'Griffin, despite his talents as a creative designer, was throughout his life unbusinesslike and dilatory. He had tremendous energy and capacity for design, but lacked the administrative ability to run the simplest project without getting into trouble'. It is clear that he was no Haussmann.

NCDC Planning and Development

The combined effects of a world-wide economic depression in the 1930s and a consistent lack of political will meant that there was very little construction in Canberra during the thirty years following Griffin's departure. In 1954, because of concern at the lack of material progress, a Senate Select Committee of Inquiry was set up to inquire into the development of Canberra in relation to the Griffin plan.

The Committee concluded that there was no sign of any determination on the part of successive governments to complete the National Capital. It accordingly recommended that a powerful and expert authority be constituted with sufficient finance to enable it to carry out a balanced programme of long-term urban development. In 1957 the National Capital Development Commission (NCDC) was established to 'plan, develop and construct' Canberra as the national capital and seat of government of Australia. The NCDC is essentially a development corporation, and upon completion of planning and construction the finished works and buildings are handed over to the relevant administrative department or authority.

In the twenty years of the Commission's existence the population of Canberra has grown from 41 000 in 1958 to just over 210 000 at the present time. The Commission's two most significant achievements — relative to the historical evolution of town planning — have been, first, the transformation and extension of Griffin's plan into a metropolitan plan capable of accommodating more than half a million inhabitants and, second, the ability to co-ordinate a large-scale urban development programme whose current expenditure rate is just over $200 million per year.

In the case of Canberra's central area the Commission accepted Griffin's plan as the basis for its own detailed land use planning and urban design. It has consistently attempted to identify his underlying planning principles and re-interpret them in the light of contemporary needs and aesthetic values.

The land axis has been clearly expressed by the construction of Anzac Parade as a formally landscaped ceremonial avenue. By 1964 the lake had been built thus fulfilling the concept of Griffin's water axis. During the next ten years the National Library, Treasury, National Gallery and High Court were completed or commenced as part of the architectural build-up that Griffin envisaged in his central triangle between Capital Hill and the Lake foreshores. Two nodes, Civic and the Defence complex at Russell, have been substantially built-up and are growing towards one another along the line of Constitution Avenue.

During the 1960s the Commission formulated a series of metropolitan plans whose purpose was to lay down a structure of land uses and communications, capable of progressively accommodating 250 000 people by 1980 and in excess of half a million by the end of the century. This so-called Y-Plan envisaged a metropolitan area divided into a series of separate 'towns' — Woden,

A. J. W. Powell

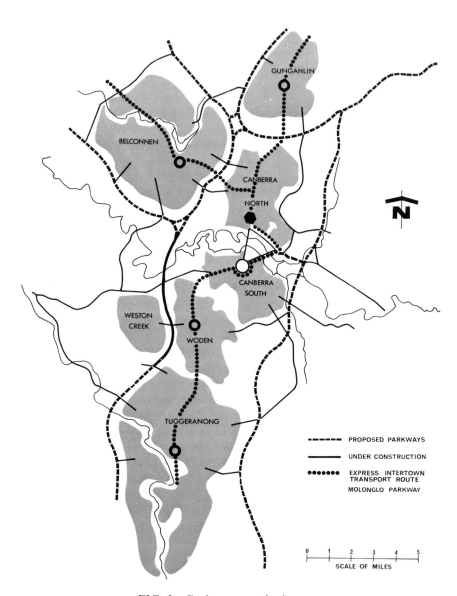

FIG. 3   Canberra growth plan

Belconnen, Tuggeranong, Gungahlin — each with its own town centre providing office employment and retail services thereby achieving a significant degree of self-containment. Each of these towns is linked by a central transport spine connecting the town centres. There are in addition peripheral highways which carry fast-moving through traffic outside the urban areas in what is basically a linear city form. In urban design terms the urban areas of each town are situated in adjoining valleys and are accordingly separated by intervening ridges and hilltops, preserved largely in their natural state as part of a continuous metropolitan open space system.

Within each town the basic planning unit is the residential neighbourhood, centred on the primary school and having sufficient shops and recreation space to cater for local needs. Through-traffic is discouraged and diverted to the distributor road system running between neighbourhoods and defining their spatial limits. The neighbourhood unit is regarded by the Commission as a functional rather than a sociological concept. Comparative studies show that it works effectively because it encourages relatively high proportions of safe pedestrian movement and coincides fairly closely with areas of local interest.

The town centres of Woden and Belconnen are developing as important locations of tertiary employment and retail services. The Commission has a specific policy of discouraging office development in Civic in those instances where other town centres appear to offer a potentially viable alternative. Town centre retailing is similarly controlled in order that a balanced distribution is available throughout the metropolitan area rather than having a high concentration in a single centre. Canberra is one of the few cities in the world where there has been effective decentralization of employment at the metropolitan scale related to the capacity of available transport systems, both bus and private car.

The skeleton of the Y-Plan is the transport system. Recent studies have shown that for a population of less than half a million the most feasible public transport system is a bus fleet running on an at-grade arterial road network. As public transport capacity increases above about the 250 000 population level a grade-separated roadway used exclusively by buses is desirable, the initial parts of which are currently under construction. The peripheral parkway network exists only in embryonic form. Part of the Tuggeranong Parkway and the Molonglo Arterial are built or under construction and by 1981 will link Tuggeranong and Civic.

The overall transport system is being developed in accordance with a transport policy jointly formulated by the Commission and the city adminis-tration (Department of the Capital Territory). The primary elements of road capacity, parking space and public transport capacity are balanced in relation to overall forecasts of transport needs. The joint policy aims to achieve a progressive shift towards increasing use of public transport. Added capacity in the bus system is counter-balanced by lesser increases in commuter road capacity and/or greater control over public parking space in town centres.

Because the various key elements of land use, roads, parking space and public transport are all integrated in terms of planning, development and operation, the conflicts which exist in most other cities are avoided and a coherent policy with explicit objectives can be maintained and implemented.

Apart from its effectiveness as a built environment Canberra is also significant because of the way in which the city is being developed. In other words the 'process' of urban development in Canberra offers important object lessons for others. The NCDC operates in the manner and style of Haussmann in the sense that it understands — as he did — that the city must be seen as essentially a technical problem. It is a viewpoint whose implications are not often recognized, and even more rarely accepted as a basis for action.

Town planning is not, in any real sense, concerned with the 'quality of life' of city dwellers despite the grandiose claims frequently made for it in this regard. All categories of professional endeavour can be said to possess a basic humanistic concern but town planning can in practice only provide physical space or containers for shelter, in much the same manner as engineering or architecture. The quality of social action and of community life depends in a more direct manner on factors which are for the most part non-physical.

Haussmann was a supreme organizer and administrator who understood that the diverse components of urban development were above all an exercise in co-ordination. Apart from his ability to utilize diverse technical skills he also recognized — as Giedion points out — the importance of controlling the complex machinery of credit and finance. He was frequently opposed in his schemes by Parliament and by landowners who felt their interests threatened by his schemes. As one means of coping with such opposition he set up a public works budget as a secure source of finance under his own control and thus not subject to the vagaries of the City Council. His budget was based on the idea that urban development was inherently profitable due to the fact that public sector works, such as roads and parks, created value in the land thus serviced. It was accordingly intended to be self-financing and to act as a secure source of finance for his works programmes.

In a similar vein the NCDC is established by Parliament with a clear power to carry out an annual works programme supported by a specific budget, and made relatively free from the typical bureaucratic controls which cause so many public authorities in Australia to be both inefficient and ineffective. The Commission operates on the basis of an appropriation through the national budget within which it allocates funds to specified projects. It is able to vary its construction priorities in order to meet forecast needs in terms of housing, utility services, education, health and so forth.

The Commission's unique skill is to set up and manipulate a highly-complex programme of urban development, on a scale far greater than any other comparable 'new town' in the world. It does this within a framework of comprehensive planning controls and utilizing both public and private sector resources. Within the Commission's annual works programme there is a wide variation in development 'lead' times. A primary school, for example may take three years to design and build whereas a dam or sewerage treatment plant could take from ten to twelve years. A new residential neighbourhood takes at least seven years from initial planning to the completion of the first house on a serviced block yet at the time the first resident moves in he expects to have water, reticulated sewerage, schools, public transport and landscaped recreation areas. The programming techniques to achieve such a high degree of coincidence must be co-ordinated and comprehensive, and the resulting built environment must be functional and aesthetically pleasing.

It is unfortunately a commonplace in the minds of most Australians that the high quality and manifest attractiveness of Canberra's physical environment is due solely to unlimited funding by the Federal government. It is not the amount of money but rather the way it is expended which really accounts for Canberra's success as a public enterprise. The standards adopted by the Commission for engineering works or schools, for example, are the same as those used in the States. Probably the most significant difference is that Canberra with a highly integrated works programme, deliberately oriented towards identified community needs and priorities, avoids the diseconomies inherent in the piecemeal approach which characterizes urban development elsewhere.

By virtue of its comprehensive planning powers and its skill in co-ordinating a long-term works programme the Commission is able to achieve more efficient development than appears to be the case in most other cities. For this reason its techniques and procedures are increasingly being studied and its assistance sought by development corporations and government agencies in other countries.

The Future Canberra

Canberra has reached a watershed in terms of its future development and planning. During the past twenty years its growth has been sustained by the transfer of public servants from Melbourne and Sydney in accordance with the intentions of the Constitution that the national capital is to be the centre of Commonwealth government administration. Virtually all of the Federal departments are now established in Canberra and after 1980 there is unlikely to be any significant degree of inward migration resulting from further transfers.

The Commission's current forecasts indicate that Canberra will continue to grow at a slightly higher rate than the national average, consistent with the trend displayed by national capitals generally as the powers and responsibilities of central government continue to expand.

The effect of a lower population growth rate, currently at about 3 per cent compared to an annual average of around 10 per cent during the period 1958–

73, will be to reduce the demand for normal basic requirements such as serviced land, schools, health facilities, etc. The concerted efforts required during the last twenty years to build the 'functional' city in response to high rates of population growth will not be required in the future. Urban development can be handled through what are now well-established, efficient procedures.

Of critical significance during the next two decades is the need for a deliberate effort, supported by clear political determination, to realize Canberra as an effective national capital. This is a goal which, in the light of Washington's experience and the efforts of the Senate Park Commission, should be achievable by the turn of the century. Apart from the National Gallery and the High Court — at present under construction — the city does not possess many of the significant national institutions which would make it a truly effective national capital. It is not always regarded by the Federal government as the obvious location for international meetings in the way that London or Paris would be unquestionable choices in similar circumstances.

Canberra does not yet possess a place in the minds of most Australians similar to the significance that Washington has for most Americans. Reps is able accurately to state: 'Washington stands, in a very real sense, as the civic centre of America, and the hundreds of thousands of visitors who annually throng to the city bear witness to the special character of its townscape and to the near reverence with which it is regarded by every citizen of the nation'.

In the case of Canberra there is considerable scope further to develop what is at best only an emergent national capital. It is proposed that the National Archives will be built during the early 1980s. The Museum of Australia has already been the subject of an official inquiry following which the Commission has carried out preliminary site planning pending a formal decision by the government that the project is to proceed. With the completion of the High Court of Australia in 1980 it would be desirable from a national capital viewpoint that the Arbitration Court — a uniquely federal institution — be moved to Canberra so as to confirm an important precinct of national legal institutions reflecting the judicial arm of government.

With regard to the physical or visual image of the city there is no doubt that the most significant lack is a crowning work of architecture in the form of the new and permanent Parliament House. In 1974 Parliament determined by statute that the site for its permanent building is to be Capital Hill. This is consistent with Griffin's proposals for his central triangle in that his so-called Capitol was to be the largest and most visible piece of architecture, although he saw its function not as the legislature but ideally as a place of popular assembly. A joint Parliamentary Committee is currently engaged in a programme of investigations, assisted by the Commission, which hopefully will result in the first stage of the permanent Parliament House opening in 1988, the 200th anniversary of European settlement on the Australian continent.

The provisional Parliament building was completed in 1927 having an anticipated life of fifty years. It is undistinguished as architecture and is not remembered as the location of historic national events. It is overcrowded and in a state of poor repair. It cannot adequately accommodate the present numbers of members and their support staff, nor is there space for all the parliamentary committees which are a growing feature of contemporary democratic government. Ancillary services, such as Hansard and library research facilites, are progressively being shifted to buildings well away from the Parliament with consequently less effectiveness for members and with more constraints on the adoption of up-to-date parliamentary procedures.

Apart from functional considerations it is all too easy to under-estimate the powerful ethos that can be embodied in a dominant piece of architecture, particularly when it houses the supreme political power of the nation. The visual form and siting of the Houses of Parliament at Westminster, or the Sydney Opera House, are examples of buildings which symbolize a nation or a city.

Similarly, Canberra will not register strongly as a national capital in the minds of Australians until it possesses a major work of architecture to house its Parliament. Fortunately the nominated site on Capital Hill offers outstanding potential for a visible symbol which could dominate the city in the positive way that the Acropolis at Athens epitomizes the institutions of classical Greece.

At the present time the Parliamentary triangle possesses only a scatter of buildings set amidst vast lawns stretching from the provisional House to the foreshores of Lake Burley Griffin. The scene from Parliament House steps impresses somewhat by virtue of extensive space but does not exist as a composition of architectural and landscape elements in the manner that Griffin envisaged. The result is a 'national place' that is unattractive to pedestrians and impractical for tourists.

Although the National Gallery and High Court will become important new tourist attractions the Commission takes the view that other national cultural institutions should be located along the edges of Griffin's land axis in order to create a feeling of urban space. Such a built-form would have a better chance of promoting pedestrian movement and a feeling of vitality throughout the triangle, and thus a sense of life and usage which at present it rarely expresses.

Unfortunately the prevailing view of successive governments, and of many Members of Parliament, has been that few if any buildings should be placed in the triangle and it is accordingly to be regarded as uninterrupted open space — a green setting rather than an urban setting. In historical terms such a viewpoint is naive. It denies the important contrast that the Griffin plan proposed would exist between the city and the embracing framework of near hills and distant mountains. So long as this attitude persists Canberra will be prevented from becoming a significant city in the sense that the history of urban development identifies Athens, Rome, Paris and Washington as significant, and also marks them as the precursors of Canberra in terms of town planning and urban design. The next two decades are likely to be critical for Canberra's continuing evolution, particularly in terms of attracting further national institutions and building up land use densities in Griffin's central triangle.

At the metropolitan scale the Y-Plan is under review by the Commission in order to take account of environmental factors now recognized as important. Studies of the region's air and water systems are attempting to gauge their capacity to handle large-scale concentrations of urban development and the extent to which they should accordingly be accepted as a constraint on future growth.

In the political realm there are growing pressures for a measure of self-government for the Territory which will mean a more complex political-administrative structure than that which currently exists between the Commonwealth government, its departmental administration, and the NCDC. The almost universal experience is that efficient urban development and co-ordinated planning are not possible if dictated by the demands of a local constituency. A national Capital can only be built on the basis of national aspirations and attitudes.

Canberra as a Prototype

Canberra is the most prolonged, most complex and most far-reaching work of national development in Australia since the laying down of the State railway networks in the latter half of the nineteenth century. It is the largest inland city in Australia but as yet can only be described as an emergent national capital. It is a major town planning achievement but has still to realize its potential in the realms of urban design and architecture. It is not yet a symbol of national consciousness because it is not an important focus of national culture.

It is, nonetheless, significant in universal terms because, as a physical manifestation of the art and science of town planning, it has reached a sufficient stage in its physical development for it to offer useful object lessons to others.

What Canberra demonstrates is that the existence of a clear and boldly imaginative plan is essential if the classical ideals of town planning and architecture are to be realized in practice. Griffin's plan goes further than the approaches of Haussmann or L'Enfant in the way that it uses Renaissance and Baroque elements but combines them with a fundamental insight into the topographical and landscape features of the site. In the absence of noble architecture and dynamic engineering structures, the initial stages of the plan are made to rely on these natural features and in this way the intentions of the long-term plan appear quickly enough to the layman's eye, thereby generating early community support which is so critical if the plan is to be persevered with by governments. Brazilia, for example, has proceeded in an opposite manner whereby initial emphasis has been placed on large-scale architectural and engineering works in the government centre whilst suburban development and metropolitan scale planning has been relatively neglected.

The Commission has found Griffin's plan to be adaptable to changing community needs and the availability of new technologies. Canberra's joint transport policy is a good example of how different urban components can be viewed in terms of their inter-dependent relationships and manipulated one against the other to achieve specific objectives, in this case a gradual shift in favour of public transport.

Although it is too early to make a definite assessment Canberra's metropolitan form and structure, as expressed in the Y-Plan, may offer distinct advantages over concentric patterns of organic urban development as typified by other Australian cities. It is already apparent that Canberra's linear form achieves a more satisfactory relationship between 'town and country' because it facilitates ready access to metropolitan and regional open space. There are indications also that the adverse effects of air pollution can be more easily mitigated by a lineal urban pattern. It is hoped that from a transport viewpoint the separation of public transport and arterial parkways to the centre and periphery respectively will eventually prove to be an efficient and economical way of handling metropolitan transport systems, which in all cities elsewhere is probably the most difficult urban planning and city management problem for which no solution is in sight.

Finally, Canberra's methods of programming and co-ordinating urban development offer potentially the most useful lessons of all yet, by their very nature, they are the most difficult processes to describe and disseminate. It is not often realized, for example, that the Snowy Mountains Scheme was of great potential significance, not because its dams and power stations were remarkable, but because of the manner in which the SMHEA as the responsible authority was organized and the way in which it performed its tasks. Its organization has disappeared, its procedures are unrecorded and unrecognized so that to all intents and purposes the potential lessons have been lost.

Canberra is not yet complete but it may already be one of the great works of man in the twentieth century. In his 1957 review of Canberra's planning and development Lord Holford commented that its future direction would not depend so much on finance but on 'an effort of will'. He went on to state that 'It was this which brought Canberra into being in the first place. Federal capitals are political acts of faith and do not have their roots implanted in the facts of economic geography, as other cities do'. It would be a tragedy if the 'act of faith' is not sustained, and increasingly taken up by the nation at large.

It is likely that in future a considerable proportion of new urban settlements will come about through deliberate choice, in the main by governments, rather than through organic processes involving economic factors and fortuitous geographical circumstances. The use of town planning techniques will accordingly increase in importance because they offer a means of organizing and controlling future urban development, not necessarily to produce radically new forms of city, but more to identify particular architectural and urban design elements that are still valid. Town planning also offers procedures for programming and co-ordinating urban development so as to meet community needs and accord with social priorities. Because Canberra stands as a physical manifestation of what the art and science of town planning can actually achieve, it is a potential source of positive lessons for others, in addition to its importance as a functional and symbolic National Capital.

References

1. Morris, A. E. J., *History of Urban Form: Prehistory to the Renaissance*, George Goodwin, London 1977.
2. Giedion, Sigfried. *Space, Time and Architecture*, Harvard University Press, Cambridge, Mass. 1959.
3. Reps, John W. *Monumental Washington: The Planning and Development of the Capital Center*, Princeton University Press, 1967.
4. National Capital Development Commission, *Tomorrow's Canberra*, ANU Press, Canberra 1970.
5. National Capital Development Commission, *Twentieth Annual Report*, 1976–7.

P. B. JONES

Teaching Surveying in a School of Civil Engineering

THE SYLLABUS

The aim of the surveying course is to teach the student:

(a) The basic principles of measurement — this part of the course is analytical, statistical, geometrical. The principles apply to all types of measurement and should be borne in mind in all laboratory work.

(b) Methods of taking field measurements and computing the results of various types of surveys which a young engineer may be called upon to carry out himself. This part of the course is essentially practical in its aim. A young engineer must be able to determine the levels of a few points competently just as he must be able to carry out a slump test on concrete or determine the Brinell hardness of a steel specimen. The *techniques* of surveying and of calculation generally result, however, from an analysis of the sources of error which must be dealt with.

While a technician can take measurements competently merely by following a routine, the emphasis of this surveying course will be to teach the principles and design methods from which the techniques follow, rather than the techniques themselves.

(c) The principles of astronomic, geodetic, photogrammetric and topographical surveying. It is unlikely that a civil engineer would carry out this type of work himself; he will, however, have to use the results of such surveys and it is necessary that he have a clear understanding of the principles involved in order that he may intelligently call for and make use of these disciplines when the occasion arises. Frequently, the overall planning of a project is the responsibility of a civil engineer and this planning both influences and is influenced by the methods of surveying.

It is not the aim of the course to teach students all of the basic survey methods which they should know or are likely to meet, and be required to carry out themselves, in civil engineering practice. Without doubt a civil engineer should be able to set out the transitions to a circular curve. This material, and other similar matters, will not be discussed in the course; the new intellectual content is small, and the subjects are dealt with quite adequately in the recommended texts. It is the student's own professional responsibility to learn these practical applications for himself.

The above statement is given as a preamble to the syllabus for the Surveying I and Surveying II courses. The emphasis is on *analysis and design*: on the analysis of sources of error and their likely magnitudes, and on the design of techniques whereby the effects of these errors can be satisfactorily controlled.

Students frequently hope for direct closed-form solutions to problems. In

91

civil engineering design this is generally an impossibility. Often a designer can make a shrewd estimate of the sizes of members in a frame and then proceed to use these trial values to assess loads and determine strengths. Often the design of a survey follows along a similar path. One must be able to estimate the method and likely precision of elements of a survey and then check whether the whole will be adequate or not.

The design process in simple surveys is quite straightforward. The detail survey is designed first, then the control survey is designed to be two or preferably three times more precise than the detail survey. In this way the errors in the control survey have a negligible effect on the detail survey.

The structural notion of flexibility is analogous to variance (that is, to the square of the standard deviation) in a survey. Thus a three-fold increase in precision is the same as a nine-fold reduction in variance or a nine-fold reduction in flexibility. If a joint in a frame were nine times stiffer than other joints we would often be willing to treat the joint as rigid, i.e. as *inflexible* for the design purposes, so analogously, the control survey can be treated as effectively error-free relative to the detail survey.

The *design* consists in examining the main sources of error and checking that the standard deviation of the errors is less than the allowable values. At times it may be necessary to average a number of readings, or to close and adjust a traverse (for level or for position) or to reduce the distances measured over, in order to increase precision.

DESIGN EXAMPLE

Let us consider a simple example of design. A plan is required at a scale of 1 in 500 and with 0.5 metre contour interval of an undulating, lightly-timbered area about 400 metres long by 200 metres wide. What is an economical method of surveying the area?

We could carry out our survey by determining bearing and distance of detail from control points. The radiations could be taped, which is relatively precise but slow and expensive, or measured by stadia or diagram tacheometry which is relatively economical but of much lower precision than taping. Electronic distance measurement is very precise, and in some configurations very fast, but the capital cost at present is such that few young engineers will have access to the equipment, at least for small surveys.

Let us consider stadia tacheometry. If control-points are set at approximately 100 metre intervals as shown in Fig. 1, the area to be surveyed from each control point would lie inside a circle of radius $\frac{\sqrt{2}}{2} \times 100 = 70$ metres approximately. It will be seen that there is considerable overlap between these circles. If we ignore this overlap, the average sighting-distance to points within a circle will be equal to the polar radius of gyration of the circle $= \frac{2}{3} \times 70 = 50$

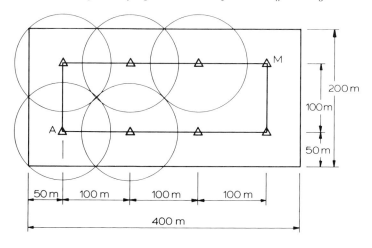

FIG. 1

metres approximately. We can thus analyse our survey assuming an average
sighting-distance of 50 metres.

Radial Error

The horizontal distance s and rise r from the ground-mark under the
theodolite to the staff position can be calculated from:

$$s = \frac{b}{\gamma}\cos^2\beta$$

$$r = \frac{b}{\gamma}\sin\beta\cos\beta + HI - C$$

where b is the staff-intercept cut off by the parallactic angle γ subtended by the
stadia wires, β is the angle of elevation from theodolite to the staff-reading C to
which the centre-hair of the theodolite is pointed, and HI is the height of
instrument above the ground-mark.

It follows that if we consider small errors $\Delta\gamma$, Δb and $\Delta\beta$ in γ, b and β
respectively, the resulting error Δs in s is given by:

$$\frac{\Delta s}{s} = -\frac{\Delta\gamma}{\gamma} + \frac{\Delta b}{b} - \frac{2\sin\beta\cos\beta\,\Delta\beta}{\cos^2\beta}$$

$$= -\frac{\Delta\gamma}{\gamma} + \frac{\Delta b}{b} - 2\tan\beta\,\Delta\beta$$

The error $\Delta\gamma$ in γ arises from differential refraction of the two rays defining the
parallactic angle. This differential refraction is proportional to distance and
hence the resulting error in distance

93

$$\Delta s = -s\frac{\Delta \gamma}{\gamma}$$

will be proportional to the square of the distance. The error also depends markedly on the minimum height of the rays above the ground; the higher the readings, the less the error.

If sighting distances are of the order of 100 metres and the lower ray is allowed to drop as low as 0.5 metre above the ground, field experience shows that the standard deviation σ_γ of γ will be in the range of from 2″ to 5″. Thus with $\gamma = \frac{1}{100}$ radian $= 2063″$,

$$\frac{\sigma_s}{s} \sim \frac{2″ \text{ to } 5″}{2063″} = \frac{1 \text{ to } 2.5}{1000}$$

If we restrict sighting distances to about 70 metres and keep our lower hair reading above one metre we may take the lower error limit:

$$\frac{\sigma_s}{s} \sim \frac{1}{1000}$$

for this source of error.

It is relatively simple to estimate tenths on a staff divided to centimetres at distances of less than 100 metres. Even if the staff interval were only interpolated correctly to the nearest 3 millimetres (implying a maximum error of $\pm \frac{3}{2}$) σ_b, the standard deviation of reading the staff-interval b, would only reach:

$$\sigma_b = \frac{1}{\sqrt{12}} \times 3 = 0.9 \, \text{mm}$$

Hence we may accept

$$\sigma_b = 1 \, \text{mm}$$

under reasonable conditions of visibility. If we take our average sighting distance as 50 metres, then since

$$b = s\gamma \sec^2 \beta$$

we will have

$$b = 50,000 \times \frac{1}{100} \times \sec^2 \beta$$
$$\sim 500 \, \text{mm}$$

since if $\tan \beta = 0.2$, $\sec^2 \beta = 1.04$ and b only increases to 520mm for a 20% grade and so we can treat $\sec^2 \beta$ as 1 for this error analysis. We thus obtain

$$\frac{\sigma_b}{b} \sim \frac{1}{500} = \frac{2}{1000}$$

When considering height determination we shall see that we require the standard deviation σ_β of measuring the angle of elevation β to be of the order of

$$\sigma_\beta \sim 20''$$

Under these conditions for a slope of $\tan\beta = 0.2$ we obtain

$$\frac{\sigma_s}{s} = -2\tan\beta\,\sigma_\beta = -2 \times 0.2 \times \frac{20''}{206265''} \sim \frac{-0.04}{1000}$$

which is completely negligible in comparison with the other terms.

There remains one other important source of error: the staff may not be vertical. Rocking the staff and taking the lowest reading will not help because the lines of sight will not be horizontal and so we must rely on a staff-bubble to ensure staff verticality. European experience has shown that the standard deviation σ_δ of the staff tilt δ from the vertical is about

$$\sigma_\delta \sim \frac{1}{100} \text{ radian}$$

for a hand-held staff with a staff-bubble. The resulting error in distance Δs can be shown to be

$$\Delta s \sim (r + c)\delta$$

and hence

$$\frac{\sigma_s}{s} \sim \frac{(r + c)}{s}\sigma_\delta$$

If we take

$$c = 1.5 \text{ metres}$$
$$s = 50 \text{ metres}$$
$$\tan\beta = 0.2$$

then

$$\frac{\sigma_s}{s} \sim \frac{(10 + 1.5)}{50} \times \frac{1}{100}$$
$$\sim \frac{2}{1000}$$

The errors which we have considered are independent. Hence the variance of the sum of the errors will be given by the sum of the variances so that the total effect is given by

$$\left[\frac{\sigma_s}{s}\right]^2 = \left[\frac{\sigma_\gamma}{\gamma}\right]^2 + \left[\frac{\sigma_b}{b}\right]^2 + \left[2\tan\beta\sigma_\beta\right]^2 + \left[\frac{r+c}{s}\sigma_\gamma\right]^2$$

$$= \frac{1}{10^6} + \frac{1}{10^6} + 0 + \frac{2^2}{10^6}$$

$$= \frac{6}{10^6}$$

so that

$$\frac{\sigma_s}{s} \sim \frac{2.5}{1000}$$

or for

$$s = 50 \text{ metres,}$$
$$\sigma_s \sim 125 \text{ mm on the terrain.}$$

Map Specification

A common method of specifying the precision of a map at a scale of 1/20,000 or larger has been to state that 90 per cent of points of well-defined detail should be plotted within 0.8 mm of the required positions. It should be immediately obvious that if we accept the meaning of the words as they are written, then this specification is *not* referring to the precision of *coordinates* but rather to the *vector errors* in position of plotted points. Thus we are *not* dealing with a normal distribution as has been commonly believed; the errors in the X and Y coordinates of points will be approximately normal, but the vector error ΔR will not. If the variance is the same in all directions viz σ^2, then

$$\frac{(\Delta R)^2}{\sigma^2} = \frac{(\Delta X)^2}{\sigma^2} + \frac{(\Delta Y)^2}{\sigma^2}$$

will be distributed as χ^2 (2), and

$$P\left\{\chi^2 = \frac{(\Delta R_0)^2}{\sigma^2} > \chi_0^2\right\} = 0.10$$

gives

$$\chi_0^2 = 4.60 = 2.15^2$$

whence

$$\Delta R_0 = 2.15\sigma = 0.8 \text{ mm}$$

$$\sigma = \frac{0.8}{2.15} = 0.37 \text{ mm}$$

The more generally, and incorrectly, calculated

$$\sigma = \frac{0.8}{1.65} = 0.5 \text{ mm}$$

would apply if we were considering the error *component* in any given direction. If we adopted $\sigma = 0.5$ mm then the probability of vector errors less than 0.8 mm would be given by

$$P\{\Delta R < 0.8\} = P\left\{\left(\frac{R}{0.5}\right)^2 < \left(\frac{0.8}{0.5}\right)^2\right\}$$
$$= P\{\chi^2(2) < 2.56\}$$
$$= 0.68$$

which is somewhat less than the 90 per cent originally called for.

Let us adopt the literal specification and aim at producing a map for which the standard deviation σ of a plotted *coordinate* satisfies

$$\sigma \le 0.37 \text{ mm}$$

on the manuscript. The variance of the error *vector* is thus

$$\sigma_R^2 = 2\sigma^2 = 0.27 \text{ mm}^2$$

and

$$\sigma_R = 0.52 \text{ mm}$$

Feasibility

Let us examine whether this precision can be attained or not.

Dimensional changes in the map base will not be considered in this discussion. It will be assumed that the manuscript does not change size during the interval of time in which the map is drawn. Hence the *scale* of the map and the *scale* of the graticule may be assumed to be the same, apart from accidental plotting errors. If the positions of points are later referred to the graticule, the effect of general scale-changes may be allowed for.

Plotting

Consider the sources of accidental errors in the drafting of the map:

(i) drawing the graticule (X *and* Y)

(ii) plotting control points relative to the graticule from co-ordinates (X *and* Y)

(iii) centring a protractor over a given control point *and* orienting it with a given bearing along a line drawn to another control point, or parallel to a grid line.

(iv) drawing a radiation (bearing *and* distance) to a detail point.

Note that each of the steps (i) to (iv) involves *two* operations. Let us assume that each of the 8 operations makes an equal, independent, contribution to the

positional error of a typical detail point relative to reference graticule lines along the left-hand and the lower edges of the map sheet. Let us further accept that these errors are at least approximately normally distributed with a standard deviation, per operation, of 0.15 mm.
Then

$$\sigma_{plot}^2 = 8 \times 0.15^2$$
$$= 0.18 \text{ mm}^2$$
$$\sigma_{plot} = 0.42 \text{ mm}$$

corresponding to standard deviations in coordinate directions of

$$\sigma_{plot \ coord} = 0.3 \text{ mm}$$

Let us examine how large the survey errors may be if the total error of survey + plotting is to remain within specification.

If σ_{detail} is the standard deviation of the error vector from the survey of a point of detail relative to the control point from which it is fixed, then we require

$$\sigma_{control}^2 + \sigma_{detail}^2 + \sigma_{plot}^2 \leq \sigma_R^2$$

If we restrict $\sigma_{control}$ to between $1/2$ and $1/3$ of σ_{detail}, then the errors introduced by the control survey will be negligible in comparison with those from the detail survey and we can write

$$\sigma_{detail}^2 + 0.18 \leq 0.27 \text{ mm}^2$$

or

$$\sigma_{detail} \leq 0.3 \text{ mm on the manuscript}$$
$$= 500 \times 0.3$$
$$= 150 \text{ mm on the terrain.}$$

In terms of coordinate errors, we could write

$$\sigma_{detail \ coord \atop (allowable)} = \frac{1}{\sqrt{2}} \sigma_{detail}$$

$$= 105 \text{ mm on the terrain.}$$

This allowable standard deviation is somewhat less than the $\sigma_s \sim 125$ mm calculated for a radiation by stadia. It is clear however that the largest source of error in the radiation arose from the effect of staff tilt. If we restrict our survey to slopes of 10 per cent, then $r + c$ will be restricted to less than $5 + 1.5 = 6.5$ metres and the term

$$\left(\frac{r+c}{s}\sigma_\delta\right)^2 \sim \left(\frac{6.5}{50} \times \frac{1}{100}\right)^2 = \frac{1.69}{10^6}$$

instead of $\dfrac{4}{10^6}$ as formerly. The resultant is thus given by

$$\frac{\sigma_s}{s} = \frac{2}{1000}$$

or

$$\sigma_s \sim 100 \text{ mm}$$

for $s = 50$ metres.

Thus provided slopes are not too steep — or more correctly, provided rises do not exceed 5 metres — our detail survey will be adequately precise as regards length of radiations.

Tangential Error

If bearings are recorded to the nearest $5'$, the standard deviation of bearing will be

$$\frac{1}{\sqrt{12}} \times 5' \sim 1.5'$$

corresponding to a tangential error of

$$\frac{1.5'}{3438'} \times 50{,}000 \sim 20 \text{ mm}$$

at a distance of 50 metres. Sighting the telescope to the centre of the staff at a height of 3 metres (rather than to the perhaps not visible base) would produce a tangential 'plumbing' error of

$$3000 \, \delta \text{ mm}$$

if the staff is tilted laterally by δ radians. It follows that with $\sigma_\delta = \dfrac{1}{100}$, this error component has a standard deviation of

$$3000 \times \frac{1}{100} = 30 \text{ mm}$$

The 'plumbing' error and the round-off error combine to give a resultant tangential standard deviation of

$$\sqrt{(20^2 + 30^2)} \sim 36 \text{ mm}$$

This is well inside the allowable standard deviation of 105 mm.

Positional Error

If we calculate the variance of the positional error — which is *not* distributed normally, nor as χ^2 — we obtain

P. B. Jones

$$\sigma^2_{TOTAL} = 100^2 + 36^2$$

whence

$$\sigma_{TOTAL} \sim 107 \text{ mm}$$

which is not much different from the larger, normally distributed, distance component. There is much to be said for determining the allowable *vector* error for the case when the error components are equal in two directions at right angles:

$$\sigma_x = \sigma_y$$

leading to

$$\sigma_R = 0.52 \text{ mm}$$

as above and then accepting any survey for which the total variance is less than σ^2_R regardless of whether the component errors are equal or not. In the extreme case where one component error vanishes, say $\sigma_y = 0$, we have a normal distribution in X only and 90% of error will be within $\pm 1.65\,\sigma_x$. Noting that $\sigma_x = \sigma_R$ in this case we have

$$1.65\,\sigma_{R\,allowable} = 0.8 \text{ mm}$$

$$\sigma_{R\,allowable} = \frac{0.8}{1.65}$$

$$= 0.48 \text{ mm}$$

which is only a little different from the 0.52 mm which comes from the two dimensional, equal error case.

If we adopt this empirical approach and design on total variance it is clear that we do not need to limit our slopes to 10 per cent. Using the original figures, we obtain

$$\sigma^2_{TOTAL} = 125^2 + 36^2$$

whence

$$\sigma_{TOTAL} = 130 \text{ mm}$$

which is well inside the allowable vector error of

$$\sigma_{detail\,allowable} = 150 \text{ mm}$$

Rises

Let us consider the error in determining rises. We had

$$r = \frac{b}{\gamma}\sin\beta\cos\beta + HI - C$$

100

whence, putting $h = \dfrac{b}{\gamma}\sin\beta\cos\beta$, we have

$$\Delta r = -h\frac{\Delta\gamma}{\gamma} + h\frac{\Delta b}{b} + 2\frac{b}{\gamma}\cos 2\beta\,\Delta\beta + \Delta HI - \Delta C$$

If we restrict our survey to maximum slopes of

$$\frac{h}{s} \sim \tan\beta = 0.2$$

then for
$$s = 50 \text{ metres},$$
$$h = 10 \text{ metres}$$

and

$$h\frac{\sigma_\gamma}{\gamma} = 10000 \times \frac{2''}{2062''} = 10 \text{ mm}$$

$$h\frac{\sigma_b}{b} \sim 10000 \times \frac{1}{500} = 20 \text{ mm}$$

and

$$2\frac{b}{\gamma}\cos 2\beta\,\sigma_\beta \sim 2 \times 500 \times 100 \times \frac{20''}{206265''} = 10 \text{ mm}$$

If we read HI and C to the nearest centimetre, the standard deviation of round-off will be

$$\frac{1}{\sqrt{12}} \times 10 \text{ mm} \sim 3 \text{ mm}$$

Hence

$$\sigma_{HI} \sim 3 \text{ mm}$$
$$\sigma_c \sim 3 \text{ mm}$$

There remains the error from the staff tilt δ:

$$\Delta h \sim \tan\beta\,\Delta s$$

from this source. Thus we obtain

$$\tan\beta\,(r+c)\sigma_\delta = 0.2 \times 11500 \times \frac{1}{100} \sim 23 \text{ mm}$$

Thus as the different components are independent, the variance of the total error in elevation is given by

$$\sigma_r^2 = \left(h\frac{\sigma_\gamma}{\gamma}\right)^2 + \left(h\frac{\sigma_b}{b}\right)^2 + \left(2\frac{b}{\gamma}\cos 2\beta\,\sigma\beta\right)^2$$

$$+ \left(\sigma_{HI} \right)^2 + \left(\sigma_c \right)^2 + \left(\tan \beta (r + c) \sigma_\delta \right)^2$$
$$- 10^2 + 20^2 + 10^2 + 3^2 + 3^2 + 23^2$$
$$= 1150 \text{ mm}^2$$

whence

$$\sigma_r \sim 35 \text{ mm}$$

Contouring

The standard adopted for contouring in New South Wales is that 90 per cent of points of well-defined detail should lie within half a contour interval. Assuming errors to be normally distributed we obtain

$$1.65 \, \sigma_{allowable} \leq 0.5 \times \text{contour interval}$$

i.e.

$$\sigma_{allowable} \leq \frac{0.5}{1.65} \times \text{contour interval}$$
$$= \frac{0.5}{1.65} \times 500 \sim 150 \text{ mm}$$

for our survey.

It should be obvious that most of our error in contouring will come from the choice of spots at which reduced levels are to be determined and from the interpolation of contours between these spot levels: only a small part of the error will come from the determination of the reduced level itself. This 'levelling' error will be only a negligible part of the total error if we restrict the levelling error to one-half of the allowable error

$$\sigma_{levelling} = \frac{150}{2} = 75 \text{ mm}$$

The allowable standard deviation of the 'contouring' as opposed to the levelling would thus follow from

$$\sigma^2_{contouring} = \sigma^2_{allowable} - \sigma^2_{levelling}$$
$$= 150^2 - 75^2$$
$$\sigma_{contouring} \simeq 130 \text{ mm}$$

Thus if we restrict the standard deviation of our levelling to 75 mm, these errors will only reduce the allowable standard deviation of contouring to 150 mm as compared with 130 mm which would apply if the levelling were completely error-free. Note that we have only considered the error in determining the rise from a control-point to a point of detail. The question arises as to how the elevations of the control points are to be determined.

If we determine heights by tacheometry around the whole traverse, and take sighting distances of 100 metres (the approximate distance between stations) rather than the average detail distance of 50 metres, then we should take

$$\sigma_\gamma = 5''$$

instead of

$$\sigma_\gamma = 2''$$

The error component becomes 25 mm instead of 10, and we get

$$\sigma_{r\,(traverse)} \sim 40 \text{ mm}$$

This error can be reduced in two ways. Firstly we can read the rise both forwards and back along each traverse line and secondly we can *close* the traverse. Each procedure will halve the variance of the final rise calculated between diagonal points of our traverse.

If we assume that our levelling errors are mainly accidental in nature, the standard deviation of the sum of n rises will equal $\sqrt{n}$ times the standard deviation of a single rise. Thus the adjusted rise between a pair of diagonal points will have a standard deviation of

$$\frac{1}{\sqrt{2}} \times \frac{1}{\sqrt{2}} \times \sqrt{4} \times 40 \text{ mm} = 40 \text{ mm}$$

Thus if σ_{LIN} is the allowable standard deviation of levelling in to the control traverse we can have

$$\sigma_{detail}^2 + \sigma_{traverse}^2 + \sigma_{LIN}^2 = 75^2$$

that is

$$\sigma_{LIN}^2 = 75^2 - 35^2 - 40^2$$
$$= 2800 \text{ mm}^2$$
$$\sigma_{LIN} = 53 \text{ mm}$$

It is clear that the levelling in could also be done by tacheometry, provided the distance from the nearest bench mark was short enough. If there are N legs of 100 metres of tacheometry observed in both directions on each leg, and the levelling traverse is run both forwards and back, then we could have N up to the largest value which satisfies

$$N \times \tfrac{1}{2} \times \tfrac{1}{2} \times 35^2 \leq 2800$$

that is

$$N \leq 8$$

Control Survey

The control survey can be readily designed to ensure that the standard deviation of the coordinates of any point (relative to any other point of the

103

traverse as origin) is negligible in comparison with the standard deviation of the detail survey.

Our allowable (vector) standard deviation of the detail survey was 150 mm.

Let us take one corner of the traverse as origin and let us design the traverse so that the vector standard deviation of the station diagonal to the origin is

$$\tfrac{1}{3} \times 150 = 50 \text{ mm}$$

It can be shown that if we consider a *related traverse* obtained by taking the original traverse from the origin to the mid-point along the length of the traverse, *and then* taking the mirror image reverse of the remainder, that is, reverse the bearing of each traverse line after the mid-point, the variance of the mid-point of the original traverse, if adjusted by Bowditch Rule, is equal to one quarter of the calculated variance of misclose of this (fictional) related traverse. This variance of misclose of the related traverse can be written as

$$I_{\rho\rho}\sigma_\theta^2 + \sum_i \sigma_{si}^2$$

where σ_{si}^2 is the variance of measuring the ith side of the traverse and $I_{\rho\rho}$ is the polar moment of inertia about its centroid of unit masses at each of the stations of the related traverse.

The related traverse for our example is shown in Fig. 2. From A to M the traverse is the same as the original, thereafter the directions of the traverse lines are reversed. The coordinates of the stations of the related traverse are listed below, relative to the arbitrary axes shown in the figure

X	Y	X^2	Y^2
0	0	0	0
100	0	10000	0
200	0	40000	0
300	0	90000	0
300	100	90000	10000
400	100	160000	10000
500	100	250000	10000
600	100	360000	10000
600	200	360000	40000
3000	600	1360000	80000

It follows that

$$I_{\rho\rho} = (1360000 + 80000) - \tfrac{1}{9}(3000^2 + 600^2)$$
$$= 400000 \text{ m}^2$$

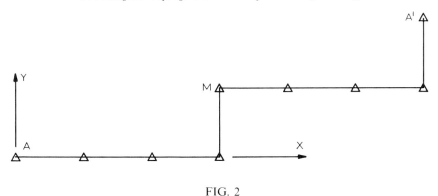

FIG. 2

Thus if all 8 distances are measured with the same precision, then we have

$$(50 \text{ mm})^2 = \tfrac{1}{4}(400000 \times 10^6 \sigma_\theta^2 + 8\sigma_s^2)$$

If we assume as a first trial that angles and distances contributed equally to our variance of position, then

$$\tfrac{1}{2} \times 50^2 = \tfrac{1}{4} \times 400000 \times 10^6 \sigma_\theta^2$$

and

$$\tfrac{1}{2} \times 50^2 = \tfrac{1}{4} \times 8\sigma_s^2$$

whence

$$\sigma_\theta = \frac{50 \times 206265''}{\sqrt{2} \times \sqrt{10 \times 100000}} \sim 22''$$

$$\sigma_s = \frac{50}{2} = 25 \text{ mm}$$

It is clear that these precisions can be very readily achieved by a simple theodolite traverse with angles read once on each face to 10″ or 20″ and with distances measured by electronic distance measurement or by catenary chaining.

To complete the design we should examine the standard deviation of closure of our initial traverse in bearing and in position and determine acceptable miscloses for these in order to gain some protection against accepting work that contains blunders. The essence of the design is however as outlined. Similar approaches can be made to the design of more complex surveys, to field astronomy, to levelling, to resections and so on. More importantly, a basically similar approach can be made to the design of a (simple) measurement process and it is this fact which really justifies the teaching of surveying within a school of civil engineering.

Much of the 'design' should be reflected in the field-work. If we are measuring distances by tacheometry we must allow for a standard deviation of

$$\sigma_s \sim 100 \text{ mm}$$

in distance. Under these circumstances it is both uneconomical *and* ludicrous to plumb the theodolite to within millimetres. It is uneconomical *and* ludicrous to read bearings to a few seconds. Techniques must be consistent in precision and we achieve this by designing our surveys.

C. R. LONGWORTH

Twenty-five Years of Australian Engineering and Resources Development

Introduction

My chosen subject is very broad and I will therefore mention superficially events and developments, which I think have influenced this quarter century of progress. The contribution will appear to emphasize certain aspects of this period, at the expense of scant mention of some and the absence of others. This is as I have seen the change, and not as a historian would have dealt with the task. I have attempted firstly, to look at what preceded this period, then to give a macro analysis of the twenty-five-year span and to conclude by speculating on some aspects of the future. In the rush and nervous haste of technological progress, our profession is no doubt guilty of raising too few historians to establish our heritage. Unfortunately, this contribution is an impression, with little of use to engineering historians. Society and man's ingenuity never progress at a uniform rate. Some reflection on the past will help to place our last twenty-five-years of development into context. Innovation and the tempo of engineering activity has over the years been closely linked to economic activity.

Let us look back for a moment into the days of the industrial revolution, with the harnessing of steam power and the development of the great railways of England. Names such as Thomas Telford, Robert Stephenson, I. K. Brunel [1] and many others, come to mind as prodigious contributors to the progress of this era. The innovations of men such as these unquestionably stimulated phenomenal development. They also served to establish a level of professionalism and dedication, of which this age knows no equal. Scientific enquiry, mated with engineering art, has resulted in surges of progress. The fiscal potentates have given us much historical explanation for these surges, but in this age, they have not succeeded in the level of economic control that we would hope to achieve for steady growth. Our rate of development has been sporadic and far from uniform.

Historically, periods of economic buoyancy were associated with full employment and varying degrees of inflation. In the mid-1920s prices were approximately twice what they were a decade before [2]. A period of depression ran through Australia and the world in the late 1920s resulting in falling prices and great suffering. More recently, we have witnessed recession within the 'First World' countries.* Contrary to the past, we have experienced increasing prices and decreasing employment and economic activity. It is difficult to reconcile the contemporary coexistence of high unemployment and high inflation if the concept of 'demand pull' forces are the principal factors considered. As a way out of this dilemma and to quote the Canadian Imperial Bank of Commerce 'Some economists have come to view the bargaining power of strong labour unions and other economic groups as a source of inflation which can arise even in the absence of excess demand' [3]. Another is no doubt associated with oil and the price of energy, about which I will say more later. One should also not ignore the influence of environmental requirements in first-world countries when compared with those of the second and third world. The price of skill and labour is now intimately geared to man's technological advance and his productivity increase. Here we have a challenge in the 60s and 70s that would have been unknown to engineers of I. K. Brunel's time. The past has seen the artisan and miner perform under conditions the likes of which the modern world will, we trust, never again tolerate. Politicians will claim much of the credit for our reform of the past, but how can one legislate health and safety without the prescience and ingenuity of the engineer and scientist?

Engineers, along with the rural fraternity, have been one of the greatest groups of desecrationists known. It is no exaggeration to say that engineers from all disciplines are now, without question, the most active contributors of skills in the applied environmental field. Ironically, penance by the profession is now contributing markedly to the quality of living. A full realization of the wide ramifactions of the oil price increases has not yet emerged in the energy-hungry nations, which include Australia.

The Australian gold rush days of the 1850s saw the country producing almost 40 per cent of the world's gold [4]. Such production left little in the way of stability or sound technological foundation. This was 'high grading' at its worst. Australia's establishment of base metal industries in the late nineteenth century, followed a little later by the steel industry, have been the harbingers of the phenomenal industrial setting of the past twenty-five years. These twenty-five years have been an age of resources development, unprecedented in economic significance in this land, and phenomenal by world standards. In the 1960s, during the Menzies Government's era, the export controls on iron ore were lifted. This was the genesis of Australia's ascendency to the position of the world's greatest exporter of the commodity reaching approximately 86 million

---

* 'First World' countries: the capitalist democracies — U.S.A., Western Europe, Japan, Canada, Australia, etc. highly industrialized countries that import raw materials and energy from the 'Third World'. These countries have 18 per cent of the world's people but consume over 65 per cent of the world's income. 'Second World': the Socialist communist countries and their respective allies. They are self sufficient in raw materials and energy. 'Third World': the non-industrialized one hundred or more countries producing raw materials which are sold to the 'First World'. The majority of these are poverty stricken and experiencing a population explosion.

tonnes in 1977 [5]. There are other equally graphic illustrations of this quarter-century leap which will bear some further mention. Power generation, transportation, manufacturing and engineering service industries, all grew phenomenally during this period, to complement our extroverted stance. The bankers of the world shared our optimism and our risk with a firm degree of aggression. Their assessment has not been wrong.

To mention the major projects and engineers of this era would lead to boredom and risk offence from those within the shadow of my fickle memory. Suffice it to mention, within the space available, a few of these developments which form the character of this period of engineering achievement. The engineering setting of Australia has been tempered by the influence of expertise from abroad as well as the development of our own local talents and standards. We preserve a strong technical character and independence. Anyone who has exported any of the various forms of engineering to Australia will bear witness to this fact. They will, in some cases, consider that our character is rooted in obstinacy and quote our various rail gauges. I remind you that I. K. Brunel's Great Western Railway had a seven-foot gauge which no doubt in part reflected the man [6].

New engineering disciplines have developed and come of age during this period. The country's engineering teaching and training facilities have had to adapt and grow, to provide the skills needed in a rapidly changing technical environment. Practising engineers in all fields have been exposed to change, and the challenge to adapt to, and apply these new disciplines. The consulting engineer was a part of the national scene well before my discussion period. He did not initially enjoy the spectrum of work, that came his way subsequently. His exposure to this age has assisted immeasurably in his ability to market his skills abroad.

The growth of professional groups and associations both nationally and internationally has been prolific over this quarter century. In this way technical stimulation has been sustained, and forums established for the review of problems common to many specialists. Air travel and communications are now taken for granted. These two factors have had greater significance in Australia, during this period, than would be the case in many other first world countries. Through easier travel, our engineers have had exposure to the minds of their confrères abroad, and benefited first hand from a sharing of their experiences.

Engineering Setting

Australia is among the great continents of the world in area, and yet, has the lowest population density of any land, of comparable size. Its population is centred predominantly in a dozen cities, which are widely separated and it has the lowest average annual rainfall of any first-world country. Infrastructure has, therefore, been the greatest single challenge to the Australian engineer, and the period under review is no exception. Colloquially, the country rode for a century on the 'sheep's back' even though isolated spurts of mineral activity occurred, during this time. Until recently, our steel industry was unable to satisfy the home market, let alone export. This was due to our growth. The winds of change have now come.

In 1963–4 minerals in one form or another earned $200 million in exports or about 8 per cent of the country's total exports. This was some five-fold less than pastoral exports. The stimulus of exploration and engineering development raised the 1974–5 equivalent exports to, in excess of $3,000 million, or 37 per cent of total exports. In spite of the recent economic vicissitudes it is not unrealistic to predict export earnings from this hidden wealth, of more than $5,000 million by the year 1980. Much of our mineral wealth is in unpopulated areas, which tests our ingenuity, and limits the viability of projects to those of large production, or those associated with high grade ore. W. S. Robinson, one time Chief Executive of The Zinc Corporation and a father of the Australian mining industry, once said 'A pennyweight of gold in Threadneedle Street is worth more than an ounce of gold at Hall's Creek' [2]. This quotation typifies the Australian scene aptly although gold no longer occupies a premier position in the country's mineral basket.

Resources Industries

The resources industries stand out as a dominant influence in the development and character of our engineering of the last quarter century. There has been a phenomenal growth in consulting engineering activities during this period in order to share in the activity. The global significance of our resources has attracted numerous overseas mining houses to our shores along with overseas engineering consultants and contractors. Many of the engineers of this era have been asssociated directly or indirectly with this exciting leap forward. Our engineering progress, and sophistication, would have been but a mere fraction of that attained, had resources not dominated. I feel that it is appropriate to devote some space to the mining industry, to explain the past and project the future. At present, the prices for certain minerals have receded on the world market, from the 'heady' days of the inception of many of the projects.

Weaknesses are now apparent in many of the resources industries as a result of falling markets and rising production costs. Curtailment of production, and closure of some mines has been necessary in Australia, and a number of other countries. All of this is not new to grey-haired miners. The rate of Australian mining development dropped to a snail's pace after 1973, following the Whitlam Labor Government's election. This has been a period which experienced decreases in world metal prices, coupled with a steep hike in oil prices. The development of mineral resources of many third-world countries also commenced in earnest. It is not paramount that these emerging nations produce at a profit, but principally to earn overseas currency or satisfy local need. Many markets have deteriorated further since 1973. Gold, tin, bauxite and scheelite have been notable exceptions to this trend. In spite of this, our industry has grown in overall terms, with national coal production now exceeding 70 million tonnes, to name one area of success.

Prior to the 1950s there was no bauxite, iron ore or nickel exported from Australia, and we had made no worthwhile oil or gas discoveries. Metallurgical and steam coal, stalwarts of our domestic steel and energy market, were not exported, although significant strides had been made in the mechanization of a number of N.S.W. coal mines. Production costs were at this time becoming extremely attractive by world standards [7]. The late 1950s and 1960s saw the intensification of exploration, which led to the establishment of the high-grade bauxite deposits at Weipa, the Darling Ranges and Gove. The Pilbara region of Western Australia was tamed into disgorging some of its iron ore with the construction of mines, ports, railways, pellet plants, townships, airfields and communications. Up to 1975, in excess of $1.5 billion had been spent in the aluminium and iron ore industries alone. Our next step forward, in the aluminium industry, took us to the production of the finished metal, and we became the world's largest alumina exporter. We have since joined the world producers of nickel, even though the price for this metal is at present very low. The industry will survive, and see better days, even though some casualties may be inevitable.

Australia has become a dominant supplier of metallurgical coal and iron ore to the Japanese steel industry. The approach to the sale of iron ore and coal is now based upon long-term contracts which were hitherto new to the mining world. Thus finance for the project was guaranteed. Some resentment exists among Australians, because the greater part of this leap forward has been accomplished principally by overseas companies. I do not share this resentment. I do not believe that we could have accomplished the genesis of such projects, let alone the technical achievement within the time span subsequently expended. Our engineers were major contributors to all facets of the design and construction of these projects, and received an exposure to the philosophy of large multi-disciplinary design and construction management teams, whose presence in Australia had been sporadic in the past. One had only to travel the world, during the latter part of this great leap forward, to experience first hand, the interest being taken by the Western world in our progress.

Since 1960, no fewer than twenty towns were built to house the mine workforces and their families. Railway construction resulted in the laying of over 1700 kilometres of heavy duty line to connect mines and ports. Eleven ports with bulk handling facilities were constructed, not to mention airfields and communications systems to serve much of the area. Infrastructure, in a country like Australia, is predominantly the key to exploitation of bulk minerals. Government have been able to provide but a small part of this infrastructure. It has been the lot of mining companies, consulting engineers

111

and contractors to achieve the goal, within the government guidelines. Up until 1975 it has been conservatively estimated that $1.5 billion, or an average figure of $100 000 per employee, was spent on mining community facilities. A comparable present-day figure would be more like $160 000 per employee. This illustrates the setting of much of the Australian resources scene, and the influence of infrastructure on economic viability. Australia, South Africa and Canada, have been the only first world countries to make major strides in coal exports. The Bowen Basin has developed into one of the great coal areas of the world, exporting a prime metallurgical product.

Australia's measured first and second order black coal reserves presently amount to 2.2 billion tonnes [8]. Intensive exploration has only been conducted over a small proportion of these coal-bearing lands. Engineers are now, more than ever before, being associated with increased productivity. Their effort in the past twenty-five years in the New South Wales underground coal industry is one of great achievement. In 1948 there were 138 underground mines in New South Wales employing 17 283 men and producing annually 10.47 million tonnes of coal. This represented an output per man shift of about 3 tonnes [9]. In 1976, 71 mines produced 32.18 million tonnes of coal employing 14 716 men, which is equivalent to 10 tonnes output per manshift (i.e. approximately 2200 tonnes per man year) or over a threefold increase in productivity.

The rationalization and increase in production is a tribute to the work of the mine owners and engineers of this period, and is even more meretorious when it is realized that the mine working week decreased from 40 to 35 hours during this time. The yearly output per man for 1976 quoted in Australia is approximately 2000 tonnes. This should be compared with current outputs in West Germany, United Kingdom and France of 500, 420 and 280 respectively [10]. Our endowment of thick seam coal should not be overlooked when contemplating this comparison.

While this is the era of open-pit mining with big machines we should not lose sight of the progress being made overseas in underground coal mining with longwall mining technology. It is in this area that many of the next generation of mining engineers will be remembered and it is interesting to reflect upon some of the results already achieved outside the country. Longwall units are in operation now which are consistently producing between 2000 and 4000 tonnes of raw coal per day over a twelve-month period allowing for moves. Units such as these require a five-man crew. In 1976, at the Robinson Run No. 95 mine in U.S.A., the world's record was set when a longwall unit produced 12 395 tonnes of coal in a twenty-four hour period with a five-man crew [11].

Growth of Engineering Technology

The period under discussion has seen the birth of many new disciplines, and the practical application of others hitherto still in their shawl of theory. Even through Karl Terzaghi's monumental 'Erdbaumechanik' dates back to 1925, the practising engineering world did not adopt a widespread application of theoretical soil mechanics before 1950. The art of rock mechanics has followed more recently. In Australia, sub-surface investigation methods around the early 1950s were very basic in all but major works. No discipline can sustain virile independent progress. Interaction with its neighbours occurs to varying degrees, and from time to time, some dominant technical force becomes a reality changing the whole course of events. The dominant tool of this quarter century has been the computer. Its influence dwarfs man's other technological efforts without comparison. Many of us would be forgiven, for underestimating the course of engineering, with the advent and development of the computer, in the early 1950s. There have been no garlands for pessimism, as its progress has subsequently and is continuing to prove. Here arrived a means which enabled structural engineers to crack the nut of indeterminacy with ease. Their reward came early, but it was not long before the application of the science throughout the profession became universal.

The principle of prestressing of concrete preceded the last twenty-five years by an even greater time span. It rested with the engineers of the 1950s to test the technique which was emerging in Europe and North America. Progress was initially slow, but the establishment in Australia of a number of U.K. consulting engineering firms did, I believe, provide stimulus to the local scene. We now have a number of fine bridges and buildings to record this period of our engineering heritage.

Developments in photogrammetric survey techniques, coupled with computer methods have revolutionized the work of the road engineer, particularly in inhospitable country. The use of satellite fixation and imagery systems are now a commercial reality. Our quarter century has witnessed the growth of the specialist. This has propagated through the industry from artisan to academic. It is just as richly illustrated in the relationship of contractors and sub-contractors, as it is in the academic cloisters or consultants' row. Complex engineering works resulted in the development of methods of control such as the critical path concept. From this emerged our age of engineering managers, to better control the fragmentary construction and manufacturing packages, that have been our liability of progress.We now have disciplines of industrial engineering, and engineering management, which brings the profession closer to the men of 'profit'.

While the journalists commenced to produce much copy on the environment in the 1970s, many engineers hitherto practised their art in varying disguises. Many unfortunately didn't, including some miners, and throughout the world developed a backlash. It is only now, some five years since the advent of environmental legislation, that a definition is emerging in the interplay between engineers, scientists, politicians and the man in the street. Engineers are now challenged, over a wide front, in matters environmental. Their skills are developing within the applied field, and embrace in particular those of good design with adequate safeguards. Environmental awareness is now being ranked with literacy and numeracy in our schools. Some of this awareness is based on fact, but much still on self-interested groups and humbug. The engineer, with his balance of theory and art, is oftentimes the most appropriate person to dispel the abstract from the environmental argument. The next generation will be called upon more and more to assert their judgement in the course of our development.

Environmental acceptance is founded to a large degree on safeguards of various forms. There are now demands for the use of tried and proven systems. No scope exists for major project development based upon unproven systems. We are now forced to reconsider many firmly established techniques and processes. A requirement also exists, at the planning stage, for the formulation by engineers, of management policies for safeguard systems. The engineers of the 1970s are now becoming increasingly involved in the field of safeguards, and will play an even greater role in the next twenty-five years. Frustration, previously associated with the development of projects is now giving way to an acceptance of the overall system. Industrial leaders, entrusted with developments, should strive for a better level of competency among those professionals within governments who establish and maintain our environmental standards.

Experience is beginning to show us that it requires a high level of competency to assess the influence of environmental legislation on industry, mining and general development. Ill-considered legislation can result in extensive disruption to any country's welfare. Implementation of the new strip mining legislation in the United States is a good example of such a disruption. The limitations on Australia's technological resources has, in the past, necessitated our study of the legislation of other developed nations. We have tried to balance overseas experience objectively with our aims, before establishing our plan. There is now an even greater need for this approach, in view of the world's problems of population concentrations and energy.

Engineering Progress

Some idea of our progress, from the 1950s to the 1970s, can be gleaned from the works achieved, and the significance that they now bear to our technical maturity. In 1949, the Snowy Mountains Hydro-Electric Power Act was passed by the Chifley Government. This project came many years after those works of a similar character already started in Tasmania. It fortuitously, at the time of enactment, paved the way for an Australian Engineering Corporation. This Corporation has now asserted itself, along with many other Australian consulting engineers and contractors, in exporting their expertise, principally within Southeast Asia, although some have gone further afield than this. Our governments have too rarely realized the role they can play in catalysing talent within the country, to the ultimate benefit of our exports.

114

The last twenty-five years have seen a phenomenal growth in consulting engineering and contracting skills within Australia. These skills have been fostered, in some cases, by the patronage of governments in awarding works of a major, or sometimes specialized nature, to contractors and commissions to engineers. This provides the incentive and the level of credibility for Australian organizations to compete internationally. The extent of dam building and associated works has never been surpassed in the country's history, both in respect of size and novelty of design. The quarter century in review saw a development of the large embankment dams of zoned materials, and those of rockfill with upstream membranes. Dams such as Talbingo, Blowering, Eildon, Ord River and Cethana are but a few examples of these works. There were, of course, some fine concrete dams such as Warragamba, Tumut Pond, and Devils Gate constructed during the same period. The economic trend is now more in favour of the earth and rock structures, where site conditions are favourable. This has been accentuated by the phenomenal progress in equipment development capable of performing such works.

Skills in undergound works have raced forward during this era, principally due to improved drilling techniques and support systems. Mechanically bored tunnels in hard and soft ground have now come of age in Australia, and will see a much wider application in civil engineering and mining works before the close of the century. Highway and traffic engineering has resulted in great changes to all Australian cities, in keeping with our other first-world members. Consistency of the policies of governments, quite apart from finance, has made it very difficult to achieve the level of road transportation efficiency that a country of our disposition warrants. Transportation and materials handling, in one form or another, still constitute a disproportionate level of cost, in comparison to many countries of similar prosperity.

Australia, with its vast coastline and widely separated seaboard population centres, should be geared to shipping. It is a sad reflection on our industrial scene that, with the exclusion of coastal bulk freights, this quarter century has seen a retreat in this mode of transport. Widespread port works have been undertaken to accommodate containers and RO/RO systems throughout the nation, with advantages to the shippers and waterside workers. Industry and the public are the odd couple out in the gains accomplished. Australian engineers and contractors, in most instances with venture assistance in various forms from colleagues abroad, paved the way for offshore engineering in the 1960s and 1970s. The Bass Strait oil and gas discoveries, along with Queensland coal, Western Australian iron ore ports and Port Latta in Tasmania, are all expressive of this age. Australia now has a nucleus of offshore engineers who will accept the challenges for developments in this field, as come they will in the next decade. Air travel has seen a phenomenal expansion of airport construction throughout the land to cope with changing aircraft types and traffic.

Our twenty-five-year step has not been one of exclusively rose-tinted engineering success. Progress is invariably achieved in the face of some adversity as the great cathedral builders of England and Europe found. Engineering failures ought to be *sotto voce* in any superficial engineering eulogy such as this. Suffice it to say that patience, perseverance and in some cases loss of life resulted in technological lessons from the failures of the King Street and Westgate Bridges in Victoria. Natural disasters of hitherto unknown proportions, in the form of the Meckering earthquake and the Darwin cyclone, have shown the ignorance of many of our nation's physical characteristics and prove a medium for progress.

I am sure that our engineering forefathers did not live in the same age of dispute, that now exists in this industry throughout the world. Litigation is now an established facet of our society. Though it be counter-productive, our education and training systems have to adapt and to expose the up-and-coming professionals to the realities under which they will be expected to perform. Energy in one form or another is essential for a country's progress. Australia has been well served by far-sighted power development schemes. Our heavy dependence on fossil fuels for electrical energy has been most fortunate as events have subsequently proved. Many of our power stations, situated at mine mouth, have been designed with much prescience. Uranium exploration took on a new look with the advent of airborne radiometric methods of prospecting. The 1970s will be recorded as a period when Australia established approximately 22 per cent of the world's reserves of uranium. It will rest with the 1980s to see the commencement of its exploitation.

The Association of Consulting Engineers (ACEA) was established in Sydney in 1952 to cater for the special needs of the consulting engineering profession. Previously, the Institution of Engineers had established panels within each state to fulfill this need. The ACEA has now developed into a national body of 596 members who practice in Australia and overseas.

Many foreign firms have established in Australia during the last quarter century. These firms have brought to our ranks wide ranging skills and competition. Australia has no restrictions on the entry and commissioning of foreign firms, although much lobbying exists in favour of the local profession where government commissions are at stake. Joint ventures between Australian and foreign firms have become more popular in recent years as a means of complementing the local expertise. All of these measures have led to greater maturity and scope of activities within the country. Consulting engineers are now exporting their services and many have established operations overseas. The industry is always a 'bell wether' of development and further growth abroad will help to preserve continuity in a home market, which is subject to rather violent swings of prosperity and adversity.

The Future

From now till the turn of the century will result in a continuing development of resources industry and services within Australia. Energy will be the key to much of our development. World oil production is expected to peak and decline during the next ten to twenty-five years [12]. Access to good coal will provide our primary energy needs during this period. Our interest in nuclear power should be rejuvenated towards the year 2000. Coal will therefore be a significant but transitory source of primary energy. Under the Gorton Government, Australia had the option in 1971 to enter the nuclear age with the Jervis Bay Power Station. We opted not to proceed. This was a monumental decision in Australia's energy file, the implications of which will become more evident in the next twenty-five years.

In 1974 coal accounted for 18 per cent of the primary energy consumed in the world outside communist countries. This compares with 34 per cent consumed in 1960. Oil and gas have dislodged coal from its dominant position in the past twenty-five years. A comeback by coal is now emerging and will intensify in the next decade. This will result in increasing exports of steam coal from Australia in spite of the pessimistic outlook at present expressed from the industry. Much of the world's coal has traditionally been developed in the northern hemisphere temperate climate countries. The tropics and southern hemisphere have not experienced comparable exploration. Australia will consolidate its position as a major coal exporter. It has been estimated that the measured reserves of bituminous coal in New South Wales and Queensland are, in calorific terms, comparable with the proven oil reserves of Saudi Arabia. To quote Wilson: 'By almost any criterion, world coal resources can be regarded as ample. What is in doubt is the willingness and ability of the world to accept large increases in coal production and use' [12]. Australia is therefore well endowed with primary energy at favourable prices. This will enable a far greater degree of processing of raw materials to a semi-finished state than has existed in the past. It will lead to further establishment of high energy, low labour intensive industries. To achieve this will require a steady expansion of our mining, power generation, transmission and service industries. Transport systems will require development to suit our needs. The movement of mineral products and in particular coal by pipeline will receive increased attention and in all likelihood become reality. Land transport by rail and improvements of transport of dry bulk commodities and semi-finished products will be an essential part of our future development. Infrastructure will be even more important in the future than the past.

Service industries will develop to cater for the demands of our resources pattern. The engineering and scientific professions will suffer a deficiency of experienced graduates and some reappraisal of the professions will occur with the next generation of students. Our progress will, like the past twenty-five years, be at variable pace; it does however, promise to be as exciting and diverse as the 'technocrats' wish to make it.

In conclusion, in this age that teems with teaching aids and dispensed leisure, there is a need for us to find time to look back. Our engineering capacity and finesse are in good shape. Let not the bustle tempt us to forget that this profession is very much an art tempered by science and consummated finally in the excellence or otherwise of our judgement.

References

1. Pannell, J. P. M., *An Illustrated History of Civil Engineering*, Thames & Hudson, London 1964.
2. Robinson, W. S., 'If I Rightly Remember' in Geoffrey Blainey (ed.), *W. S. Robinson Memoirs*, Cheshire, Melbourne 1967.
3. Commercial Letter, Issue No. 4 1975, Canadian Imperial Bank of Commerce.
4. 'What Mining Means to Australia', Australian Mining Industry Council, 1976.
5. *Skillings Mining Review*, June 1977.
6. Pugsley, Sir Alfred (ed.), *The Works of Isambard Kingdom Brunel*, The Institution of Civil Engineers, London 1976.
7. Ellis, M. H., *A Saga of Coal*, Angus & Robertson, Sydney 1969.
8. 'Australian Black Coals 1976', The Queensland Coal Board and the Joint Coal Board.
9. Smith, M. J., 'New Areas of Development of the Coal Mining Industry in New South Wales', The Association of Mining Electrical and Mechanical Engineers, 1976 Annual Convention.
10. 'The Current Situation Regarding the European Coal Industries', *World Coal*, Vol. 3, No. 9, 1977, p. 57.
11. Chironos, Nicholos P., 'Consolidations Record Production Runs', *Coal Age*, August 1976.
12. Wilson, Carrol L., *Energy Global Prospects* 1985–2000. Report on the workshop on alternative energy strategies. McGraw-Hill, New York 1977.

Foundation Settlement Analysis Using Elastic Theory

1. INTRODUCTION

The application of elastic theory to the prediction of deformations in soil masses has many obvious limitations, and these have led to the total rejection of elastic theory by some geotechnical engineers. However, it has been well proven that, if applied judiciously with due recognition given to its limitations, elastic theory can be an extremely useful tool for settlement prediction of all types of foundations. The objective of this chapter is to describe the rational application of elastic theory to settlement analysis and to summarize some of the characteristics of foundation behaviour which the theory reveals. Attention is confined to the magnitude of settlement of foundations on clay soils, and consideration is not given to the question of the rate of settlement. Section 2 discusses the behaviour of an ideal two-phase elastic soil and how the ideal soil differs from a real soil. It then describes the principle of settlement prediction via elastic theory and discusses the determination of the required soil parameters. Section 3 outlines some of the available techniques for obtaining elastic solutions for foundation applications while Section 4 presents some typical solutions for shallow pad foundations and lists some of the conclusions regarding the settlement characteristics of this type of foundation. Raft and pile foundations are treated in Sections 5 and 6.

Most of the work described in this chapter has been developed over the last twenty years within the School of Civil Engineering at the University of Sydney.

2. APPLICATION OF ELASTIC THEORY TO SOIL MASSES

2.1 *Soil as an Ideal Two Phase Elastic Material*

The simplest rational model of saturated soil is a two-phase elastic material consisting of an elastic homogeneous solid phase (the skeleton of soil particles) and an incompressible liquid phase (the pore fluid filling the voids in the skeleton). If it further assumed that the material is isotropic, its deformation properties are characterized by two fundamental deformation parameters, the Young's modulus of the skeleton E', and the Poisson's ratio of the skeleton, v'.

Provided that the effective normal stress changes σ'_x, σ'_y and σ'_z on a soil element are known, the consequent strains can be calculated from elastic theory e.g. the vertical strain ε_z is given by

$$\varepsilon_z = \frac{\sigma'_z - v'(\sigma'_x + \sigma'_y)}{E'} \tag{1}$$

Under drained conditions, when there are no excess pore pressures, equation (1) gives the final (or drained) strain of the element and hence v' and E' represent the drained elastic parameters of the soil.

Under undrained conditions, the strain of an ideal soil element can be calculated from equation (1), provided that the effective stress changes (and hence the initial excess pore pressures) can be calculated. It may readily be shown that, under general three-dimensional conditions, the initial excess pore pressure Δu due to changes in total normal stresses σ_z, σ_x and σ_y, is

$$\Delta u = \tfrac{1}{3}(\sigma_x + \sigma_y + \sigma_z) \tag{2}$$

However, for practical purposes, it is convenient to characterize the undrained behaviour of a soil by a pair of equivalent parameters, E_u and v_u, which describe the behaviour of the soil in terms of changes in *total* stress rather than effective stress. It can be shown that, for a saturated soil, $v_u = 0.5$ (i.e. the soil exhibits no volume change) and E_u is related to the fundamental parameters E' and v' as

$$E_u = \frac{3E'}{2(1 + v')} \tag{3}$$

The vertical undrained strain ε_{zu} can then be calculated in terms of the total stress changes as

$$\varepsilon_{zu} = \frac{\sigma_z - 0.5(\sigma_x + \sigma_y)}{E_u} \tag{4}$$

It is also possible to relate other commonly used soil parameters to E' and v'. For example, the coefficient of volume decrease m_v is given by

$$m_v = \frac{(1 + v')(1 - 2v')}{(1 - v')E'} \tag{5}$$

and the coefficient of lateral earth pressure at rest, K_0, is given by

$$K_0 = \frac{v'}{1 - v'} \tag{6}$$

For many natural soil deposits, it may be more appropriate to consider the soil skeleton as being anisotropic rather than isotropic. The simplest case of anisotropy is cross-anisotropy, for which all horizontal directions are equivalent from the point of view of stress-strain response. Definition of the deformation behaviour of a cross-anisotropic soil skeleton requires five independent parameters of the skeleton, rather than the two required for an isotropic skeleton. It is possible to derive relationships between the vertical strain and these parameters, and also between the undrained and drained parameters of the cross-anisotropic soil. However, the practical utility of the cross-anisotropic elastic model is at present limited because of the difficulties involved in measuring the required parameters. Some measurements have been reported [1, 2], but the laboratory techniques and equipment are far too complicated for practical purposes. Hence, attention will be restricted herein to an isotropic soil skeleton.

2.2   Limitations of Elastic Theory

The effective stress-strain response of real soils is complex and differs from that of the ideal elastic two phase elastic material in a number of ways, including the following:

(a) the stress-strain relationship is non-linear;

(b) strains are generally not fully recoverable on reversal of stress;

(c) strains under constant effective stress are generally time-dependent i.e. the real soil skeleton exhibits creep behaviour;

(d) under some conditions, the application of shear stress produces a volume change; this is the phenomenon of dilatancy.

Furthermore, because real soil has a finite shear strength, the shear stresses induced in the soil by a loaded foundation may reach the shear strength of the soil at certain points within the mass as the loading is increased; this is particularly likely to occur in clays under undrained loading conditions. Local yielding will then occur, and if the foundation loading is further increased, a redistribution of stress must occur within the soil so that the shear stresses nowhere exceed the shear strength. As a result, the strains at a point in the soil will be greater than the values which would occur in an elastic soil. Moreover, these strains will no longer depend solely on the stresses at that point but will be dependent on the stress state within the entire soil mass.

It is therefore obvious that the application of elastic theory to real soils must be carried out judiciously if satisfactory predictions of settlement are to be made. Two important aspects of this judicious application are:

(i) allowance should be made for the possible effects of local yield in estimating immediate or undrained settlements;

(ii) the elastic parameters of the soil should be determined for a stress path and stress range appropriate to the problem.

Modern techniques of analysis, particularly the finite element method, enable the above aspects to be taken into account and, in addition, allow consideration of factors such as creep and dilatancy of the soil. However, because there are many circumstances in which such sophisticated analyses are not feasible, attention here will be confined to hand methods of calculation using available solutions from elastic theory. The calculation of creep settlements will not be described here although there are methods available which utilize elastic theory and which are extensions of the approach used for calculating immediate and consolidation settlements [3].

2.3   Calculation of Settlements

The method of calculating settlements is based on the elastic approach described by Davis and Poulos [4, 5] and similar approaches by Kerisel and Quatre [6] and Egorov *et al.* [7]. However, it also incorporates a modification for the effects of local yield on immediate settlement, as described by D'Appolonia *et al.* [8].

The total final settlement S_{TF} (excluding creep) is calculated as the sum of the immediate (or undrained) settlement S_i and the final consolidation settlement S_{CF} i.e.

$$S_{TF} = S_i + S_{CF} \tag{7}$$

Following D'Appolonia *et al.* [8], the immediate settlement is calculated as

$$S_i = \frac{S_{ielas}}{F_R} \tag{8}$$

where S_{ielas} = immediate settlement calculated from elastic theory

F_R = factor to account for local yield under undrained conditions

The final consolidation settlement is given by

$$S_{CF} = S_{TFelas} - S_{ielas} \tag{9}$$

where $S_{TF\,elas}$ = from total final settlement calculated from elastic theory

Equation (9) is strictly only correct for purely elastic conditions, but Small [9] has found that it is a reasonable approximation to the final consolidation settlement of a soil which has undergone undrained local yielding prior to consolidation.

Thus, from equations (8) and (9),

$$S_{TF} = \frac{S_{ielas}}{F_R} + (S_{TFelas} - S_{ielas}) \tag{10}$$

The yield factor F_R has been evaluated for a strip footing on a layer by D'Appolonia *et al.* [8], using an elasto-plastic finite element analysis. For shallow foundations on clay, F_R is primarily a function of the applied stress ratio q/q_u (the inverse of the factor of safety) and an initial shear stress ratio f, defined as

$$f = \frac{(1 - K_0)\sigma_{vo}'}{2s_u} \tag{11}$$

where $\quad K_0$ = coefficient of lateral earth pressure at rest
σ_{vo}' = initial vertical effective stress
s_u = undrained shear strength

It has been found that the values of f for real soils is largely dependent on the overconsolidation ratio (OCR). For a normally consolidated soil (OCR = 1), f typically is between 0.6 and 0.8, but decreases rapidly as OCR increases, being about 0.2 for OCR = 2 and about zero for OCR = 4.

Some values of F_R are reproduced in Fig. 3. It should be noted that the evaluation of this factor requires an estimate of undrained bearing capacity q_u, so that undrained strength values are needed both for this estimate and also to evaluate f.

When carrying out hand computations, S_{ielas} and S_{TFelas} may be calculated either by summation of vertical strains beneath the foundation or directly by the use of elastic displacement theory.

(i) *Summation of strains*: This procedure is analogous to the one-dimensional method, and is useful for non-homogeneous or stratified soil deposits. S_{TFelas} is given by

$$S_{TFelas} = \Sigma \frac{1}{E'}\{\sigma_z - v'(\sigma_x + \sigma_y)\}\delta h \tag{12}$$

where $\quad E', v'$ are the drained Young's modulus and Poisson's ratio of the soil skeleton, the values being those appropriate to the changes of stress in each layer;

$\sigma_x, \sigma_y, \sigma_z$ are the stress increases due to the foundation, estimated from elastic stress distribution theory, for the value of v'; and

δh is the thickness of each stratum or layer.

Similarly,

$$S_{ielas} = \Sigma \frac{1}{E_u}\{\sigma_z - v_u(\sigma_x + \sigma_y)\}\delta h \tag{13}$$

where $\quad E_u, v_u$ are the undrained Young's modulus of the soil (for a saturated soil, $v_u = 0.5$)

$\sigma_x, \sigma_y, \sigma_z$ are the stress increases due to the foundation, for the value of v_u.

(ii) *Elastic displacement theory*: If the soil stratum is reasonably homogeneous and appropriate average values of the soil moduli can be assigned to the whole soil profile, the elastic settlements may be calculated from equations of the following general form:

123

$$S_{TFelas} = \frac{qBI}{E'} \qquad (14)$$

where q = foundation pressure
      B = some convenient dimension of the foundation (e.g. breath)
      I = influence factor given by elastic displacement theory for Poisson's
          ratio $v = v'$ and for the particular geometry of the problem
      E' = drained Young's modulus of the soil

$$S_{ielas} = \frac{qBI}{E_u} \qquad (15)$$

where I = influence factor from elastic displacement theory for $v = v_u$
      E_u = undrained Young's modulus of soil.

Various solutions for stresses and the influence factor I for various foundation
types have been presented by Giroud [10] and Poulos and Davis [11]. Some
of these solutions are summarized in Sections 4 to 6. A number of displacement
solutions for layered soils and soils having a varying modulus with depth are
also available.

It should be noted that the principles of utilizing elastic theory also apply to
calculations carried out by more sophisticated numerical analyses i.e.
immediate or undrained movements are determined by inputting the undrained soil parameters into the analysis while the total final movements
require the use of the drained soil parameters. With the development of finite
element analyses of consolidation, it is now possible to carry out a single
unified analysis using only the effective stress-strain properties of the soil [12].
Such an analysis can provide the complete time-settlement behaviour of a
foundation on a soil which exhibits non-linear and anisotropic behaviour, and
thus obviates the need to artificially separate stability, deformation and
consolidation analyses. The computational capability of the geotechnical
engineer has therefore been increased enormously; nevertheless, for most
routine settlement calculations, the use of such sophisticated analyses is not
warranted, and use is frequently made of simpler elastic parametric solutions,
at least for preliminary estimates of settlement. Elastic displacement solutions
are particularly useful in this regard.

2.4   Determination of Soil Deformation Parameters

The elastic soil parameters E_u, E' and v' required for settlement predictions are
generally determined either from in-situ tests or laboratory tests. Commonly
used field tests include plate loading tests, the pressuremeter, static cone
penetration tests and screw plate tests. Many of these tests do not measure
directly the required parameter but rely on empirical correlations between the
test results and that parameter, e.g. the correlation between cone penetration

resistance and Young's modulus. A variety of these correlations are summarized by Mitchell and Gardner [13] who also discuss the interpretation of load tests in terms of elastic theory to determine the soil modulus. This procedure is particularly valuable when applied to pile foundations [14] and it appears that the most reliable value of average soil modulus is obtained by backfiguring from the results of a pile load test.

Laboratory testing is generally only feasible for obtaining soil parameters for the settlement of shallow pad or raft foundations. For the determination of the required parameters in an elastic-based settlement analysis, two rational procedures have been developed:

(i) the 'stress-path' approach, in which the soil sample is subjected to the field stress path and the resulting strains used to calculate the required soil parameters;

(ii) the 'SHANSEP' approach (Stress History and Normalized Soil Engineering Parameters), in which the soil parameters are normalized with respect to the initial overburden stress and related to the overconsolidation ratio.

Details of the stress-path procedure and its interpretation in terms of elastic theory are given by Davis and Poulos [4, 5] while the principles behind the SHANSEP concept are described by Ladd and Foott [15] and Ladd *et al.* [16].

Stress path testing enables E_u, E' and v' (and also the coefficient of consolidation) for a particular stress path, to be determined from a single test. In some cases involving a thin relatively homogeneous deposit, it may be possible to select a single representative depth for the stratum and carry out tests simulating only the behaviour of the soil element at that depth. This depth is generally between one-quarter to one-third of the layer depth, but should not exceed 0.9 times the foundation breadth. However, for deeper deposits, the use of a single representative depth may lead to inaccurate settlement predictions and tests should be undertaken to simulate conditions at various depths in the layer.

The SHANSEP method requires considerably more testing than the stress path approach in order to define the variation of the normalized elastic parameters with overconsolidation ratio. However, it has the advantage of providing a rational framework for the presentation of data in a compact form and of enabling a progressive accumulation of data for a particular soil type. Another major advantage is that it enables the effect of effective stress changes on the soil parameters to be evaluated, e.g. the increase in modulus or strength at any point in a soil due to partial consolidation under a surcharge fill. SHANSEP also has some limitations, notably that it is generally limited to reasonably regular deposits for which the stress history is well-defined. Its successful use requires a good knowledge of stress history and preconsolidation pressures. It is also doubtful whether the method is applicable to cemented or highly structured soils.

Whichever approach is taken, one of the most important requirements for accurate parameter determination is that the laboratory samples should be initially reconsolidated under stress conditions, and to an overconsolidation ratio, appropriate to the field situation. In particular, if K_0 conditions exist initially in the field, initial reconsolidation of the sample in the laboratory should be carried out under K_0 conditions. The common practice of initially consolidating samples under hydrostatic initial stress conditions, rather than under K_0 conditions, may lead to values of E_u and E' which are too large, and values of v' which are too small. As the accuracy of a settlement prediction is highly dependent upon the soil deformation moduli, it is well worthwhile attempting to reproduce the field stress conditions as accurately as possible in laboratory tests.

3. METHODS OF OBTAINING ELASTIC SOLUTIONS FOR FOUNDATION PROBLEMS

In this section, some of the methods for obtaining elastic solutions for foundation problems will be reviewed. These methods will be classified as follows:

(i) direct integration of basic solutions;

(ii) 'complex' integration of basic solutions;

(iii) finite difference methods;

(iv) the finite element method.

3.1 Direct Integration of Basic Solutions

Many of the most commonly used solutions for the settlement of shallow foundations have been obtained by direct integration, over the shape of the foundation area, of the basic equations for a point loading on an elastic mass. The most common basic equations are those derived by Boussinesq for a point load on the surface of an isotropic semi-infinite mass and by Burmister [17] for a point load on the surface of an isotropic layer of finite depth. These equations can be integrated directly if the distribution of contact pressure between the foundation and soil is known; most commonly, this applies to uniformly loaded flexible foundations. A large number of solutions for various foundation shapes are summarized by Giroud [10] and Poulos and Davis [11].

Because of the relatively simple nature of the basic elastic solutions, derived solutions for foundations are generally restricted to simple cases involving a semi-infinite mass or a single isotropic homogeneous layer.

126

3.2 'Complex' Integration of Basic Solutions

The title refers to methods which involve the following five stages. First, the division of the foundation into a number of elements of appropriate shape, each subjected to uniform stresses of unknown magnitude. Second, the integration of basic elastic solutions for concentrated loading over the shape of the elements to determine the stress and/or displacement at any point in the elastic mass. Third, the use of the above integrated solutions to derive equations relating the displacements of the soil adjacent to each element of the foundation to the unknown element stresses and the soil properties. Fourth, the derivation of equations relating the displacements of the foundation itself to the known element stresses and the material properties of the foundation. Fifth, setting up and solving the set of compatability equations obtained by equating the displacements of the soil and the foundation at each element, together with the appropriate equilibrium equations. The element stresses are thus obtained and from these, the displacement of each element can be determined.

This approach is a very useful method of examining foundation-soil interaction problems and was probably first used for obtaining the settlement and contact pressure distribution due to rigid surface foundations. Subsequently, it has been widely used for analysing the behaviour of rafts [e.g. 18, 19, 20] and pile foundations [e.g. 21, 22]. The basic Boussinesq and Burmister point load solutions have been used for rafts while the analyses of pile foundations have utilized the solutions of Mindlin [23] for subsurface point loading within an isotropic semi-infinite mass. Some of the solutions for rafts and piles will be reviewed in Sections 5 and 6.

As with solutions derived by direct integration, those obtained by the 'complex' integration technique are generally restricted to a homogeneous soil mass. However, it is possible to consider, in an approximate fashion, the effects of non-homogeneity of the soil profile as well as the effects of non-linear soil behaviour.

3.3 Finite Difference Methods

This approach was developed by Cumming and Gerrard [24] and Gerrard and Mulholland [25] and requires the expression of the basic equations of elasticity in terms of displacements gradients; these equations are then written in finite difference form and lead to a series of equations relating the vertical and horizontal displacements at points on a suitable grid representing the soil mass. By solving these equations, together with the appropriate boundary conditions, the displacements at each grid point may be determined. The stresses can then be obtained from the displacement gradients.

This method has been used to analyse isotropic and anisotropic multi-layer systems [25, 26]. However, although it is in principle, a versatile method,

irregular soil profiles or boundaries are awkward to analyse and it has now
largely been superseded by the finite element method.

3.4 *Finite Element Method*

This method has been described in detail by Zinkiewicz [27] and Desai and
Abel [28] and consists of the following steps:

 (i) the discretization of the soil and the foundation into a system of finite
    elements;
 (ii) the derivation of the stiffness matrix for an individual element, using the
    stress-strain relationship of the material;
 (iii) assembly of the overall stiffness matrix [K] for the entire mass from the
    individual element stiffness matrices to obtain the relationship between
    the total load vector {R} and the nodal displacement vector {δ}.

$$[K]\{\delta\} = \{R\} \tag{16}$$

 (iv) solution of equation (16) to obtain the nodal displacements {δ}.
 (v) calculation of element stresses from the nodal displacements.

The above calculations require the use of computer and a vast number of
programs are now available. The finite element method is capable of taking
account of complicated geometry and boundary conditions, loading and
construction sequences, non-homogeneity and non-linear stress-strain behaviour. It has also been used to examine problems involving large strains,
such as those occurring during the construction of an embankment on very
soft clay [29]. Moreover, the settlement and stability of a foundation can now
be examined by means of a single analysis rather than having to artificially
separate these problems as has been customary in the past. By also
incorporating the consolidation behaviour of the soil into the analysis, it is
possible to perform a complete time-settlement analysis of a foundation
supported by a non-linear soil mass [12].

Because of the time and expense involved in carrying out finite element
analyses, they are probably best suited to 'one-off' solutions rather than
extensive parametric solutions, although a number of such solutions have
been obtained [e.g. 30].

At the University of Sydney, attention has been concentrated on the
complex integration approach although the finite element method has played
an increasingly important role in recent years. In the following sections, some
of the available solutions for foundation settlement will be described and the
theoretical characteristics of foundation behaviour will be discussed. Only
isolated shallow foundations, rafts and piles will be considered, but it should
be emphasized that elastic solutions also exist for many other cases, for
example, earth dams, embankments on compressible layers, earth retaining
structures and anchors.

4. SHALLOW FOUNDATIONS

A considerable number of elastic solutions for the settlement of various types of loaded areas have been collected by Giroud [10] and Poulos and Davis [11]. Most are for a footing on a homogeneous isotropic soil layer, and typical of these are the solutions for the settlement of a rigid circular footing on a finite layer, shown in Fig. 1. For most practical purposes, rigid footings of other shapes can be treated with sufficient accuracy as a rigid circular footing of equal area. Fig. 2 gives solutions for the corner of a uniformly loaded strip foundations on a homogeneous isotropic layer. The settlement of other points on the surface may be obtained by superposition. If the strip footing is rigid its settlement can be approximated closely as the mean of the centre and edge settlements of the corresponding uniformly loaded (flexible) strip.

To allow for the effects of local yield on immediate settlement, D'Appolonia *et al.* [8] have evaluated values of the local yield factor F_R, and these are

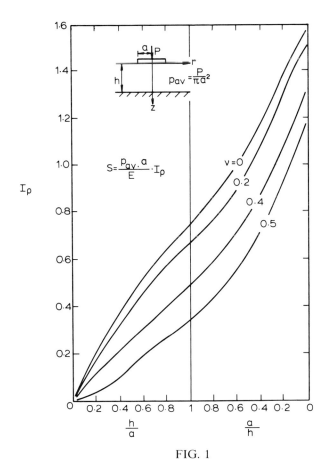

FIG. 1

129

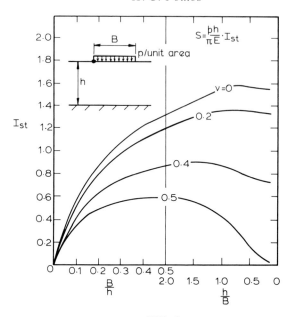

FIG. 2

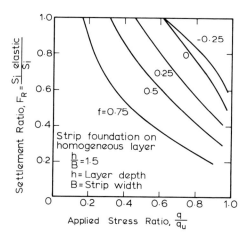

FIG. 3

plotted in Fig. 3 as a function of the applied stress level (q/q_u) and the initial shear stress ratio of f (equation 11). Although these solutions strictly apply only to a uniformly loaded strip, they can be applied approximately to other footing shapes.

Solutions for foundations on a cross-anisotropic mass have been presented by Gerrard and Harrison [31], while Gerrard et al. [32] have examined the

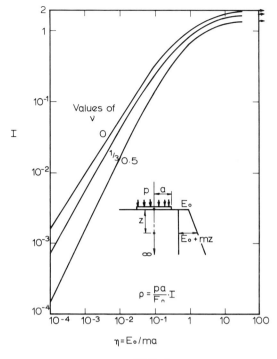

FIG. 4

errors involved in assuming that an anisotropic soil mass is isotropic. They show that significant errors may occur in the calculated settlements if the horizontal modulus is greater than about 1.5 times the vertical value and if the soil is incompressible.

A series of solutions of considerable geotechnical relevance has been obtained relatively recently for the settlement of a foundation on a soil mass whose modulus increases linearly with depth [33] (this soil has been termed a 'Gibson soil' after R. E. Gibson [34] who first obtained a rigorous analytical solution to this problem in 1967). The Gibson soil is a more satisfactory approximation to a normally consolidated soil deposit than is a homogeneous soil, although the latter may often adequately represent an overconsolidated deposit. Solutions for the settlement of a uniformly loaded circular area on a Gibson soil are shown in Fig. 4. Corresponding solutions for rectangular areas have been published by Brown and Gibson [35].

One of the more useful roles of elastic theory is to determine the main characteristics of foundation behaviour, for example, the factors which influence settlement, the relative importance of immediate settlement, the relative importance of immediate settlement and the effect of three-dimensional geometry on settlement. Some of the more significant conclusions

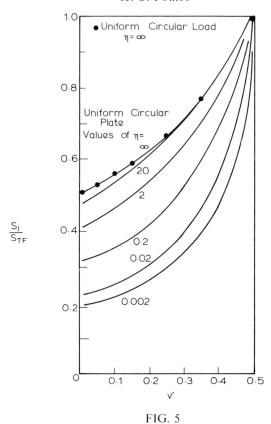

FIG. 5

regarding shallow foundation behaviour, as derived from an examination of the relevant elastic solutions, are as follows:

(i) the main factors affecting settlement (apart from the soil modulus) are the layer depth (relative to the footing size) and the distribution of Young's modulus with depth. The rigidity of the footing does not have a great effect on the maximum settlement; the difference between the settlements of a rigid and perfectly flexible footing generally does not exceed about 21 per cent. Also, for a given area of footing, the maximum settlement is not greatly affected by footing shape.

(ii) the settlements outside a footing decay relatively rapidly if the layer depth is relatively shallow or if the soil modulus increases with depth.

(iii) the ratio, S_i/S_{TF}, of immediate to final settlement is frequently in excess of 0.5, particularly if the drained Poisson's ratio v' is close to 0.5, the soil layer is relatively deep or the distribution of soil modulus with depth is relatively uniform. However, as the soil becomes increasingly non-homogeneous, the relative importance of immediate settlement decreases. Fig. 5 plots S_i/S_{TF} against v' for various degrees of non-homogeneity, as expressed by the parameter $\eta - E_0/ma$, where E_0 — surface modulus, m = rate of increase of modulus with depth and a = circle radius. Small values of η imply a very non-homogeneous soil while $\eta = \infty$ represents a homogeneous soil. From a practical point of view, these results can be considered as indicating that immediate settlement forms a larger proportion of the final settlement for stiffer overconsolidated clays (η large) than for softer normally consolidated clays (η relatively small). These theoretical conclusions are supported by data collected by Simons and Som and quoted by Burland and Wroth [36]. For 12 case records of settlement of major structures on overconsolidated clay, a range of values of S_i/S_{TF} from 0.32 to 0.74 was found, with an average of 0.58. However, 9 case histories of buildings on normally consolidated clay indicated a range of S_i/S_{TF} of 0.08 to 0.21, with an average value of 0.16.

(iv) the final settlement calculated from one-dimensional theory, S_{oed}, gives a close approximation to the actual total settlement S_{TF} in many cases involving foundations on a homogeneous oil layer. Fig. 6 plots S_{oed}/S_{TF} against relative layer depth and v', and shows that for small v' (less than about 0.3), S_{oed}/S_{TF} is close to unity, even for relatively large soil layer thicknesses. However, if the soil is non-homogeneous and S_{oed} is calculated in the usual way using the stress increases for a homogeneous soil layer, S_{oed}/S_{TF} may be considerably less than unity i.e. the one-

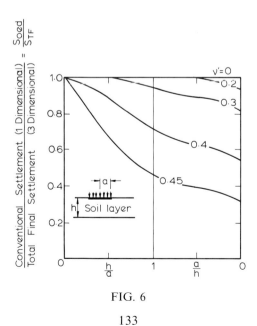

FIG. 6

133

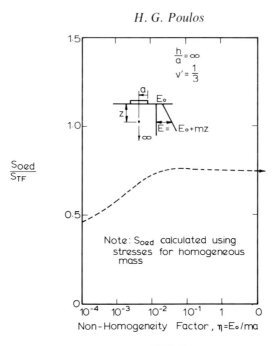

FIG. 7

dimensional settlement significantly underestimates the final settlement. The variation of S_{oed}/S_{TF} with the non-homogeneity parameter η, is shown in Fig. 7. The theoretical conclusions drawn from this figure are consistent with the practical conclusions reached by Burland et al. [37] that, for soft normally consolidated clays (for which small values of η are appropriate), the oedometer settlement underestimates the *total final* settlement, although it gives a relatively good estimate of the final *consolidation* settlement.

(v) the use of the stresses for a homogeneous semi-infinite mass in equations (12) and (13) to calculate settlements in a layered soil profile generally leads to values of acceptable accuracy unless the soil layer is very shallow and $v = 0.5$, or the soil profile is highly stratified with the upper layers much stiffer than the lower layers.

(vi) the effects of local yield on immediate settlement may be significant with normally consolidated clays having high values of the initial shear stress ratio (>0.5). In such cases, local yield may commence at safety factors as large as 8.

5. RAFT FOUNDATIONS

The relative rigidity of the foundation and the detailed distribution of loading on the foundation are generally not of great importance in calculating the settlement of shallow pad foundations. However, they assume much greater significance for raft foundations owing to their layer dimensions, and because of these additional factors, a comprehensive set of parametric solutions for rafts, covering these and other important parameters, is not feasible. Among available solutions are those for a strip raft subjected to concentrated loading [38], and uniform loading [39], a circular raft subjected to uniform loading [19, 20] and concentrated loading [40] and a rectangular raft with uniform loading [41] and concentrated loading [42]. In addition, Gorbunov-Possadov and Malikova [18] treat these and other cases in their comprehensive book.

Solutions for the differential settlement (between centre and edge) and maximum moment in a uniformly loaded circular raft on a finite soil layer of depth h are shown in Figs 8 and 9. The relative rigidity of the raft is defined by a factor K_c, where

$$K_c = \frac{E_r(1 - v_s^2)}{E_s}\left(\frac{t}{a}\right)^3 \qquad (17)$$

where $\qquad E_r =$ raft modulus

$t =$ raft thickness

$a =$ raft radius

$E_s, v_s =$ soil modulus and Poisson's ratio.

Poisson's ratio of the raft, v_r, is 0.3. Figs 8 and 9 indicate the rapid decrease in differential deflection, and the corresponding rapid increase in maximum

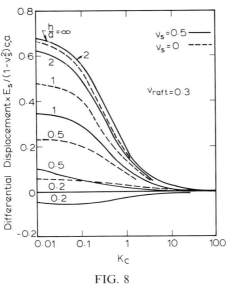

FIG. 8

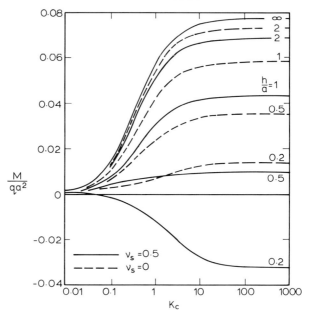

FIG. 9

moment, as the factor K_c increases (i.e. the raft becomes stiffer) or the relative layer depth, h/a, increases.

The effects of soil non-homogeneity on raft behaviour have been examined by Brown [43] for a uniformly loaded circular raft on a Gibson soil. He shows that the bending moments are significantly less than for a homogeneous soil if the degree of non-homogeneity is significant. It is also found that, for practical purposes, the effects of non-homogeneity can be approximately accounted for by using, in the solutions for a homogeneous soil, the modulus at a depth equal to the radius of the raft.

Figs 10 and 11 show distributions of moment and deflection along a strip footing subjected to a concentrated vertical load at various locations along the strip. In this case, the relative rigidity, K_s, is defined as

$$K_s = \frac{16 E_r I (1 - v_s^2)}{\pi E_s L^4} \tag{18}$$

where
$$I = \text{moment of inertia of strip}$$
$$L = \text{length of strip}$$

and the other symbols are as before.

Values of K less than about 10^{-4} indicate a very flexible strip while a strip having K greater than about 0.1 can be considered as rigid.

Most raft foundations in practice are basically rectangular in shape. While a

136

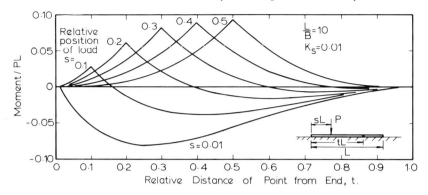

FIG. 10

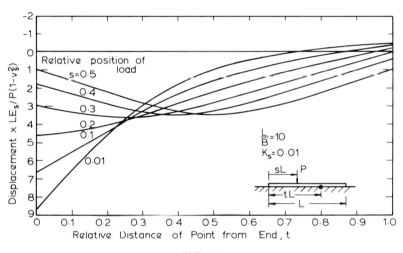

FIG. 11

limited number of solutions are available, it is obviously impossible to obtain an adequate, yet compact, series of parametric solutions for rectangular rafts and it is therefore tempting to consider division of the rectangular raft into strips and then using the available solutions for strip rafts to determine the distribution of moment and deflection in each direction of the rectangular raft. Unfortunately, such a procedure produces deflections and moments which are considerable less than those from a proper rectangular raft analysis, probably largely as a result of ignoring the interaction between adjacent strips. Thus, it would appear necessary to carry out a proper rectangular raft analysis if a realistic assessment of the behaviour of a rectangular raft is to be obtained. The finite element method offers a very useful means of making such an analysis, as described by Hain and Lee [44], Hain [45] and Fraser and Wardle [41]. The

137

computer programe developed by Fraser and Wardle is particularly versatile as it can handle layered or anisotropic subsoil profiles without the need to use three-dimensional elements. Hain [45] and Weisner [46] have extended the finite element analysis to allow consideration of piled rafts.

While elastic parametric solutions for rafts have a more restricted utility than for other types of foundations, they are nevertheless extremely valuable in indicating behavioural trends. Some of the characteristics of raft behaviour indicated by elastic theory are as follows:

(i) The major factors influencing raft behaviour are the relative rigidity of the raft, the nature of the loading, the shape of the raft and the relative thickness of the soil stratum. The first three factors are much more important for rafts than for shallow pad footings.

(ii) The range of relative raft rigidity over which most rafts change from being 'flexible' to 'rigid' is relatively small, generally only about 2 to 3 orders of magnitude. Consequently, over this range, rapid variations of bending moment and differential deflection occur with changing relative rigidity.

(iii) Long-term bending moments in rafts will tend to be greater than those developed under undrained conditions, as the long-term value of relative raft rigidity will be greater than the undrained value (since the drained soil modulus is less than the undrained modulus). Laboratory measurements on model rafts have confirmed this conclusion.

(iv) Because of the sensitivity of differential deflections to raft stiffness, it may be important to consider interaction between the structure, the foundation and the soil. The stiffness of the structure may well result in an effective increase in overall stiffness of the raft, with consequent redistribution of column loads and differential deflections. An indication of the circumstances under which structure-foundation interaction may be important is given by Brown [47] while methods of carrying out more complete analyses are described by Lee and Brown [48], King and Chandrasekaran [49] and Lee [50].

(v) Comparisons between elastic solutions and those derived from subgrade reaction theory (sometimes referred to as the Winkler theory or the 'beam on elastic foundation' theory) show fair agreement for isolated concentrated loading on the raft. However, as the number of loads or the density of loading increases, there is an increasing difference between the two theories, due to the inability of the subgrade reaction theory to reproduce the general 'dishing' of the raft. In the limiting case of uniformly distributed loading, the subgrade reaction theory predicts zero moments in the raft, irrespective of the raft stiffness, whereas the elastic theory indicates significant moments, particularly if the raft is relatively rigid. Thus, there appears to be little justification for the continued use of subgrade reaction theory, particularly as its major advantage over elastic theory, that of simplicity of analysis, is no longer a valid one with the availability of elastic finite element programs.

6. PILE FOUNDATIONS

Wide use has been made of both the 'complex' integration approach and finite element analysis to obtain solutions for the settlement of single piles and pile groups. For homogeneous soils, it has been found that both approaches yield very similar solutions for single pile settlement and that even for non-homogeneous soils, approximate solutions from the complex integration approach agree well with finite element solutions, provided that rapid variations of soil modulus with depth do not occur.

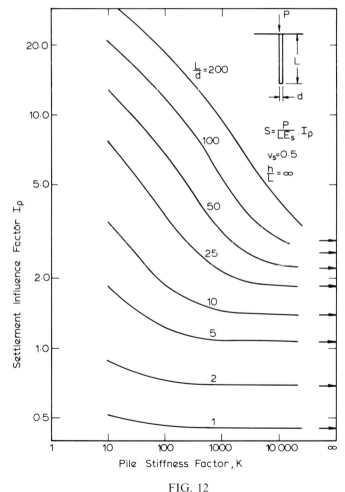

FIG. 12

139

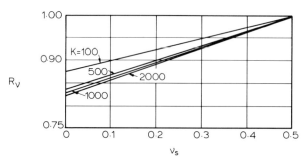

FIG. 13

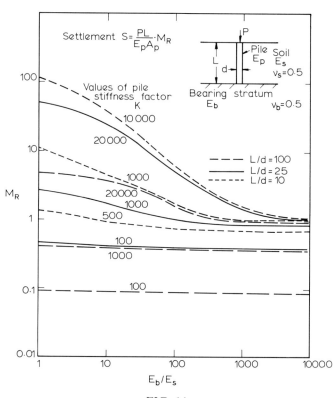

FIG. 14

Typical solutions for a single friction or 'floating' pile in a deep homogeneous soil mass are shown in Fig. 12. Correction factors for the effect of soil Poisson's ratio v_s are shown in Fig. 13. Solutions for an end-bearing pile in a homogeneous soil mass resting on a stiffer elastic stratum are shown in Fig. 14 in terms of a factor M_R by which the elastic compression of the pile (considered as a simple column) are multiplied to obtain the settlement of the top of the pile. In all cases, the pile stiffness factor K is defined as

140

$$K = \frac{E_P}{E_S} \cdot R_A \qquad (19)$$

in which E_P = Young's modulus of pile

          E_S = Young's modulus of soil

          R_A = area ratio of pile, the ratio of the area of the pile section to the gross cross-sectional area; for solid piles, $R_A = 1$.

An alternative form of presentation of these and other solutions is given by Poulos [51].

Some solutions for the settlement of a relatively stiff pile in a Gibson soil suggest that the settlement may adequately be estimated in many cases by using the corresponding solutions for a homogeneous soil having a modulus equal to that at about 0.67 L, where L is the embedded pile length.

For pile groups, the most convenient form of analysis is based on the superposition of 'interaction factors' for two piles. The interaction factor, α, is obtained from an analysis of two identical equally loaded piles within an elastic mass and is the ratio of the increase in settlement of a pile due to the presence of the adjacent pile, to the settlement of a single isolated pile. α is a function of the pile spacing, the pile stiffness factor K, L/d, the relative depth of the soil layer, the distribution of soil modulus with depth and the nature of the bearing stratum. Solutions for interaction factors have been presented by Poulos [52], Poulos and Mattes [53] and Poulos [54]. By employing superposition of these interaction factors, it is possible to analyse the settlement and load distribution within any pile group. From this analysis, it is then possible to derive theoretical values of the group settlement ratio R_S, the ratio of the group settlement to the settlement of a single pile carrying the same average load.

The settlement of the pile group S_G can then be calculated as

$$S_G = R_S \cdot S_{1\,av} \qquad (20$$

where $S_{1\,av}$ – single pile settlement under the averal pile load.

$S_{1\,av}$ may be calculated from the theoretical solutions for a single pile or, alternatively, from a pile load test. Theoretical solutions for R_S are shown in Fig. 15 for pile groups in a uniform soil mass. The effect of the pile tip support condition, spacing and number of piles in the group are shown in this figure. A more extensive tabulation of results is given by Poulos [54]. An interesting feature of these solutions is that, at a given pile spacing, R_S increases almost linearly with the square root of the number of piles for groups of more than about 16 piles. Thus, for relatively large pile groups, R_S can be obtained by extrapolation as follows:

$$R_S = R_{16} + (\sqrt{n} - 4)(R_{25} - R_{16}) \qquad (21)$$

where R_{16}, R_{25} = values of R_S for 16 and 25 piles

                    n = number of piles in group

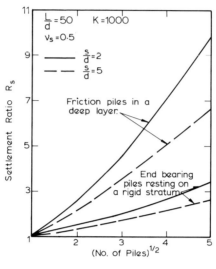

FIG. 15

R_S is influenced by the distribution of soil modulus with depth; R_S for a Gibson soil is less than the value for a homogeneous soil, particularly at larger spacings. Banerjee and Davies [55] have presented some solutions indicating this effect.

If compressible soil layers underlie the pile group, their contribution to the group settlement can be calculated approximately from the elastic solutions described by Poulos and Mattes [56] and Poulos [54].

The main characteristics of single pile behaviour revealed by the elastic solutions are as follows:

(i) The major part of the settlement of a single pile occurs immediately on application of the load. Typically, the ratio S_i/S_{TF} exceeds 0.8. This theoretical conclusion is supported by pile load test results at normal working load levels (at loads approaching the ultimate, a considerable amount of time-dependent settlement may occur due to shear creep). Thus for single piles, the estimation of the rate of consolidation settlement is unlikely to be as significant as for shallow foundations.

(ii) The effects of pile compressibility are most pronounced for long slender piles. The settlement of such piles at working loads is not significantly influenced by conditions at the pile tip i.e. whether it is 'floating' or 'point-bearing', or whether the pile base is enlarged.

(iii) For piles of normal proportions in softer soils, the load-settlement behaviour is substantially linear up to at least half the ultimate load. Thus, elastic theory can be applied directly to single pile settlement prediction. This conclusion is not confined to a purely linear elastic soil model as the

142

finite element analyses of Esu and Ottavianni [57] have shown that, even when the soil exhibits a hyperbolic stress-strain response, the load-settlement behaviour is still substantially linear up to relatively high load levels.

For pile groups, the following conclusions have been drawn from the theoretical solutions:

(i) The settlement depends mainly on the group dimensions rather than on the number of piles. Thus, for a given size of pile cap, increasing the number of piles will lead to only a negligible reduction in settlement unless the piles are widely spaced. This conclusion is consistent with field measurements of group settlement.

(ii) For a given number of piles, the configuration of the piles does not greatly affect the settlement, provided the same centre to centre spacing between adjacent piles is maintained.

(iii) The decay of pile interaction with increasing spacing is more rapid in a Gibson soil than in a homogeneous soil mass.

(iv) The ratio of immediate to final settlement, S_i/S_{TF}, decreases as the group size increases, and approaches the value for a shallow foundation for very large groups.

(v) If the pile cap is in contact with the surface, there is only a relatively small reduction in settlement as compared to the case of free-standing piles, unless the piles are relatively short or widely spaced.

There has been a steady accumulation of comparisons between theoretical and observed settlement behaviour of single piles and pile groups, and the agreement obtained indicates that the major aspects of pile behaviour are remarkably well-reproduced by the theory.

7. CONCLUSION

The objective of this chapter has been to describe the use of elastic theory for foundation settlement prediction, to review some of the available useful solutions and to summarize some of the more significant characteristics of settlement behaviour of shallow foundations, rafts and piles. Space limitations have precluded a detailed discussion of specific case histories and practical applications of elastic theory, but it is clear that, despite the simplifications involved in applying elastic theory to real soils, the theory gives a good indication of the main features of behaviour of the various foundation types. Provided that appropriate soil parameters can be measured or estimated, reasonable estimates of the magnitude of immediate and final settlement can be made.

One advantage of elastic theory is that it provides a simple but unified method of analysing foundation settlements and of obtaining theoretical solutions covering a wide range of parameters. Such solutions can provide the geotechnical engineer with a 'feel' for the factors which may be important in analysing the settlement of a particular foundation type. While more sophisticated methods of analysis are now available and more realistic stress-strain characteristics can be employed for the soil, simple hand methods of settlement analysis based on elastic theory still have an important role to play, both for obtaining preliminary estimates of settlement and as a means of checking the results of more complicated computer analyses.

References

1. Atkinson, J. H., 1975. 'Anisotropic Elastic Deformations in Laboratory Tests on Undisturbed London Day', *Geotechnique*, Vol. 25, No. 2, pp. 357–74.
2. Lo, K. Y., Leonards, G. A. and Yuen, C. M. K., 1977. 'Interpretation and Significance of Anisotropic Deformation Behaviour of Soft Clays', *Laurits Bjerrum Memorial Volume* (Addendum), NGI.
3. Poulos, H. G., De Ambrosis, L. P. and Davis, E. H., 1976. 'Method of Calculating Long-Term Creep Settlements', *Jnl. Geot. Eng. Divn*, ASCE, Vol. 102, No. GT7, pp. 787–804.
4. Davis, E. H. and Poulos, H. G., 1963. 'Triaxial Testing and Three-Dimensional Settlement Analysis', *Proc. 4th ANZ Conf. Soil Mechs. Fndn. Eng.*, pp. 233–43.
5. Davis, E. H. and Poulos, H. G., 1968. 'The Use of Elastic Theory for Settlement Prediction Under Three-Dimensional Conditions', *Geotechnique*, Vol. 18, No. 1, pp. 67–91.
6. Kerisel, J. and Quatre, M. 1968. 'Settlements Under Foundations', *Civ. Eng. Pub. Works Review*, May, June.
7. Egorov, K. E., Kuzmin, P. G. and Popov, B. P., 1957. 'The Observed Settlements of Buildings as Compared with Preliminary Calculation', *Proc. 4th Int. Conf. Soil Mechs. Foundn. Eng.*, London, Vol. 1, p. 291.
8. D'Appolonia, D. J., Poulos, H. G. and Ladd, C. C., 1971. 'Initial Settlement of Structures on Clay', *Jnl. Soil Mechs. Fndns. Divn*, ASCE, Vol. 97, No. SM10, pp. 1359–77.
9. Small, J. C., 1977. 'Elasto-Plastic Consolidation of Soils', PhD thesis, University of Sydney.
10. Giroud, J. P., 1973. *Tables Pour le Calcul des Fondations*, Dunod, Paris.
11. Poulos, H. G. and Davis, E. H., 1974. *Elastic Solutions for Soil and Rock Mechanics*, John Wiley and Sons, New York.
12. Small, J. C., Booker, J. R. and Davis, E. H., 1976. 'Elasto-Plastic Consolidation of Soil', *Int. Jnl. Solids and Structs*, pp. 431–48.
13. Mitchell, J. K. and Gardner, W. S., 1975. 'In-Situ Measurement of Volume Change Characteristics', *Proc. Conf. on In-Situ Msmt. of Soil Properties*, ASCE, Vol. 2, pp. 279–345.
14. Poulos, H. G., 1974. 'Some Recent Developments in the Theoretical Analysis of Pile Behaviour', *Soil Mechanics — New Horizons*, I. K. Lee (ed.), Newnes—Butterworths, London, pp. 237–79.
15. Ladd, C. C. and Foott, R., 1974., 'New Design Procedure for Stability of Soft Clays', *Jnl. Geot. Eng. Divn*, ASCE, Vol. 100, No. GT7, pp. 763–86.
16. Ladd, C. C., Foott, R., Ishihara, K., Schlosser, F. and Poulos, H. G., 1977., 'Stress-Deformation and Strength Characteristics', State of Art *Report*, 9th Int. Conf.

Soil Mechs. Fndn. Eng., Tokyo, Vol. 2, pp. 421–94.

17. Burmister, D. M., 1943. 'The Theory of Stresses and Displacements in Layered Systems and Applications to the Design of Airport Runways', *Proc. Highway Res. Board*, Vol. 23, pp. 127–48.

18. Gorbunov-Possadov, M. I. and Malikova, T. A., 1973. *Calculations of Structures on Elastic Foundation* (In Russian), 2nd edn, Stroizdat, Moscow.

19. Brown, P. T., 1969a. 'Numerical Analyses of Uniformly Loaded Circular Rafts on Elastic Layers of Finite Depth', *Geotechnique*, Vol. 19, pp. 301–6.

20. Brown,P. T., 1969b. 'Numerical Analyses of Uniformly Loaded Circular Rafts on Deep Elastic Foundations', *Geotechnique*, Vol. 19, pp. 399–404.

21. Butterfield, R. and Banerjee, P. K., 1971. 'Elastic Analysis of Compressible Piles and Pile Groups', *Geotechnique*, Vol. 21, No. 1, pp. 43–60.

22. Poulos, H. G. and Davis, E. H., 1968. 'The Settlement Behaviour of Single Axially-Loaded Incompressible Piles and Piers', *Geotechnique*, Vol. 18, No. 3, pp. 351–71.

23. Mindlin, R. D., 1936. 'Force at a Point in the Interior of a Semi-Infinite Solid', *Jnl. Appl. Phys.*, Vol. 7, No. 5, pp. 195–202.

24. Cumming, D. A. and Gerrard, C. M., 1964. 'Computation of Stresses in Pavements', *Proc. 2nd Conf. Aust. Road Res. Board*, Vol. 2, pt. 2, p. 729.

25. Gerrard, C. M. and Mulholland, P., 1966. 'Stress, Strain and Displacement Distribution in Cross-Anisotropic and Two-Layer Isotropic Elastic Systems', *Proc. 3rd Conf. Aust. Road Res. Board*, Sydney, Vol. 3, Pt. 2, pp. 1123–67.

26. Gerrard, C. M., 1967. 'Stresses and Displacements in Layered Cross-Anisotropic Elastic Systems', *Proc. 5th ANZ Conf. Soil Mechs, Fndn. Eng.*, Auckland, p. 205.

27. Zinkiewicz, O. C., 1971. *The Finite Element Method in Engineering Science*, McGraw Hill, London.

28. Desai, C. S. and Abel, J. F., 1972. *An Introduction to the Finite Element Method*, Van Nostrand Reinhold, New York.

29. Carter, J. P., 1977. 'Finite Deformation Theory and its Application to Elastoplastic Soils', PhD thesis, University of Sydney.

30. Milovic, D. M., 1974. *Stress-Strain Analysis in Soil Mechanics*, Instietut za gradevinarstvo SAP Vojvodine — Subotica, Yugoslavia.

31. Gerrard, C. M. and Harrison, W. J., 1970. 'Circular Loads Applied to a Cross-Anisotropic Half-Space', CSIRO Aust. Div. Appl. Geomech., Tech. Paper No. 8.

32. Gerrard, C. M., Davis, E. H. and Wardle, L. J., 1972. 'Estimation of the Settlements of Cross-Anisotropic Deposits Using Isotropic Theory', *Aust. Geomechs. Jnl.*, Vol. G2, No. 1, pp. 1–10.

33. Brown, P. T. and Gibson, R. E., 1972. 'Surface Settlement of a Deep Elastic Stratum Whose Modulus Increases Linearly with Depth', *Can. Geot. Jnl*, Vol. 9, No. 4, pp. 467–76.

34. Gibson, R. E., 1967. 'Some Results Concerning Displacements and Stresses in a Non-Homogeneous Elastic Half-Space', *Geotechnique*, Vol. 17, pp. 58–67.

35. Brown, P. T. and Gibson, R. E., 1973. 'Rectangular Loads on Inhomogeneous Elastic Soil', *Jnl. Soil Mechs. Fndns. Divns. ASCE*, Vol. 99, No. SM10, p. 917.

36. Burland, J. B. and Wroth, C. P., 1974. 'Settlement of Buildings and Associated Damage', *Proc. Conf. Settl. of Structures*, Cambridge, Pentech Press, pp. 611–54.

37. Burland, J. B., Broms, B. B. and De Mello, V. B. F., 1977. 'Behaviour of Foundations and Structures', State of Art *Report*, 9th Int. Conf. Soil Mechs. Founds. Eng., Tokyo, Vol. 2, pp. 495–546.

38. Brown, P. T., 1975a. 'Strip Footings with Concentrated Loads on Deep Elastic Foundations', *Geot. Eng.*, Vol. 6, No. 1, pp. 1–13.

39. Brown, P. T., 1972. 'Longitudinal Bending of Uniformly Loaded Strip Footings on

Deep Elastic Foundations', *Aust. Geomechs. Jnl*, Vol. G2, No. 1 pp. 28–31.

40. Borowicka, H., 1939. 'Druckverteilung unter elastischen Platten', *Ingenieur Archiv*, Vol. X, No. 2, p. 113–25.
41. Fraser, R. A. and Wardle, L. J., 1976. 'Numerical Analysis of Rectangular Rafts on Layered Foundations', *Geotechnique*, Vol. 26, No. 4, pp. 613–30.
42. Brown, P. T., 1977. 'Rectangular Rafts', Lecture 8 of 'Geotechnical Analysis and Computer Applications', School of Civ. Eng., University of Sydney.
43. Brown, P. T., 1974. 'Influence of Soil Inhomogeneity on Raft Behaviour', *Soils and Foundations*, Vol. 14, No. 1, pp. 61–70.
44. Hain, S. J. and Lee, I. K., 1974. 'Rational Analysis of Raft Foundations', *Jnl. Geot. Eng. Divn*, ASCE, Vol. 100, No. GT7, pp. 843–60.
45. Hain, S. J., 1975. 'Analysis of Rafts and Raft-Pile Foundations', *Soil Mechanics — Recent Developments*, University of N.S.W., pp. 213–94.
46. Weisner, T. J., 1977. 'The Behaviour of Piled Raft Foundations', PhD thesis, University of Sydney.
47. Brown, P. T., 1975b. 'The Significance of Structure-Foundation Interaction', *Proc. 2nd ANZ Conf. Geomechs.*, Brisbane, pp. 79–82.
48. Lee, I. K. and Brown, P. T., 1972. 'Structure and Foundation Interaction Theory', *Jnl. Struct. Divn*, ASCE, Vol. 98, No. ST11, pp. 2413–31.
49. King, G. W. and Chandrasekaran, V. S., 1974. 'An Assessment of the Effects of Interaction Between a Structure and its Foundation', *Conf. on Settl. of Structures*, Cambridge, Pentech. Press, pp. 368–83.
50. Lee, I. K., 1975. 'Structure-Foundation-Supporting Soil Interaction Analysis', *Soil Mechanics-Recent Developments*, University of N.S.W., pp. 255–94.
51. Poulos, H. G., 1972. 'Load-Settlement Prediction for Piles and Piers', *Jnl. Soil Mechs. Fndns. Divn*, ASCE, Vol. 98, No. SM9, pp. 879–97.
52. Poulos, H. G., 1968. 'Analysis of the Settlement of Pile Groups', *Geotechnique*, Vol. 18, No. 4, pp. 449–71.
53. Poulos, H. G. and Mattes, N. S., 1971a. 'Settlement and Load Distribution Analysis of Pile Groups', *Aust. Geomechs. Jnl*, Vol. G1, No. 1, pp. 18–28.
54. Poulos, H. G., 'Estimation of Pile Group Settlements', *Ground Engineering*, March 1977, p. 50.
55. Banerjee, P. K. and Davies, T. G., 1977. 'Analysis of Pile Groups Embedded in Gibson Soil', *Procs. 9th Int. Conf. Soil Mechs. Fndn. Eng*, Tokyo, Vol. 1, pp. 381–6.
56. Poulos, H. G. and Mattes, N. S., 1971b. 'Displacements in a Soil Mass due to Pile Groups', *Aust. Geomechs. Jnl*. Vol. G1, No. 1, pp. 29–35.
57. Esu, F. and Ottavianni, M., 1975. Discussion. *Jnl. Geot. Eng. Divn.*, ASCE, Vol. 101, No. GT7, pp. 693–5.

Twenty-five Years of Consulting Engineering

As I commence this segment of the book to commemorate John Roderick's term at the School of Civil Engineering at the University of Sydney I find it difficult to appreciate that a quarter of a century, a generation has passed since I ceased to be his pupil and became his professional engineer colleague. It was with great pleasure and some humility that I accepted the invitation to join the select group of people to contribute — a pleasure because it presented me with an opportunity to look back over my own twenty-five years in the challenging and rewarding consulting engineering profession; humble because there are other consulting engineers from among the earliest lists of John Roderick's graduates who have equal or better qualifications than I have to tackle this aspect of our profession since then.

The Association of Consulting Engineers, Australia

It is perhaps a coincidence that the birth of the Association of Consulting Engineers, Australia took place in 1952, the first full year of John Roderick's reign in the School of Civil Engineering and in fact my own final year at the School at the end of which I joined the firm with which I am still associated.

The consulting engineering profession in New South Wales, or indeed in Australia, naturally did not commence with the formation of the ACEA, but before I make further mention of the Association I would like to sketch briefly how the profession managed before then. Before World War I there appears to have been little scope for consultants and few firms carried organized staffs of engineers or draughtsmen. Civil engineering work was done by permanent staffs of government and semi-government departments and local authorities, while there was even less scope for structural consultants because few buildings were of a type involving more engineering skill than could be provided by the architect. Mechanical and electrical consultants were rare as most design work in these fields was done either by staffs of public bodies or by firms handling agencies for equipment or by contractors.

From 1918 until the depression in the early 1930s there was some increase in opportunities for civil consultants particularly in the local government field, and in the late 1920s new ground was broken when a prominent mechanical and electrical engineer acted as a secondary consultant to architects. Commencing in the early 1930s and continuing over the next two decades or more, Consulting Engineers' Panels were set up within the Institution of Engineers in all states, while in 1933 the Association of Consulting Structural Engineers in N.S.W. (ACSE) was formed with eighteen foundation members including some illustrious names which have continued on in the business names of consulting firms such as Everingham, Macdonald, Morrison, Stanley and Wagner.

The idea for the formation of the ACSE had first germinated in 1924 and in the nine years it took before that Association was born it is recorded that, while competition between those offering engineering services was quite cut throat at times and far from being in the best interests of the profession, the long gestation period had provided the opportunity for most, if not all, the foundation members to establish a close relationship and understanding which far surpassed those which would have resulted had the Association been launched at an earlier date.

The various Institution Panels and the ACSE applied themselves during the 1930s and 1940s, disrupted naturally by World War II, in formulating conditions of engagement, scales of charges, codes of ethics and the like in order to rid the profession of the 'law of the jungle' which it is said tended to exist before those times. It is of interest to note that it was in 1939, just prior to the commencement of the second major world war this century, that ACSE submitted its scale of charges to the Institution of Engineers, Australia, for ratification and adoption.

Turning now to 1952, the year which I indicated earlier saw the birth of the ACEA, it is considered that the action of the Association of Professional Engineers Australia (APEA) in serving a log of claims on a number of practising consulting engineers probably expedited the establishment of an association to speak for all consulting engineers. Of course having been established and having successfully negotiated an acceptable industrial relationship with APEA the question was asked 'To what matters of interest to consulting engineers should we now turn our attention?' The Institution of Engineers Consulting Engineers Panels were well established and were active in varying degrees in different States, so there was danger of duplication in any development of the activities of ACEA. With developing interest in the fledgeling association in most states throughout Australia, it became evident that an association completely independent of the Institution of Engineers could function more freely in providing for the business needs of consulting engineers. At about the same time, due mainly to efforts by several Melbourne consultants, there was a move to form the individual State panels into a Federal body. This was approved by the Institution and the first meeting of the joint panels took place early in 1953.

Late in 1953 the Joint Committee of this Federal body resolved to hold a discussion with the ACEA and from that time the role of the panels diminished and by 1967 the last of the State panels held its final meeting. Throughout the whole of the time from the 1920s onwards the role of the Institution as an umbrella for the Consulting Engineers has been of inestimable value. I have heard that the Institution has at times felt that the time consumed in its deliberations by attending to the affairs of consultants has not been in the best interests of the main body of its members. Nevertheless the Institution has been fundamental to the interests of consultants in that it has set the standards for discipline and ethical behaviour and has conferred the privilege of status on the profession. With the phasing out of the Institution's panels there could have been inevitably some weakening of the profession's ties with the Institution. However, a glance down the lists of presidents and division chairmen of the Institution will show that since 1961, when the winding down of the panels commenced in earnest, consultants have provided a major and increasing number of those leaders.

That year just mentioned, 1961, was the turning point really in the ACEA's history as the 'struggle' to establish an organization to serve all the needs of consulting engineers was over. In 1959 a move had been made to form a Victorian branch of ACEA, which had been established in Sydney, the home of the aforementioned ACSE of N.S.W. The latter Association did not in fact amalgamate with the ACEA until the early 1960s. During the next two years expansion to other States occurred, rules for branches were formulated and membership of FIDIC, the International Association of Consulting Engineers, was achieved.

At that time the Association appointed a part-time paid secretary — a decade later it appointed a full-time director and full-time secretary, membership having grown from the original 25 from 12 firms in 1953 to 100 members from 40 firms in 1962 and on to 600 members from 260 firms employing approximately 5500 people twenty-five years after inauguration.

The ACEA not only retains membership of FIDIC but since 1963 and 1968 respectively has actively participated in the Building Industry Advisory Council with architects and quantity surveyors, and in the Australian Professional Consultants Council with architects, surveyors, quantity surveyors and agricultural consultants which primarily co-ordinates the activities of professionals in those fields in work outside Australia.

From these brief notes it is seen that in exactly the same twenty-five years that John Roderick has been responsible for the preparation of civil and structural engineering graduates from the University of Sydney the Association of Consulting Engineers, Australia has been born from various groups and panels of consultants and has grown to the present body with status and stability and with a uniform voice in the community across Australia.

Consulting Engineer Firms

In 1953 when I entered the consulting engineering profession as a raw graduate my own firm, with offices in Sydney and Brisbane, had a total staff of twenty-three and I made it up to twenty-four. One or possibly two other firms in the whole of Australia had staff numbers larger than that. Five years later my firm had trebled in size and the largest firm was twice that again, and in New South Wales more and more of John Roderick's graduates were entering the consulting profession.

During the early 1960s, due to the rapid population growth throughout Australia, many engineers, particularly from government departments, saw the opportunities ahead in consulting engineering and by the end of the 1960s during the so-called 'boom' period there were many firms with more than fifty on the staff and several with between 250 and 750 staff members, all in addition to the individual consultant working on this own, or to the 'sole trader' with perhaps only a couple of draughtsmen and a typist.

The last five years of the two and a half decades which have been the period covered by this book have seen a general decline in the staff numbers in consulting engineering firms — due I believe to many reasons including increase in efficiency of operation technically and commercially as well as a general downturn in capital works which have been undertaken by the public and private sector in the mid 1970s.

Until 1970 consulting engineers were obligated to practise in partnerships or as individual owners of the firms. In 1970 following the lead set by architects several years before, the rules of the ACEA were changed to allow membership of the Association by consulting engineers who were directors of companies providing consulting engineering services in addition to those who were members of partnerships or sole traders. This change did not and has not made any difference by and large to the operation of the professional consulting practices with respect to the service given and the responsibilities undertaken. It has, however, facilitated continuity of practices by simplifying the entry of younger principals and the retirement of those approaching an age requiring them to step aside. It also enables participation by principals (directors) in staff superannuation schemes whereas principals in a partnership were denied that opportunity.

In the sections which follow I will touch briefly on a number of aspects of consulting and matters within the consulting engineer's practice which have developed or undergone change during John Roderick's twenty-five years.

Multi-Discipline Practices and Overseas Associations

Twenty-five years ago there were virtually no consulting practices which provided multi-disciplinary services. In the civil/structural field some firms specialized in one or other with about half the practices doing work in both areas. The same applied to the mechanical/electrical consultants. However, at about that time, particularly in projects associated with storing and handling of grains and sugar, there was a need for one consultant to act as the primary consultant with the other disciplines being provided by specialists as secondary consultants, much the same as had been traditionally adopted by architects.

By the end of the 1950s several firms, including my own, found it more effective (both from efficiency and economy points of view) to provide some, or all, of the external major disciplines 'in house'. During the 1960s with the development of Australia's minerals on a grand scale and the exploitation of oil and gas reserves, all with the attendant expansion of industry generally, many firms diversified their activities such that recent years have seen the larger firms capable of providing not only the traditional civil/structural, mechanical and electrical services but with expertise in chemical and mining engineering and even in a few cases in-house architectural services as well.

As the firms grew larger during the 1960s more and more services were required of them particularly as projects grew larger in size, and more often than not more complex in nature, and therefore involving the expenditure of vast sums of money. To meet these demands other skills were added such as purchasing officers, expeditors, cost accountants, industrial officers and the like.

Moreover, with the advent in the 1970s of the ecologists, 'environmentalists' and other 'friends of the Earth', consulting engineers became involved, on behalf of their clients, in the preparation of environmental impact statements. Depending on the project, the services of biologists (both land and marine), zoologists, botanists, sociologists and many other 'ists' were required in addition to the many engineering disciplines, geologists, surveyors and others traditionally associated with consulting enginering. Some firms have opted in recent years to add some of these scientists to their engineering staffs.

I indicated earlier that presently there are some 260 firms which have principals who are members of ACEA. By far the majority of these still practise in one (or perhaps two) disciplines of engineering, however there are, in each state of Australia, several firms which now provide multi-disciplinary services.

Perhaps the biggest influence in steering many of these larger firms into the broader fields of service was the advent in the 1960s into Australia of several of the large engineer-constructor firms from the U.S.A. These were brought into the country more often than not by the financial arm of the mining companies which required large-scale, short-time expenditure on projects usually more remotely located than had been the case in the preceding years. Many Australian consultants were able to participate as secondary or sub-consultants to these firms and local expertise was quickly acquired to enable more and more of the services to be provided by direct engagement of the local firms.

By the 1970s many consultants felt that there was a great injustice for the 'big ones' from across the Pacific Ocean to be handed, in particular, all the major mining and mineral processing projects, but, although the number of jobs going overseas has reduced, naturally in the eyes of Australian consultants that reduction has not reached a satisfactory level as we move well into the second half of this decade. Perhaps the future will see a change — hopefully for the better.

With Australia continuing to develop its vast natural resources and with modern technology changing so rapidly it is difficult for Australian consulting engineers to keep pace and so be in a position to provide all the services required for any likely project or client. To assist, however, many consultants have formed associations with other consultants in many countries of the world with the accent mainly on the U.S.A., Canada, the U.K. and some European countries. These associations, the earliest of which were probably actually made in the late 1960s, vary from formally set-up companies to partnerships to *ad hoc* project to project associations to 'don't call me I'll call you' arrangements. Whichever method, considerable success has been achieved in these joint ventures with the consequent realization by clients that, when projects are looked at realistically, the basic engineering skills available from most Australian consultants represent by far the major requisite, and the specialist skills are really quite a small component. It is pleasing to note that the 1970s are tending to reduce the 'tail wagging the dog' situation.

Export of Australian Consulting Engineering Services

Despite my comments above that many projects have been and are still being engineered by large overseas engineer-constructor organizations, Australian consultants have had considerable success in providing services outside Australia.

At the commencement of the quarter-century under review Australian consulting engineers had provided services outside the country mainly in Fiji, New Zealand and New Guinea and this situation continued for the next ten years or so. However, during the 1960s some members of the profession who had had the opportunity of travel into Southeast Asia or, and more particularly, who had in their younger days worked with United Kingdom consultants which had provided services in the 'colonies' saw the possibility of diverting some of the consulting work towards Australia, and proceeded to establish small offices in places like Port Moresby, Singapore, Kuala Lumpur and Jakarta. This was done either by joining forces with a local consultant or 'hanging up a brass plate' and hoping for the best.

Reasonable success followed and by 1970 projects had been engineered by Australian consultants in most Southeast Asian countries, many Pacific Islands and in East Africa. Often the carrying out of projects led to the establishment of a permanent office in the country. Since then to my knowledge several South and Central American, Middle East and Indian sub-continent countries can be added to that list.

The establishment and subsequent operation of the World Bank and the Asian Development Bank have opened the door to many Australian consulting engineers to participate in appraisal missions with other professions — particularly in the agriculture, urban development and energy fields — and in the implementation of such projects. A significant number of Australian consulting engineers have accredited registration with those two and other international lending authorities and the success rate has been reasonable, although not as yet in proportion to the financial contribution to the funds by the Australian government.

The provision of consulting engineering services outside of Australia has opened up many new fields which were not (and still are not, nor I submit should they be) taught to us at university. Those of us who have operated in other countries have had to rapidly learn about currency transfers, withholding and other taxes, special cost-of-living allowances, servant allowances, provision of housing and transport, local schooling, use of untrained and semi-trained personnel, large disparities between local and expatriate salaries, foreign languages — I could go on and on. More often than not the engineering is the simple component overshadowed by the personnel problems.

All consulting engineers working outside Australia in the 1950s and 1960s were, I would suggest, 'babes in the wood' compared with our United Kingdom and European cousins; however, I do feel that we are now holding our own. But I would not like the reader to think that consulting engineering outside Australia is easier or more financially rewarding than handling assignments at home. It isn't. By the time one prepares proposal after proposal, makes visits to the countries concerned, sits for hours and even days on end while the prospective client 'negotiates' (or attempts to do so) the fees and other charges, often the profit is largely eaten up before any engineering commences. However, all that is forgotten once the project is completed, benefits to the community concerned are apparent and the occasional 'thank you for a job well done' is uttered by someone.

Consulting engineers and members of their staff who have had the opportunity of serving in countries outside Australia, more often than not in living and working conditions not nearly as comfortable as in Sydney or Melbourne or anywhere in Australia really, I do believe perform a more valuable service when they return to their home offices.

Many projects undertaken outside Australia, particularly in the latter half of the last twenty-five years have required Australian consulting engineers to train counterpart staff in an endeavour to leave some expertise behind. This naturally has related to the many developing countries where the profession has worked. This is not an easy task by any means and in many instances I am afraid not very successful. However, consulting engineers do not often have the opportunity to 'teach' in this sense and when success is achieved the rewards do approach those such as when the designer of a structure sees it actually built and acclaimed.

Marketing Consulting Engineering

Twenty-five years ago most consulting engineering assignments came from architects, and government and local government bodies. Commissions were given and accepted verbally or occasionally by an exchange of letters, rarely if ever involving the drawing up of a legally worded contract. With the increase in expenditure in the late 1950s and into the 1960s consulting firms began to grow in size and more and more engineers entered the profession. Clients found a wider choice of consultant than they had previously; the older firms found that some of their traditional clients were transferring their work to the newer firms; the younger up-and-coming architects were tending to go to the younger engineers or to the smaller firms feeling they would get a more 'personalized' service.

Before long, due I believe to the then criticized (but now applauded) 'aggressiveness' of a few consultants the profession as a whole became aware that the second half of the twentieth century required that consulting services had to be marketed, properly and professionally. Brochures were permitted by ACEA to be prepared setting out details of the firms, the fields of practice operated and scope of services provided. Also in the 1960s overseas clients began surveying the field of consulting firms and a new ball-game commenced — proposals were requested from several firms which had to set out such matters as experience, how the project would be handled, who would work on it, how fees would be charged, budget estimates of fees and the like. This required the preparation of *curricula vitae*, completed job description reports and a host of other material which the consultant hoped would convince a prospective client to use his services rather than someone else's.

From the aforementioned 'aggressiveness', grew a 'progressiveness' within the profession. However, in the late 1960s and early 1970s the business of making proposals tended to get a little out of hand with clients approaching anyone and everyone and consultants making proposals for anything and everything. By the mid 1970s I am pleased to say both clients and consultants became more selective and sensible — costs of producing became increasingly high (they still are) and out of all proportion.

Agencies such as the World Bank and Asian Development Bank require consultants to be registered and, for most projects, detailed proposals to be prepared by a 'short list' of consultants. The 'scramble' of the late 1960s and early 1970s at least provided good training and groundwork to enable consultants nowadays to put these together quickly and with reasonable economy. As in contracting there is no second prize should you lose the brief. By the same token, clients embarking on major projects of the large size and complexity seen in recent years are entitled to 'shop around' to find the best consultant, or group of consultants, to engineer these projects. Consultants make a living only by selling people's time and this can only be achieved when clients require studies, reports, designs or supervision and where competition exists so a proper and professional marketing technique is essential for survival.

In the Consulting Engineer's Office

When I joined the consulting profession twenty-five years ago I doubt whether a single design or drawing office was air conditioned. The tools of trade were a

154

slide rule, design handbooks, mathematical tables, a drawing board with tee square and a few set squares. A few years later drawing machines began to appear on the market but for quite a long time they were used mainly by the mechanical engineers and draughtsmen. During the 1960s structural and civil draughtsmen, because of the more complex structures being designed, recognized that speed and efficiency could be achieved and today I doubt whether any draughtsman of any discipline in any consulting engineer's office is not equipped with a modern drawing machine attached to a 'vertical' drawing board.

The slide rule and logarithm and other tables held a strong place in the design office alongside perhaps an adding machine until the early 1960s when computers and calculators appeared on the horizon. I well recall attempting to attend a two nights per week course about that time when the schools of Civil Engineering and Physics combined to introduce graduates of five to ten years standing to computers and programming. Nowadays all this is a normal part of the undergraduate course but in the early years of John Roderick's reign there was none of it at all. (In fact if I remember correctly another example of change is that prestressed concrete was covered towards the end of final year in about two or three lectures with no examination thereafter.)

There is no need here to attempt to trace the history of calculators and computers during the last decade or so; suffice to say that with tiny programmable pocket calculators now available no-one needs slide rules and logarithm tables — probably the younger engineers have never used either. Many consulting engineers have also in recent years obtained in-house mini-computers having formerly utilized the services of computer companies often with remote teletype consoles. Full-time computer engineers have become part of the consulting engineer's permanent staff and a new language is heard around the office — hardware, software, peripherals, megabytes, disc drives, etc. But for these advances in speed of calculation and storage of information engineering costs would I believe have been much higher — these costs still bear much the same relationship to total project cost as they did five, ten, twenty and twenty-five years ago despite the greater complexity of structures, machines and production plant and the need for finer design techniques, for more alternate designs to be studied, for a greater demand by clients on cost minimisation.

Twenty-five years ago the consulting engineer's library could fit into a medium-sized suitcase. However, with great advances in design methods and production of new materials and the tendency for consulting firms to diversify libraries began to grow rapidly. Soon it was not possible for every engineer to keep pace in his own private library in his own office or design station. Central libraries began to be established with one or more engineers, or perhaps their wives, attempting to keep it in order in their spare time. Fifteen years ago it is doubtful whether any consulting engineer firm had a full-time professional librarian on the staff — in the mid 1970s they have become an essential member of the medium to large firms not only cataloguing and watching over the books, journals, trade catalogues and the like but providing a valuable research function as well.

Facilities such as copying machines, offset and other printing machines, high-speed plan printing machines, the telex and STD telephone systems, microfilms, accounting machines, all commonplace nowadays were rarely if ever seen in the consulting engineer's office twenty-odd years ago. In-house printing facilities could not be justified then except perhaps for a duplicator using stencils cut on a typewriter and a small table top 'dyeline' plan printer. The professional printer around the corner provided these services. With the demand for maximum convenience, security of information, rapid printing and binding of reports and specifications, most consulting engineers have over the last decade or so gradually introduced all these facilities into their own offices.

What a marked effect on the consulting engineer's 'overheads' all these have had! So much so that more and more firms, commencing probably in the late 1950s began introducing full-time accounting personnel to keep track of these costs, to relieve the partners of the evening and Sunday afternoon task of making up fee accounts, to cope with ever changing tax laws and other such non-engineering matters. Included in the latter and by no means one of inconsiderable concern during the last ten or fifteen years has been the need for consulting engineers to have adequate professional indemnity insurance cover. Consulting engineers in the 1950s were more often than not secondary consultants, projects were less complex and demanding and more importantly the client and the legal profession seemed less likely to 'attack' the professional engineer than is the case today. However, major claims, particularly in the U.S.A., on accountants, the medical profession, architects and engineers during the 1960s, soon spread to Australia and the consulting engineer since then has had to be even more mindful of his legal liability position than he did a generation ago.

The Future

I believe that during the past twenty-five years consulting engineers have made rapid strides both in local and overseas consultancy and it is difficult to detect any significant declining trend in their role in the next twenty-five years. Whereas the consulting engineer's traditional role in the past has been largely one of engineering design, and preparation of drawings and specifications with some construction supervision and contract administration, the services have been widened to include feasibility studies, environmental impact statements, complete project management including purchasing and financial controls, laboratory materials tests and many areas of original research.

The technological gap that divides the developed nations and the developing nations may have narrowed a little during the past twenty-five years but I think it quite unlikely that by the end of the next twenty-five years very many of the developing countries will be designing their own minor and major projects. It has been said that computers and computer programmes will adversely affect the consulting engineer's future. However, I believe that as long as a computer cannot think the engineer will not be replaced: it is the quality of the engineer and not the machines that a consulting firm employs that ultimately determines the quality of its work. Moreover as the world population grows vast new resources of water, food and energy will be needed for its survival. In the field of water resources alone, exploitation of subterranean resources, desalination of vast surface resources, recycling of waste water, provision of protected water supplies and building of new sewerage systems will take more than the next twenty-five years and will inevitably require the services of consulting engineers. The next generation of consulting engineers can certainly be assured of as much work at least, and most probably more, as we have undertaken over the past twenty-five years.

I have enjoyed all my twenty-five years in consulting engineering and have appreciated the opportunity to participate in a wide variety of projects during that time, projects which have taken me throughout the Australian continent and to many countries of the world. I doubt whether I will continue the same level of activity for the next quarter century but hopefully a reasonable portion of it.

I have had the opportunity of working with and knowing many of John Roderick's graduates and I am sure they would all agree that he gave us all a head start into whichever field of civil engineering we elected to follow. I thank the producers of this commemorative book for inviting me to write this chapter and I wish John Roderick a long and satisfying retirement.

The Influence of the Slab on the Lateral Load Response of Concrete Buildings

INTRODUCTION

Slabs are critical elements in the lateral force resisting system for a concrete building. Experience from laboratory testing [1, 2] and from the performance of concrete structures in earthquakes [3, 4] shows clearly that slabs have a major effect on the overall three dimensional response. Yet such effects are frequently ignored or taken into account in a rudimentary manner only [5]. There are three ways in which the slab can influence the lateral load response: (i) through frame action with the columns in the direction of the lateral forces; (ii) by acting in the direction of the lateral forces as a coupling member between shear walls; and (iii) by working as a diaphragm distributing the lateral forces transversely to their resisting system. This paper summarizes the current state-of-understanding with respect to each of those three aspects of the influence of the slab.

FRAME ACTION

General Considerations

The lateral load responses of moment resistant space frames are very sensitive to the participation assumed for the slabs as they work with the beams and as they restrain the rotations of the column at the different floor levels [6]. No single parameter defines the width of the slab that works with the beam for two way floor systems. The effective width varies with the aspect ratios for the side lengths of the slab, the ratio of the flexural stiffness of the boundary beams to that of the slab, the point of application of the slab loads over the depth of the boundary beams and the ratio of the torsional stiffness of the transverse beam to the flexural stiffness of the flexural beam. While the ACI 318–71 [7] equivalent frame method is a valid concept for normal beam and slab structures subjected to lateral loads [8] it does not provide adequate guidance on many aspects of the slab's participation and should not be extended to extreme cases such as flat plates or wall beam structures.

In laboratory tests on three dimensional one bay by one bay frames, one of the more unexpected results has been the severe damage to lateral beams caused by the slab [1, 2]. The rotations of the longitudinal beam-column joints rotate the ends of the lateral beams. The slab restrains those rotations causing large torsional cracks in the lateral beams and diagonal cracks across the corners of the floor slabs. While that torsional cracking caused a significant decrease in the flexural stiffness, the torsional stiffness and the flexural strength of the lateral beams in the tests, it was not critical because the lateral loading was perpendicular to those beams. In an actual structure, however, a more skew loading is likely with accompanying torsional cracking, strength and stiffness degradation in all perimeter beams.

From the architect's and general contractor's viewpoints, the ideal frame is, as illustrated in Fig. 1a, a flat plate structure where there are no beams and the slabs are supported directly on the columns. Such frames provide the architect with maximum flexibility in his selection of the exterior form and interior spatial relationships for the structure. From the financial viewpoint flat plate framing is generally more economic than beam and column framing because the rental volume per total volume of structure is more for flat plate, formwork costs are less, the turn-around time per floor for multistory construction is less and the structural frame provides minimum impediment to the placement of mechanical and electrical services. Even where drift limitations effectively eliminate the use of flat plate framing to resist lateral loads, there is a strong demand from architects and contractors to use flat plate framing as the vertical load carrying system complementing the frames or shear walls resisting the lateral loads. However, it is then necessary, especially in seismic zones, to check the adequacy of the vertical load carrying flat plate frame at the distortions likely under the maximum lateral forces. For economic reasons it is customary to design structures in seismic zones for lateral forces less than those likely if the structure remains elastic during the maximum earthquake. A high energy absorption is provided and the structure allowed to resist the seismic forces by deforming inelastically [5]. In such cases punching at the flat plate connections is a real possibility at the lateral deformations likely in the maximum earthquake. Understanding the response of flat plate structures to lateral loading is essential to the maintenance of the economic viability and life safety of concrete buildings.

Flat Plate Framing

When flat plate framing is subjected to lateral loading the stiffness, energy dissipation and strength characteristics of the connections are the main factors determining the response of the structure. Predictions of response characteristics based on elastic theory and a homogeneous material, and the use of model tests to verify such predictions, generally provide erroneous information. Such procedures take no account of the effects of flexural and torsional cracking of the concrete, or yielding and bond slip of the reinforcing steel. The average flat plate structure is cracked at the slab to column

159

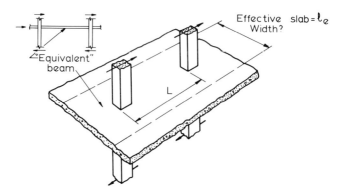

Fig. 1a   Flat plate construction

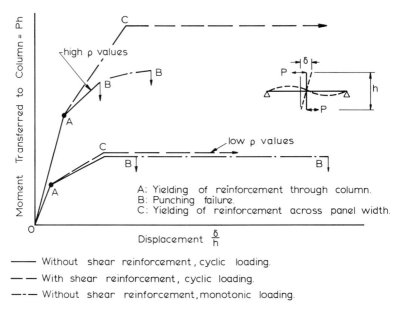

FIG. 1b   Idealized moment-displacement envelopes

connection under dead load. Further, the slab reinforcement passing through that connection yields under live load unless a large amount of the column strip reinforcement is concentrated in the column head region. Tests on full-scale connections are needed to properly define lateral load response characteristics. A sufficient number of such tests have been made to adequately define those characteristics for reinforced concrete slab-interior column connections [9–14]. By comparison, however, little testing has been done on reinforced concrete slab-exterior column connections [9, 15, 16, 17] or

160

prestressed concrete connections [18]. Further in appraising existing work, it must be recognized that most of the testing has been conducted on slab-column specimens for which conditions model more closely those for a column footing than those for a multipanel slab system. Slab-column specimens do not provide for such consequences of continuity as moment redistribution between connections and self-generated in-plane forces in the slab [9].

Slab-interior column reinforced concrete connection tests have shown that the lateral load response is strongly influenced by differing amounts and distributions of the flexural reinforcement in the slab, by amounts and extent of the shear reinforcement and by the level of shear stress transferred to a column simultaneous with a moment. Moment transferred to the column-displacement envelopes for a given level of shear stress can be idealized as shown in Fig. 1b. There is a linear response range OA in which the stiffness is determined by the cracked section properties of the slab in the column head region and which is terminated at A by yielding of the flexural reinforcement passing through the column. Beyond A the stiffness decreases with increasing displacements until a punching failure occurs suddenly at B for all specimens without shear reinforcement. Even when there is a low reinforcement ratio resulting in a connection with a shear strength considerably greater than the flexural strength of the slab, a punching failure still occurs when the slab is rotated far enough. Reversed cycling of the moment being transferred reduces markedly the displacement at which the punching failure occurs and generally results in a capacity about 10 per cent less than that for monotonic loading to failure. For specimens with high reinforcement ratios punching occurs shortly after the reinforcement passing through the column yields. Concentration of the reinforcement within lines two slab thicknesses either side of the column increases the capacity of the connection but reduces its ductility.

As indicated by the broken lines in Fig. 1b the only proven ways of maintaining capacity through large rotations have been to add properly detailed shear reinforcement consisting of either integral beam stirrups [10, 11, 13] or thin steel H sections or studs [14] anchored above and below the flexural reinforcement through the column. Shear reinforcement in the form of shearheads or bent bars increases the capacity but does not improve the ductility [10, 11]. The shear reinforcement must hold the top and bottom flexural mats together and prevent the development of a splitting crack between them.

Where concrete structures are used in seismic zones they should be proportioned so that the hysteresis loops for inelastic reversed cyclic loadings are broad ellipses of the form of curve A in Fig. 2. If they become S-shaped and thin, energy dissipation is reduced and earthquake effects become more severe. For slab-column connections hysteresis loops remain broad ellipses under reversed cyclic loading only if the reinforcement ratio within the column head area is 0.9 per cent or less and the maximum nominal shear stress less than $6\sqrt{f_c'}$ (psi units, $0.48\sqrt{f_c'}$ MPa units).

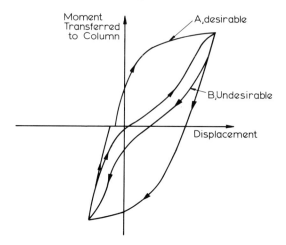

FIG. 2   Hysteresis loops

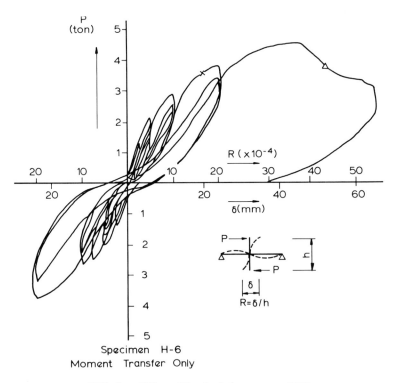

Specimen   H-6
Moment   Transfer   Only

FIG. 3a   Effect of level of shear stress [12]

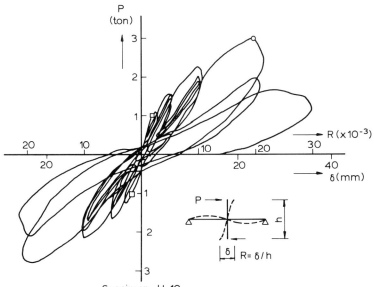

Specimen H-10
Level of Simultaneous Shear Stress $\sqrt{f'_c}$

Fig. 3b   Effect of level of shear stress [12]

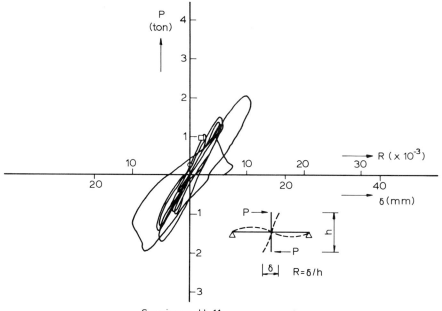

Specimen H-11
Level of Simultaneous Shear Stress $2\sqrt{f'_c}$

FIG. 3c   Effect of level of shear stress [12]

163

The level of shear stress transferred simultaneously with the moment markedly affects the form of the hysteresis loops. Shown in Fig. 3 are loops [12] for specimens similar in all respects except for increasing levels of shear stress. All three specimens were proportioned so that theoretically they would fail in flexure. The energy absorption and energy dissipation characteristics worsen rapidly as the shear stress level increases. In most building codes the effects of the vertical component of the earthquake motion are ignored. From Fig. 3 it is obvious that if flat plate framing is used in seismic regions properly detailed shear reinforcement is highly desirable unless a careful analysis is made of the maximum likely seismic deformations.

If the capacity of reinforced concrete connections is inadequate for lateral load, a designer is likely to consider prestressing the slab as an alternative to changing the geometry or providing shear reinforcement. The limited available results [18] show that prestressing increases the shear capacity and is therefore a viable procedure for wind loadings. However, for seismic loadings, the clamping force provided by the prestress reduces energy dissipation effects so that the strength problem of the reinforced concrete connection may still persist for the prestressed concrete connection. While the stiffer prestressed structure can absorb more energy, it also has less energy dissipation capacity.

The strength of flat plate connections is best assessed using beam analogy procedures [9, 19]. Such procedures permit proper recognition of slab flexural reinforcement effects and the relative contributions of shear reinforcement at transverse and side faces of a column. The linear variation in shear stress procedure of ACI 318–71 [7] overestimates the strength of connections with less than one per cent flexural reinforcement and does not provide a realistic model of torsional effects. Collapse in flexure is possible due either to a local fan mechanism centered on the column or a folding mechanism extending across the full width of the structure. The local fan mechanism is generally suppressed in the complete structure by in-plane restraint effects and only the folding mechanism need be considered. Beam analogy procedures assume that the slab sections framing into each column face can be idealized as beam sections each capable of developing the ultimate force combinations implied in building codes such as ACI 318–71. Beam analogy procedures predict that for all conditions except shear transfer only, the capacity of a connection can be increased by increasing the reinforcement ratio in the column head region. Such an approach is useful to a designer who might otherwise be forced to alter the geometry of his structure or add shear reinforcement.

While there is general agreement on reasonable methods for assessing the strength of flat plate connections, there are wide differences in opinion on the more important problem of assessing the lateral load stiffness of flat plate framing. Those differences are highlighted by discrepancies between field performance and full scale test data on the one hand and elastic theory predictions on the other. There are several medium rise structures on the East Coast of the U.S.A. where lateral load stiffnesses were assessed according to the equivalent frame method of ACI Code 318–71 and using an effective slab width equal to about one half the width centre to centre of panels. Marked cracking occurred in the columns under design wind loads and it was apparent that the moments in the columns were not properly assessed. In full scale laboratory tests stiffnesses have been as little as 50 per cent of those predicted using the ACI equivalent frame and a cracked section for the slab. Further, stiffnesses have been considerably less than those predicted by many elastic analyses [20]. Laboratory data shows that to correctly predict measured rotations account must be taken of bond slip for the slab reinforcement within the column and of the ratio of the cracked to uncracked stiffness for concrete in torsion being much less than the same ratio for bending. When the column dimension in the direction of moment transfer is greater than the anchorage length for the reinforcement in that direction, the model shown in Fig. 4 correctly predicts

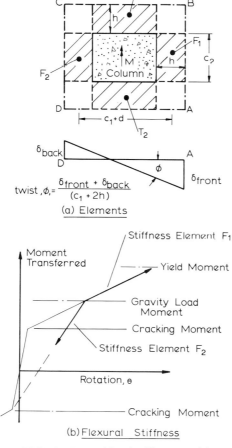

(a) Elements

(b) Flexural Stiffness

FIG. 4   Lateral load-stiffness model

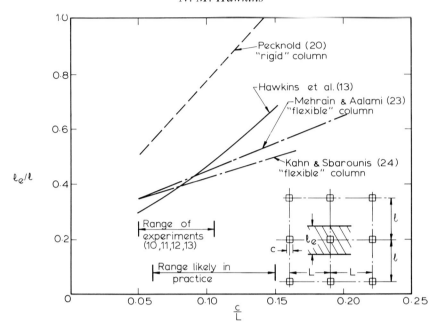

FIG. 5   Effective width of slab

the stiffness for monotonic loading for both elastic and post-yield ranges [13] for the tests reported in References 10, 11, 12 and 13. The slab is assumed attached to the column by cantilevering cracked flexural elements F_1 and F_2 and cracked torsional elements T_1 and T_2 each having the properties of those sections. The elements F_1 and F_2 have the loading and unloading stiffnesses shown in Fig. 4b and determined as outlined in Reference [2]. The torsional elements have the cracked section stiffness defined in Reference [22]. Compatability for points A, B, C and D at a distance one slab thickness, h, from the column, determines the twist ϕ. The post-yield stiffness is that obtained when the front face element F_1 is given zero stiffness. Various predictions for the effective slab width l_e, Fig. 1, that result in the same central rotation for a given moment transferred to the column as that for a beam of span length L, subject to the same central moment are shown in Fig. 5. In most flat plate structures c/L ratios lie between 0.06 and 0.15. Large scale experiments have covered only a small portion of that range. From Fig. 5 it is apparent that of the theory of elasticity methods, Pecknold's approach with the torsional stiffness effectively taken as zero gives reasonable agreement with the trends of the experimental data.

COUPLING OF SHEAR WALLS BY SLABS

Many slab and wall structures have the form shown in Fig. 6a and for lateral load analysis they are idealized as the planar coupled walls shown in Fig. 6b.

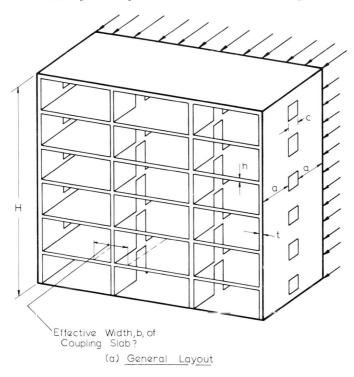

(a) General Layout

Fig. 6a   Shear wall-slab coupled structure

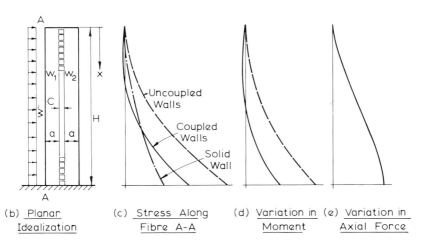

(b) Planar Idealization   (c) Stress Along Fibre A-A   (d) Variation in Moment   (e) Variation in Axial Force

FIG. 6b – e   Shear wall-slab coupled structure

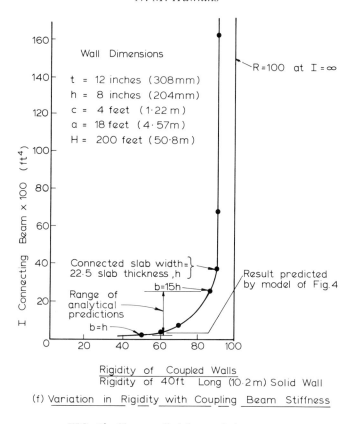

FIG. 6f   Shear wall-slab coupled structure

In Figs. 6c, d and e are shown likely stresses along the extreme fibre A-A, variations in moment over the height of the walls and forces in the walls for a solid cantilever wall (dashed-dot curve), two uncoupled walls (dashed curve), and coupled walls (solid curve). It is obvious the degree of coupling must be carefully assessed. Depending on the effective width, b, assumed for the coupling slab the behaviour can vary between an almost completely coupled and an uncoupled condition. Shown in Fig. 6f is the variation in the rigidity of the coupled walls as a function of that effective width for the case of 12 in. wide, 18 ft. deep and 200 ft. high walls coupled across a 4 ft. wide corridor by 8 in. thick slabs [25]. The range of effective slab widths recommended by various investigators are shown on Fig. 6f. In addition to the question of the effective rigidity, procedures are also needed for assessing the shear strength at the toe of the wall and the width over which the reinforcement in the slab is effective for resisting the lateral loadings.

Reinforced concrete scale model tests have been conducted at the Universities of Toronto [26] and Christchurch [27]. As in the case of flat

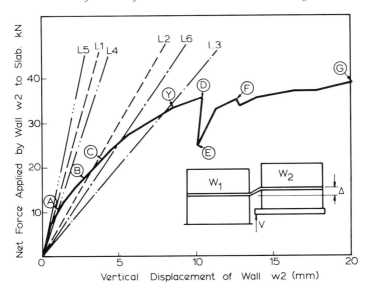

FIG. 7   Load-deflection results for slab-coupled shear walls [26]

plate framing those tests have demonstrated the marked differences likely
between elastic predictions and reinforced concrete test data. The Toronto
results are summarized in Fig. 7. Cracking at the corridor ends of the walls
occurred at A, transverse cracking across the full panel width between parallel
walls at C, and punching at the wall ends at D. After D, while the load capacity
could be regained, the shear failure spread back along the walls with increasing
deformations. Lines L_1 and L_2 in Fig. 7 are the theoretical stiffnesses for an
uncracked and cracked slab respectively with an effective width equal to half
the corridor width. Line L_3 is the theoretical stiffness, calculated as for L_2, but
on a span equal to the corridor width plus the wall thickness. Lines L_4, and L_5
are the theoretical stiffnesses for cracked coupling slabs having effective widths
determined according to the elastic theory techniques of References 28 and 29.
Those techniques considerably over-estimate the measured stiffness. Line L_6 is
the theoretical stiffness determined in accordance with the model of Fig. 5 and
assuming zero displacement at the slab's discontinuous edge. The stiffness for
line L_6 approximates reasonably well the slope of the load-deflection curve for
its cracked section range. In a real structure cracking of the slab at the ends of
the shear wall is likely due to temperature, shrinkage, and dead load effects.
The results in Fig. 7 indicate that the effective width should be taken as less
than half the corridor width for a cracked section and can probably be
realistically evaluated using the same model as that appropriate for slab-
column connections. The resulting effective rigidity is shown in Fig. 6f.

While the shear strength prediction procedures of Reference 26, shown in
Fig. 8a, are easy to apply, the same result is also obtainable using beam

169

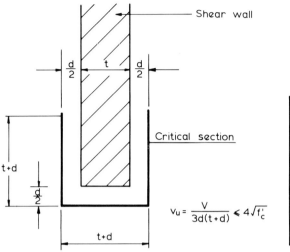

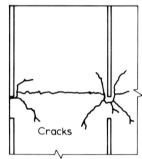

$$V_u = \frac{V}{3d(t+d)} \leqslant 4\sqrt{f_c'}$$

FIG. 8a   Prediction of slab-coupled shear wall
shear capacity [26]

FIG. 8b   Crack pattern at
load stage C [26]

analogy procedures. However, the reduced shear stress of $2\sqrt{f_c'}$ (psi units, $0.16\sqrt{f_c'}$ MPa units) recommend in ACI 318-71 for one way action must be used. The pattern of cracking that develops in the top of the slab is shown in Fig. 8b. Because that pattern is reversed on the bottom side of the slab, the width over which the reinforcement is effective for transfer of lateral load should be limited to no more than half the corridor width either side of the wall.

DIAPHRAGM ACTION

Diaphragm action refers to the transmitting of shear forces through the roof or floor of the structure to the lateral load resisting system. That action is illustrated in Fig. 9a. Diaphragms are usually classified as rigid or flexible. Rigid diaphragms transmit lateral loads to the resisting elements in proportion to the relative rigidity of those elements and cause torsional effects when their center of mass is eccentric from the center of rigidity of the resisting system. Flexible diaphragms transmit loads to resisting elements in proportion to the area tributary to each element and do not transmit rotational forces. Cast-in-place concrete floors are usually treated as rigid diaphragms and plywood floors as flexible diaphragms. Concrete slabs are not perfectly rigid and exhibit a wide range of behaviour with their actual flexibility depending on both the rigidity of the slab and the lateral load resisting system. It is incorrect to assume that slabs are rigid if their in-plane

170

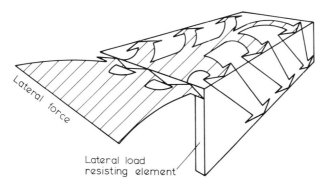

FIG. 9a   Diaphragm action

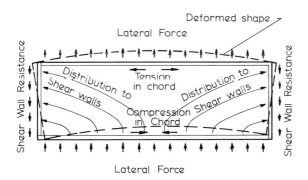

FIG. 9b   Beam action of diaphragm

stiffness is less than or comparable to the stiffness of the lateral load resisting system.

Cast-in-place concrete diaphragms can be considered as shear walls oriented horizontally. Then, as illustrated in Fig. 9b, it is apparent that items of concern can be: (1) adequate tensile ties on the perimeter of the diaphragm, (2) adequate shear strength for the web of the diaphragm and (3) distortions induced in the lateral load resisting elements by diaphragm deformations. Other concerns are: (4) lateral load distribution effects including torsion, and (5) the design of connections transferring forces between diaphragms and the lateral load resisting systems.

Lateral Load Distribution

Both flexural and shear deformations must be considered in assessing the relative rigidity of lateral load resisting elements including diaphragms. Shear rigidities determine the distribution of forces up to wall height to length ratios or diaphragm length to depth ratios of one and one-quarter. Flexural rigidities

171

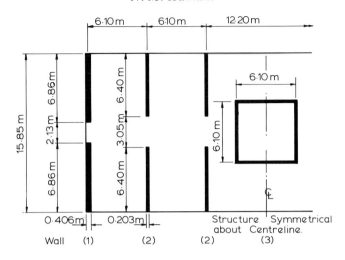

No. of Storeys = 20
Storey Height = 2·67m

(a) Plan of Structure

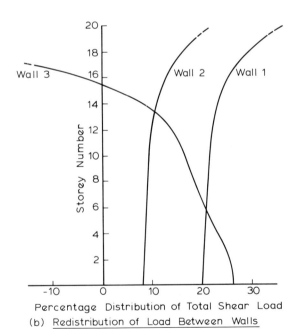

(b) Redistribution of Load Between Walls

FIG. 10   Lateral load distribution by diaphragm action

172

govern above ratios of one and three-quarters. Simple elastic analyses [30] predict that with tall buildings, the slab rigidity results in a considerable redistribution of load over the height of the structure. As illustrated in Fig. 10, while planar walls may absorb most of the lateral forces in upper levels, these shears are redistributed through the diaphragms and resisted predominately by the core at lower levels. Micro concrete models tests [31] have verified those predictions and shown that: (i) the neutral axis shifts noticeably within large panel members towards the compression side of that member before cracking occurs and (ii) flexural to shear rigidity ratios are less than those based on gross section properties. Analytical studies of inter-connected shear wall-core and flat plate structures have shown that neglect of warping effects introduces marked underestimations in core wall torques and longitudinal stresses in the core wall and columns [32].

Lateral load distribution and torsional effects are usually assessed using gross section properties. In severe earthquakes diaphragms may be highly stressed especially if cut-outs for stairs, elevators, etc. are located in critical regions. Analyses of inelastically loaded shear walls and large shear panels have shown that account should be taken of the changes in shear and flexural rigidity with cracking, of the non-closing of previously formed cracks under load reversals, of bond slip effects, and of compression softening of concrete stressed above $0.7f'_c$ [33].

Connections Between Diaphragms and Lateral Load Resisting System

At such connections the in-plane shears can be imposed on regions where gravity loads already create high negative moments and high out-of-plane shears. Reinforcement must be adequate to carry that negative moment and prevent sliding on the connection plane. In severe earthquakes diaphragm distortions have occurred due to slippage along that plane. Reinforcement must be provided to independently resist the shears, moments and normal forces acting on the plane. Shear reinforcement is best provided according to shear-friction concepts [34, 35]. For monotonic loading and dense aggregate concrete the interface shear capacity, v_u, can be taken as:

$$v_u = 0.8\rho_v f_y + 7\sqrt{f'_c} \text{ (in psi units)} \leq 0.3f'_c$$
$$= 0.8\rho_v f_y + 0.56\sqrt{f'_c} \text{ (in MPa units)} \leq 0.3f'_c \qquad (1)$$

where ρ_v is the shear reinforcement ratio. If the $\rho_v f_y$ value is less than 200 psi (1.38 MPa) the capacity should be reduced linearly from the values given by equation (1) to zero for lesser $\rho_v f_y$ values. In order for such shear reinforcement to be fully effective at least two thirds of it should be located in the flexural tension zone. Where the interface lies between concretes cast at different times the strength is very sensitive to the surface roughness. For the values given in equation (1) to apply the surface must be deliberately roughened to a depth of

173

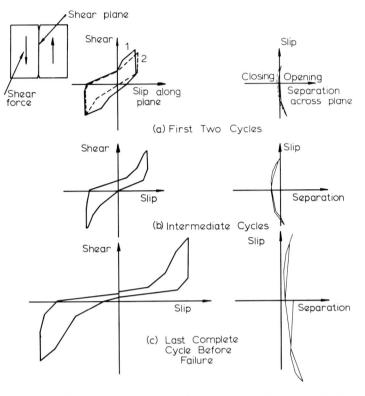

FIG. 11   Shear transfer response for reversed cyclic loading [34]

at least one quarter of an inch and all laitance removed. If the surface is not roughened the ultimate stress drops quickly with decreasing roughness to $0.6\rho_v f_y$.

If the lateral load increases monotonically until failure occurs reasonable ductility is associated with the capacities given by equation (1). If, however, there are load reversals, then the capacity decreases to about 80 per cent of the monotonic loading capacity. More importantly, as illustrated in Fig. 11, the shear stress-slip curves become distinctly S-shaped with large slips developing at low loads for small changes in stress. That action markedly affects the dynamic response characteristics of a structure and can quickly lead to shear distributions on lateral load resisting elements significantly different to that obtained assuming rigid floor diaphragms [36]. One method of avoiding such difficulties is to provide prestress across the joint. Under axial compressive loads the stiffness at zero load is partially regained, the hysteresis loops enlarged and reasonable ductility regained [37]. Connections for diaphragms composed of precast concrete units pose special problems especially for structures located in seismic zones [37].

Distortions of Lateral Load Resisting Elements

As indicated in the discussion of frame action, the restraints imposed by the diaphragm can cause torsional cracking in lateral beams and change the effective length of columns. As indicated in Fig. 9b, diaphragm stiffness also affects the deformations in boundary walls. Walls parallel to the direction of motion are subjected to significantly twisting action while those perpendicular to the motion can be subjected to both twisting and translational actions.

CONCLUDING REMARKS

Adequate information is available to make reasonably reliable assessments of the out-of-plane strength and deformation characteristics for flat plate concrete frame and shear wall construction subjected to lateral loads. Such assessments must not be based solely on elastic analyses but should consider redistribution effects associated with concrete cracking, bond slip of the reinforcement and yielding of the reinforcement. Shear reinforcement is necessary at stress concentration locations for simultaneous satisfaction of ductility and strength requirements. By contrast, little is known about the in-plane shear strength and stiffness characteristics of concrete slabs and the dependence of the lateral load response on those characteristics. Crude assumptions concerning those properties are often used by designers without regard to the importance of those assumptions for the overall safety of the structure. The information in this paper can be used to develop a procedure for checking the importance of design assumptions for those in-plane characteristics.

References

1. Nakano, K., 'Experiments on Behavior of Prestressed Concrete Four-Story Model Structure on Lateral Force', *Proceedings*, Third World Conference on Earthquake Engineering, New Zealand, V. III, January 1965, pp. IV572–IV590.
2. Wilby, G. K., 'Response of Concrete Structures to Seismic Motions', Report 75–11, Department of Civil Engineering, University of Canterbury, Christchurch, July 1975.
3. *The Venezuela Earthquake, July* 29, 1967, American Iron and Steel Institute, New York 1969.
4. *San Fernando, California, Earthquake of February* 9, 1971, U.S. Department of Commerce, National Oceanic and Atmospheric Administration, Washington, D.C. 1973.
5. International Conference of Building Officials, *Uniform Building Code*, Vol. I, 1976 edn., Whittier, California 1976.
6. Edgar, L. and Bertero, V. V., 'Evaluation of Contribution of Floor System to Dynamic Characteristics of Moment-Resistant Space Frames', *Proceedings*, Sixth World Conference on Earthquake Engineering, New Delhi, January 1977.
7. ACI Committee 318, *Building Code Requirements for Reinforced Concrete (ACI 318–71)*, American Concrete Institute, Detroit 1971.

8. Fraser, D. J., 'Equivalent Frame Method for Beam-Slab Structures', ACI Journal, 74, No. 5, May 1977.

9. ACI-ASCE Committee 426, 'The Shear Strength of Reinforced Concrete Members-Slabs', Structural Division Journal, ASCE, 100, No. ST8, August 1974.

10. Carpenter, J. E., Kaar, P. H. and Corley, W. G., 'Design of Ductile Flat Plate Structures to Resist Earthquakes', *Proceedings*, Fifth World Conference on Earthquake Engineering, Rome 1973.

11. Islam, S. and Park, R., 'Test on Slab-Column Connections with Shear and Unbalanced Flexure', *Journal of the Structural Division*, ASCE, 102, ST3, March 1976, pp. 549–68.

12. Kanoh, Y. and Yoshizaki, S., 'Experiments on Slab-to-Column and Slab-to-Wall Connections', *Japan Concrete Journal*, 13, 6, June 1975.

13. Hawkins, N. M., Mitchell, D. and Symonds, D. W., 'Hysteretic Behavior of Concrete Slab-to-Column Connections', *Proceedings*, Sixth World Conference on Earthquake Engineering, New Delhi 1977.

14. Elmasri, M. Z., Dilger, W. H. and Ghali, A., *Static and Dynamic Response of Slab-Column Connections to Shear and Moment*, Report No. CE 75-10, Department of Civil Engineering, University of Calgary, Alberta, November 1975.

15. Kanoh, Y. and Yoshizaki, S., 'Torsional Test of a Slab-Column Connection', Paper presented at Fall Convention of Architectural Institute of Japan, 1976.

16. Neth, V. W., 'Model Studies of A Reinforced Concrete Flat Plate With Edge Columns', PhD thesis, University of Calgary, Alberta, July 1977.

17. Narui, S., 'Trägfahigkeit von Flachdecken an Rand-und Eckstützen, (Ultimate Shear Capacity of Edge Column-Slab Connections)', PhD thesis, University of Stuttgart, February 1977.

18. Trongtham, N. and Hawkins, N. M., *Moment Transfer to Columns in Unbonded Post-Tensioned Prestressed Concrete Slabs*, Report SM 77-3, Department of Civil Engineering, University of Washington, October 1977.

19. Park, R. and Islam, S., 'Strength of Slab-Column Connections with Shear and Unbalanced Flexure', *Journal of the Structural Division*, ASCE, 102, ST9, September 1976, pp. 1879–902.

20. Pecknold, D. A., 'Slab Effective Width for Equivalent Frame Analysis', *ACI Journal*, 72, 4, April 1975, pp. 135–7.

21. Takeda, T., Sozen, M. A. and Nielsen, N. N., 'Reinforced Concrete Response to Simulated Earthquake', *Journal of the Structural Division*, ASCE, 96, ST12, December 1970, pp. 2557–73.

22. Hsu, T. T. C., 'Torsion of Structural Concrete-Behavior of Reinforced Concrete Members', SP-18, *Torsion of Structural Concrete*, American Concrete Institute, Detroit 1968.

23. Mehrain, M. and Aalmi, B., 'Rotational Stiffness of Concrete Slabs', *ACI Journal*, 72, 4, April 1975, pp. 135–7.

24. Khan, F. Z. and Sbarounis, J. A., 'Interaction of Shear Walls and Frames', *Journal of the Structural Division*, ASCE, 90, ST3, June 1964, pp. 307–12.

25. Popoff, A., 'What Do We Need to Know About the Behavior of Structural Concrete Shear Wall Structures', SP-36, *Response of Multistory Concrete Structures to Lateral Forces*, American Concrete Institute, Detroit 1973, pp. 1–12.

26. Schwaighofer, J. and Collins, M. P., 'Experimental Study of the Behavior of Reinforced Concrete Coupling Slabs', *ACI Journal*, 74, 3, March 1977, pp. 123–7.

27. Paulay, T., private communication, August 1977.

28. Qadeer, A. and Stafford Smith, B., 'The Bending Stiffness of Slabs Connecting Shear Walls', *ACI Journal*, 66, 6, June 1969, pp. 464–73.

29. Tso, W. K. and Mahmoud, A. A., 'Effective Width of Coupling Slabs in Shear Wall Buildings', *Journal of the Structural Division*, ASCE, 103, ST3, March 1977, pp. 573–86.

30. Coull, A. and Adams, N. W., 'A Simple Method of Analysis of the Load Distribution in Multistory Shear Wall Structures', SP-36, *Response of Multistory Concrete Structures to Lateral Forces*, American Concrete Institute, Detroit 1973, pp. 187–207.

31. Ramakrishnan, V., 'Comparison of Three Dimensional Analysis of Concrete Shear Wall Buildings and Their Actual Behavior', *Methods of Structural Analysis*, Vol. I, American Society of Civil Engineers, New York 1976, pp. 95–114.

32. Taranath, B. S., 'The Effect of Warping on Inter-Connected Shear Wall-Flat Plate Structures', *Proceedings*, Institution of Civil Engineers, 61, 2, December 1975, pp. 711–24.

33. Darwin, D. and Pecknold, D. A., 'Analysis of RC Shear Panels Under Cyclic Loadings', *Journal of the Structural Division*, ASCE, 102, ST2, February 1976, pp. 355–70.

34. Mattock, A. H., *The Shear Transfer Behavior of Cracked Concrete Subject to Cyclically Reversing Shear*, SM 74-4, Department of Civil Engineering, University of Washington, Seattle, November 1974.

35. Mattock, A. H., *Shear Transfer Under Cyclically Reversing Loading Across an Interface Between Concretes Cast at Different Times*, SM 77-1, Department of Civil Engineering, University of Washington, Seattle, June 1977.

36. Polyakov, S. V., *Design of Earthquake Resistant Structures*, MIR Publishers, Moscow 1974.

37. Hawkins, N. M., 'Seismic Resistance of Precast and Prestressed Concrete Structures', *PCI Journal*, 22, 6, November/December 1977.

Some Comparisons of the Engineering Scenes in Australia and the United Kingdom

It was with great pleasure that I accepted the invitation to contribute a paper to this book to mark the retirement of John Roderick. As one who had firstly studied under him, subsequently working in the same department, and later holding a professorial appointment in the country where he himself was educated, I have the great privilege of knowing him well and also many of his former colleagues from the years prior to his move to Sydney. Having personally left university teaching after some twenty-two years to take up an appointment in CSIRO, I felt my contribution might best be written about some observations on the engineering scenes in Australia and the United Kingdom.

The past three decades have seen many changes, both in Australia, the United Kingdom and elsewhere. These include the quality and number of undergraduate students entering tertiary establishments to study engineering, the number of institutions which offer engineering courses, and changes in the content of courses resulting from advances in knowledge and the influence of the electronic computer. The stage has now been reached where, in the United Kingdom, the Institution of Civil Engineers has made major decisions relating to professional qualification prerequisites. In Australia, where it is recognized that there is an oversupply of graduates into the market, the principal statement on engineering training, issued by the Institution of Engineers, Australia, relates to the '1980 Rule', requiring four-year courses of study at tertiary level as a prerequisite to corporate membership.

Many of the senior year undergraduates, whom John Roderick taught upon his arrival, had experienced conditions very different from those of today. Undergraduate numbers in the University had grown rapidly with the influx of returning servicemen, who were taking advantage of the post-war training schemes, and facilities were inadequate and classes were large. Students were expected to attend evening drawing office classes on two evenings per week in first year, as well as a Saturday morning workshop practice course. As the full-time academic staff was quite inadequate to cope, part-time instructors attended many of the practical classes, and one was more likely to have personal contact with these people than with the lecturers themselves. My recollections of the early years of the course were those of a very full programme, with a large amount of prescribed laboratory and drawing office work, little of which exercised the creative or critical faculties, a highly competitive and purposeful spirit, and an attitude of fending for oneself. Students or their sponsors paid fees except if they were recipients of Exhibitions, of which 200 were awarded each year throughout the State. Engineering students received a high proportion of these, and many had been awarded the maximum attainable Leaving Certificate pass.

Assignments, if not imaginative, were usually meticulously marked, with attention to detail, and the importance of producing a report, graph or drawing which communicated its message unambiguously, and followed all of the associated conventions, was soon recognized by the undergraduate. Spelling and English expression were also matters given attention. The course had no options, and the early years consisted of subjects taught within the Engineering faculty which were designed to provide a grounding in the science of engineering, together with subjects from the science syllabus, which were presented in a sequence quite unrelated to the needs of the engineers. This lack of co-ordination of material proved very difficult for many students but many graduates, in retrospect, must have identified the fact that those who survived were well placed to analyse an engineering problem, in which the data had to be obtained by one's own efforts. The courses bred self-reliant, even if over-loaded, engineers. The first two years of the course were common and a large part of the third year also, so that mechanical engineering design and electrical engineering supplemented the civil engineering subjects in that year.

Engineering undergraduates who enrolled straight from school lived predominantly in the metropolitan area, and commuted daily to university from home. A large percentage had come from State schools, several of which provided students of very high academic quality. Secondary teaching had been strict and rigorous, by well-qualified teachers who strove for high standards.

At the end of World War II Sydney University was the only one in the State, and when John Roderick arrived at Sydney, the newly-formed second university, which became the University of New South Wales, had not produced any engineering graduates. New South Wales now has five institutions conferring degrees in Civil Engineering, namely, the Universities of Sydney, New South Wales, Newcastle, and Wollongong and the New South Wales Institute of Technology. The development of the Civil Engineering School in the University of Sydney since 1951 has, of course, been outlined elsewhere in this book, and the standing of the School and its present resources are a tribute to the energy and dedication of John Roderick.

Engineering Courses in the United Kingdom

In the United Kingdom, students undertaking professional engineering courses of study attend Universities or Polytechnics.

British universities, in general, are smaller and of more recent origin than the older and larger universities in Australia. Sydney University, for example, with a present enrolment of 17,600 students, was inaugurated in 1852, whilst in the United Kingdom, Oxford, Cambridge, the Scottish Universities of St Andrews, Glasgow, Aberdeen and Edinburgh, the Universities of Durham and London are the only ones which predate it.

Most British universities were constituted in the early years of this century, and average student populations are of the order of 6,000.

English university courses in engineering are normally three years in length, whilst Scottish courses are of four years duration, with certain exemptions for well qualified entrants. Students enter University after progressing through six forms of secondary education, English students qualifying firstly at the Ordinary level and subsequently at the Advanced level of the General Certificate of Education. The entry age to university is about 18, and students enter an engineering course after selection by the department on the basis of their 'O' and 'A' level grades. Students normally study a wide range of subjects to 'O' level then concentrate on three which, for engineering, would usually include mathematics and physics.

English language to 'O' level is usually a prerequisite. Students apply to five universities through the Universities Central Council on Admissions and are conditionally accepted or rejected by the specific university departments to which they have applied. A large percentage of universities invite sixth-form students for interview, enabling them to see the department at firsthand, and to find out details about the course. At Sheffield University most Wednesday afternoons through two terms were devoted to this activity, which involved up to six members of staff. The student interviews were taken very seriously, and a conscientious effort was made to answer all of their questions, so that they had a factual basis on which to make their choice. Departments who were in any way casual would soon find that the numbers of applicants for admission dropped.

The British pattern is for students to move to a University remote from their home towns, so that it is necessary for them to find accommodation in University halls of residence or in lodgings.

As mentioned earlier, courses are normally of three years duration, with quite a spread of content from university to university. Because of time limitations, the syllabus is tailored to fit closely the perceived needs of students after graduation, and service courses have syllabuses which conform also to the requirements of the graduate engineer. A lot of attention is paid to the phasing and sequence of presentation of material, and practical classes are also arranged wherever possible, with attention to relevance.

In the final year at Sheffield, students in civil and structural engineering had the opportunity of making a selection of four subjects taken from a wide choice of options, in addition to a compulsory core comprising eight subjects. They also were required to undertake two projects, one in the first and the other in the second term of the final year, and these were selected from a long list, enabling each student to choose topics in his field of interest. The optional subjects ranged over many fields and included such diverse matters as structural plasticity, transport systems and planning, architecture and tunnel engineering. There was also a design project, set to a broad specification.

Despite very limited funds it was possible for a number of visiting lecturers to be appointed. These were senior engineers in practice, providing short lecture courses in specialist topics.

Vacation employment at the end of the first and second years was a requirement of the course, and students were expected to seek their own employment in relevant engineering work and to submit a report on their experience.

Students started to seek out employment opportunities early in their third year, and during my period in England the great majority had provisional offers before they sat for their final examinations in the third year.

Honours were awarded on the performance of the student in their final examinations, with some account being taken of second year performance.

The emphasis placed on the teaching of engineering practice varied from one university to another, and in several universities, departments of engineering science were established, with some common features with those at Oxford and Cambridge. In such a course, a student would be taught predominantly engineering science subjects in a common year and professionally oriented subjects would have a considerably less significant role. The interesting point about these courses is that they were offered largely by the newer, post-war universities, whilst those universities which had been established before World War II have, as a rule, continued to offer degree courses in the conventional disciplines.

Polytechnics provide courses in many subjects, including engineering, and their activities are governed by the Council for National Academic Awards, a body established by Royal Charter in 1964. Courses of study, establishments, examiners and other important considerations are approved by the CNAA, and CNAA degrees are awarded which are expected to be comparable in standard with those granted by universities.

One interesting feature of British universities and polytechnics is the appointment of external examiners to undergraduate courses. The role of the external examiner varies from one university to another, but normally he will be sent drafts of examination papers, plus worked solutions, for comment, and immediately after the examinations are marked, he will be sent the mark list and all, or sample, answer papers, to peruse and evaluate. This may apply to all years or perhaps just the senior years of the course. He will be invited to attend the meeting of examiners, and expected to take a major part in confirming, or perhaps questioning, the recommendations for honours, passes and failures, and he may be involved in interviewing senior students also.

External examiners are appointed usually for a three year period, so that, in time, a university professor will gain an insight into the teaching methods, course syllabus and examination procedures of a number of other universities (or polytechnics) besides his own. Moderation by these external processes ensures that universities and polytechnics do not depart significantly from generally accepted standards, whilst still admitting significant variation of course structure and content from one teaching establishment to another.

The Professional Institutions

In the United Kingdom, the senior engineering body is the Institution of Civil Engineers, founded in 1818, and receiving its Royal Charter in 1828. Many separate institutions followed and these developed their own particular traditions, and had their own prerequisites for membership.

In 1965 the Council of Engineering Institutions was incorporated by Royal Charter and those institutions which were felt to be of professional standing with comparable educational standards, became constituent members. Fifteen such 'Institutions' have participated in the CEI, and the formulation of common objectives has been a difficult task, accompanied by severe internal tensions in the Council.

Corporate members of constituent institutions are entitled to use the title of Chartered Engineer (C.Eng.), and their names are included in the Council of Engineering Institutions Register of the Chartered Engineers. The route to Chartered Membership is by the fulfilment of CEI prerequisites, but institutions such as the Institution of Civil Engineers have specific requirements appropriate to the particular needs of the profession.

In 1973, the Council of the Institution of Civil Engineers appointed a Committee of eight, headed by Dr A. H. Chilver, to look into the whole question of education and training of civil engineers in the United Kingdom. (Henry Chilver, like John Roderick, is a graduate of the universities of Bristol and Cambridge, with research interests in metal structures. He was Professor of Civil and Municipal Engineering at University College, London, and has subsequently become Vice-Chancellor of Cranfield Institute of Technology.) The Chilver Report, which was published in 1975, and approved in the same year by the Council of the Institution, aimed at ensuring the following;

(1) a restriction on membership to candidates who have received a broad early education, or shown themselves as particularly capable of benefiting from it,

(2) comprehensive technical education by the specific recognition of appropriate university degrees,

(3) better training by the approval beforehand, and the monitoring during progress, of training schemes organized by the industry, and

(4) a minimum attendance on specialized or other post-graduate courses prior to admission to corporate membership.

The aim is to restrict members to graduates with recognized degrees and an appropriately broad pre-university qualification, who must then pass two professional examinations. The first, or PE1, leading to Associate Membership, will be designed to verify the technical competence of each candidate, whilst the second, or PE2, following a period of definable professional responsibility, will be a formal interview arranged by the institution, in which evidence of competence is provided by the candidate, and written answers to questions on management topics and on the Engineer in Society.

The assessment of educational attainment is by a numerical points system in which a candidate needs to attain thirty points before being admitted to membership. These are accumulated from points awarded by O level and A level subject passes at secondary education level, further points for a recognized university degree and the possibility of extra points from certain other first degrees or higher degrees in a cognate subject.

The original recommendations had specific minimum educational prerequisites at the point of university entry and these drew widespread criticism on the basis of their inflexibility and denial of access to the profession to the 'late developer'. The Chilver Implementation Board broadened the original proposals to allow the flexibility inherent in the points system.

It is important to note the significance attached by the Institution to training, preferably under approved training agreements, for graduates to work under well thought out training schemes prepared by 'Supervising Civil Engineers'.

The Chilver recommendations allow the Institution to regulate the number of new members to its ranks, and as corporate membership of the Institution of Civil Engineers is a normal prerequisite to a senior position in the profession, the Institution will have a major influence in controlling the numbers, quality and breadth of the civil engineers in the United Kingdom.

The Institution of Structural Engineers, and Institution of Municipal Engineers, also constituent members of CEI, are considerably smaller than the Institution of Civil Engineers. They have their own rigid examination and interview procedures for entry, but are watching the implementation of the Chilver committee proposals with interest.

The Institution of Civil Engineers has an active Graduate and Students Section, and first year undergraduates are encouraged to join the Institution, for a small annual subscription. This entitles them to most of the benefits of membership, including the magazine *New Civil Engineer*, which very successfully keeps members informed of the activities in the profession, both within and outside the United Kingdom.

Programmes and paper competitions for Students and Associate Members attract considerable interest and the prizes awarded by the Institution are highly valued. For some years the Association of London Graduates and Students has run conferences to which senior undergraduates from U.K.

universities have been invited, and the Institution itself awards prizes and Certificates of Merit, on the recommendation of the Head of Department, for outstanding students in their penultimate or final years of those engineering degree courses, recognized by the Institution as qualifying eventually for Corporate membership. Prizewinners are selected not solely on examination performances but with due regard to course work and particularly ability in civil engineering design.

Since the United Kingdom entered the European Economic Community, considerable attention has been paid to the standing of the qualifications and training of the British Chartered Engineer, and their acceptance in the Common Market countries.

In Australia, by contrast, the Institution of Engineers, Australia has remained the single body fulfilling a learned society role for the engineering profession, and it is only within the last few years that colleges catering for different disciplines within the profession have been formed. As the local Institution, like its British counterparts, also has regional Divisions, its members are associated in groups determined by geography and/or branch of the profession.

In Australia many employees have traditionally placed a greater emphasis on the educational qualification than Chartered membership of the professional institution when appointing an engineer, and many a graduate, appointed to a junior position after completing a university course, has risen to a senior position without pursuing Institution membership further. For those who do so, the formalities of satisfying the professional experience requirements are less rigorous than those in the British Institutions.

The Institution of Engineers, Australia has the role of accrediting both standards and content of engineering course, and the education, training and experience appropriate to Chartered Engineer (Australia). Courses provided at universities and colleges of advanced education are assessed and recognized, after satisfying basic requirements, and under the '1980 Rule', a course must be of not less than four years' duration full time, or of sufficient duration in part-time to attain a similar standard, after the candidate had achieved a standard of secondary education not less than the general standard of examination for matriculation to an Australian university.

Particular difficulties arise in Australia in regard to a nationally measurable matriculation standard, as the six States operate different systems of examination and assessment for their secondary school courses. With progressive erosion of teaching standards in secondary schools, minimum entry prerequisites to engineering courses in Universities have fallen very substantially below those for many other professions, and in some instances colleges, unable to attract students, have touted for them with offers of special bridging courses for those failing to matriculate.

There are a significant number of small colleges of questionable viability in which engineering courses are provided, and without the close scrutiny provided by the external examiner system which operates in the United Kingdom. The whole question of education and training of engineers is currently receiving close attention by the Institution of Engineers, Australia, and it has made a submission on this subject to the Committee of Inquiry into Education and Training chaired by Professor Bruce Williams, and to State committees in Victoria and South Australia enquiring into similar issues.

Engineering Research

In the United Kingdom, industrial research is widely undertaken by universities, government laboratories, defence establishments, government agencies, research institutes and by individual companies.

University research is largely funded from grants administered by the Science Research Council and Natural Environment Research Council, which carry out research and training through their own institutes and grant-aided institutes, and which support research by awards of grants, fellowships and post-graduate awards to Universities and other institutes of higher education.

The Science Research Council was set up in 1965, taking over six national research establishments and the basic research functions of the former Department of Scientific and Industrial Research. The primary purpose of the Council is to sustain standards of education and research in the universities by helping university staff to carry out basic research at the forefront of their subjects, and by enabling suitable graduates to receive further training in either methods of research or a specialised branch of science or engineering of importance to British industry.

In addition to the provision of research studentships, the Science Research Council provides quotas of advanced course studentships to approved post-graduate courses. In the mid 1960s, a proliferation of post-graduate courses had occurred and it was recognized that many of these were either inadequately supported, or were offered by departments of less than the first rank in standing and resources, or by departments providing a curriculum which was unrelated to national needs. In the late 1960s a rationalization was made by the SRC of courses it was prepared to support, and since that time the Council has kept them under constant review. It has, however, encouraged universities to make proposals in new areas of relevance, especially where the resources and expertise of a number of institutions could be combined by joint activity. One example of this is the field of marine technology, of obvious relevance in terms of the massive offshore oil developments in the North Sea. Following seminars in London, Edinburgh and Cardiff, a task force was set up, with a large industrial representation, which pointed to priorities and needs. Interdisciplinary approach to research was advocated, and in line with SRC policy, a recommendation was made that support should be concentrated on a small number of centres of expertise, namely, Glasgow and Strathclyde Universities, Heriot-Watt University, The University of Newcastle-upon-Tyne, and at University and Imperial Colleges in London. Since these, other centres in England and Wales have been assessed.

Pure research is also funded, and proposals from individuals in Universities are evaluated after comments from referees have been received.

The SRC is the major source of funding for pure, non-goal-oriented work, but in programmes such as marine technology, mentioned above, in which large financial support is provided, considerable effort is made to ensure that the results of research are relevant and that they are appropriately communicated. The gross expenditure of the SRC in 1976/7 amounted to £127 million, of which 21 per cent was allocated to research grants and 11 per cent to postgraduate awards.

Many universities have research contracts with government ministries or agencies, or with firms, particularly those universities which are situated in the large cities.

Government research establishments also employ large groups of research workers in engineering laboratories, such as the National Physical Laboratory, National Engineering Laboratory, the Warren Springs Laboratory and National Maritime Institute, which are under the Department of Industry, whilst the Building Research Establishment, Hydraulics Research Station and Transport and Road Research Laboratory are within the Department of the Environment, the last having links also with the Department of Transport. The Ministry of Defence includes such research establishments as the Royal Aircraft Establishment, Royal Armament Research and Development Establishment and the Military Vehicles and Engineering Establishment.

The largest government research establishments employ 1,000 or more personnel and have research programmes relating to many national engineering needs. Recent government economies are causing several of these to reduce their numbers by 10 per cent during the current year.

One very significant change occurred to research establishments in the United Kingdom with the implementation of the Rothschild Report a few years ago. Rothschild proposed that the concept of contractor and customer should apply to the conduct and funding of research. In the Ministry of Defence, the customers — the military officers who know in broad terms what they want — are in close communication with those undertaking the research, and irrelevant or wasteful activity should soon be identified. In the non-defence field, however, the 'customer' may be the whole population of the nation, and in order to make the Rothschild concept operate, the government has resorted to various artifices. Requirements Committees or Boards react to proposals put up by the establishment, and funding and support depends on the result. In some cases these Boards have part-time membership of people who have to make rapid assessments, and in some others the Boards do not contain people with the technical expertise, who might best judge the merits of specific proposals. The Rothschild concept is coming under increasing criticism, and any benefits expected from attempts to ensure immediate relevance of research objectives are overshadowed by the possible stifling of longer-term work, and sheer bureaucratic inefficiency.

In the United Kingdom many industries have formed research associations. Many of these, formed with the intention of increasing efficiency by co-operative research within specific industries, are registered companies, limited by guarantee of a nominal sum, and they function as autonomous bodies determining their policy for the development of their research programmes and dissemination of results. The success and viability of these research associations depends of course on the financial support provided by the contributory firms and by government departments.

Many of these associations are set up for the manufacturing industries and some have major laboratories of their own, often placed in pleasant rural settings in the grounds of old country estates. One example is the Welding Institute, near Cambridge. Others, such as the Construction Industry Research and Information Association in London, have not established their own laboratories, but fund and promote research in outside laboratories and organizations by research contracts.

These associations have made very significant contributions to their industries and enlightened firms which have supported specific investigations have had the benefit of confidential access to the results as they became available. As industry tends to identify immediate problems, much of the research is 'tactical' rather than long-term or 'strategic', with clearly identifiable goals, tangible and predictable benefits. The Construction Industry Research and Information Association is of particular interest because of its close links with civil engineering. This association, which has its headquarters in London, has an income of the order of $750,000 per annum, of which one quarter comes from subscriptions, one quarter from special contributions from industry, and one half from governmental sources. CIRIA has six main technical committees, employs 45 people full-time and has 500 working within it or for it, in one way or another, in industry, on working parties interfacing with the association, or people working on the 70 odd projects under way. CIRIA has been very active in examining several fields of activity in the construction industry and identifying areas where research should be promoted. Many of these are in areas different from conventional technical research, for example, work associated with technical management, where improvements may often lead to substantial economies.

One must not leave the subject of engineering research in the United Kingdom without making reference to the research departments of many civil engineering contractors and research groups in some of the consulting offices.

187

In general this is *ad hoc*, but commercial organizations exist in specialized fields, such as ship and offshore oil rig design, which will undertake design, research or developmental work.

In Australia, by contrast, engineering research traditions are far less developed.

Australian engineering research has been confined largely to universities and the Commonwealth Scientific and Industrial Research Organization. The tradition of university research originates since World War II, and funding is principally by grants awarded by the Australian Research Grants Committee. Industrially-sponsored university research is commencing in a small way and it is good to see that the Civil Engineering Post-Graduate Foundation in the University of Sydney is developing, particularly since much of Australian secondary industry is unaware of, or insensitive to, the benefits of applied research.

Many of the research directors or senior research staff of industrial firms in Australia are members of the Australian Industrial Research Group, which, since 1964, has aimed at improvement of research management in industry, fostering understanding of the need for industrial research, and development of interaction and relationships with universities and other educators, and with the Federal government.

In Australia research associations are conspicuous by their absence, particularly in the manufacturing sector, and many companies prefer, or may be obliged, to draw on results of research undertaken in the United States or the United Kingdom, rather than sponsor local programmes, even though the objectives of the overseas research may not have been related to Australian conditions. As an example, much research into agriculture and development of mining machinery falls into this class.

In civil engineering, fledgling research associations are growing, but reliability of funding must be still a major cause of concern to their directors.

By far the largest research organization in Australia, which is funded by the Federal Treasury, is the CSIRO, which had its origins in the middle of World War I and was set up as the Council for Scientific and Industrial Research by Act of Parliament in 1926, to carry out research to benefit Australia by solving the problems which then faced industry and agriculture. Sir George Julius, a prominent consulting engineer, played a major role in the developmental stages of CSIR, and one of its most prominent supporters was Mr R. G. (later Lord) Casey, who trained as a mining engineer. The CSIR, which subsequently was reconstituted as the CSIRO in 1949, has developed in the fifty years of its lifetime, in accordance with problems of particular relevance to the nation at the time. Thus, with the limited resources available, the early Sections or Divisions were centred on problems of primary industry, but in 1936 through to the war years, the National Standards Laboratory, Aeronautical Research Laboratory and other Sections were set up, making important contributions to the wartime development of our secondary industry.

The Organization currently has 37 research Divisions as its principal operating units, each led by a Chief who is responsible to a small Executive for his Division's activities. Some Divisions with related interests are grouped, but their links are informal. The wide spectrum of subjects covered across the different Divisions enables interdisciplinary studies to be undertaken. For example, research into physical methods of grain disinfestation is being pursued by groups of engineers in the Division of Mechanical Engineering, in Melbourne, working in close collaboration with scientists in the Division of Entomology, in Canberra.

Many CSIRO Divisions are active in fields which impinge on civil engineering, amongst them the Divisions of Building Research, Applied Geomechanics, Mechanical Engineering, Chemical Technology and the National Measurement Laboratory.

The CSIRO has recently been examined by a Committee of Inquiry, which was set up in October 1976, to inquire into the Organization. In a lengthy and comprehensive report, the Committee has analysed the CSIRO's role and objectives, programmes, organization structure and functions, policies for employment of staff, relationship with rural industry, other industry, governments, tertiary education, and other matters.

The Committee made particular reference to the problems of the manufacturing industry in Australia, and reported that there is considerable evidence of a substantial gap between CSIRO and manufacturing industry, but stated it was of the opinion that, to a large extent, the problem arose from within the manufacturing sector itself and that alterations to CSIRO alone would not solve the problem. The Committee strongly advocated creation of industrial research associations in Australia to look after the needs of fragmented industries with small firms lacking in staff of appropriate skills and background to talk to CSIRO.

When considering CSIRO's role, and its funding, the Committee recommended that the principal type of research undertaken should be strategic mission-oriented, but fundamental and tactical problem-oriented research were appropriate when related to the Organization's role. The principal funding was considered to be best served by a specific government vote, rather than through funds to ministries which would contract, Rothschild fashion, for services.

The Future

So far I have made some comparisons of engineering education and research and of the engineering Institutions in Australia and the United Kingdom. Both countries are English-speaking and Australia has, of course, modelled many of its traditions on those of the 'Old Country'. Comparing the countries in Civil Engineering terms, however, the similarities soon end. Great Britain has an area of 228,000 sq. km, or about that of Victoria, and a population of 54 millions, or four times that of Australia. It has developed extensive communication networks, firstly by developing canals, then railways and now motorways, and a fast and efficient land network services the nation's needs. Rainfall is regular and the problem of water storage for domestic supply is an order of magnitude smaller than for cities such as Sydney. Urban renewal and reconstruction is a significant component of the work of the British civil engineer, who has to work largely in areas and on schemes in which pressures from conservationists and other groups may lead to protracted discussions and modifications of plans. The United Kingdom has already exploited most of its on-shore minerals with the exception of coal, but is directing a large part of its resources to the urgent development of the North Sea oilfields, in waters up to 250 metres depth and 100 km from the Scottish coast. Studies are in progress on development of renewable energy resources, particularly wave energy, and governmental funding has been provided for evaluation of four different wave energy systems. Thirty-three nuclear power units over 30 megawatts are in operation in the United Kingdom, with a total capacity of over 8,000 megawatts.

In Australia, by contrast, the concentration of population in a small number of large cities has brought with it problems of urban services and communication, with need for personal transport for daily commuting. Rural and interstate railways in Australia are largely utilized for transportation of freight, as passengers prefer to travel by air, and public transportation systems do not provide the role in Australia that is found in Britain.

Off-shore oil supplies in Bass Strait have catered for 70 per cent of Australian requirements but indigenous production is now declining and no major new oil fields have been discovered. Australia is plentifully supplied by solid fossil fuels conveniently placed to the major industrial centres of New South Wales and Victoria, so that the need for renewable energy resources for electricity generation will be local and specialised. Solar energy, though plentiful in Australia, will only have a major impact if it can be utilized economically, and at present low costs of conventional energy, particularly off-peak concessions, coupled with high labour costs for fitting solar collectors to existing installations, are such as to make solar energy marginally unattractive.

Australia has no national energy policy, and even at the State level, forward rational planning of energy options is not complete. It is significant, however, that it was the engineering profession which showed initiative in setting up the Institution of Engineers, Australia Task Force on Energy, and its papers and recommendations have formed a most useful reference for the National Energy Advisory Committee and other bodies making recommendations to government. Solutions to our energy problems, as with other resources problems, must be engineering ones, and civil engineers have been well represented, both on the Institution Task Force, NEAC, and in important energy inquiries.

The future progress of Australia, the United Kingdom and indeed the world is vitally dependent upon the engineering development of resources such as energy, water, food and timber, and the role of the civil engineer, as defined in the Charter of the Institution of Civil Engineers many years ago as 'the Art of directing the Great Sources of Power in Nature for the use and convenience of man', is as true now as it was then.

D. C. O'CONNOR

The Engineer and the Environment: New Challenges and Prospects

Where Are We?

It seems a very short twenty-seven years since John Roderick came to the University as Challis Professor of Civil Engineering. I was privileged to be amongst the first group of undergraduates to be introduced to new realms of structural analysis which, together with the advent of computers, ushered civil engineering into a new era. It is timely, on Professor Roderick's retirement, to look at the status of civil engineering now, and to speculate on where it might go in the next quarter century.

As a young undergraduate I was thrilled and challenged to be entering a profession defined as the art of directing the great sources of power in nature for the use and convenience of man. Something seems to have changed over the intervening years, and one senses a growing disenchantment with this approach. There seems to be emerging a world-wide distrust of technology and growth, and widespread concern about development for development sake, and if engineers are to discharge their obligations to society, they must do more than conceive systems of greater complexity. They must put these systems into the social and physical environments in such a way that our quality of life will be improved. This is where the challenge lies, and we must look ahead because engineering needs a new impetus to carry it into the next quarter of a century.

It is timely to ask 'where do we stand as a profession as far as the environment is concerned?' As practical engineers we need perspective in the face of the highly emotive terms that bombard us today — resource depletion, population explosion, technological disaster, biological time bomb, and many others. We seem to be experiencing an overkill from the doomsters. Black asks, 'Why should disasters happen *now*, in spite of centuries of warning?' [1]. He feels that there is a contemporary mythology that we are living in a unique era — a watershed — where *our* problems are always more serious, more acute, and more eruptive than those of any other generation. We seem to have developed the outlook that our lives are guided by some mysterious fate rather than by ourselves. He draws attention to dangerous implications of this way of thinking. It diverts our attention from the real issues, depriving us of a sensible

192

policy for the future, it leads us to attitudes of pessimism and gloom, and it provokes predictable over-reactions.

We are all tempted at times to ask ourselves how things got as bad as they seem to be. There is no doubt that we are all victims of what Black refers to as the same Western world view that man has dominion over nature and must use it for his own advantage. This comes to us from our Judao-Christian tradition, formalized in the book of Genesis, and it still provides the basis for our view of nature, and tends to set man apart from it. Did our definition of engineering arise in the same way, and are we as a profession sufficiently far-seeing to fashion a practical response to our environmental problems?

We are in the process of developing a social response. Our sociological conscience has to be developed, and we must allow for a certain amount of lag between the development of environmental problems and the emergence of social institutions to cope with them. We must develop institutions which not only respond to crises, but must adapt in anticipation of them. I am writing this paper as an educator, engineer and scientist, so I wish to consider what environmental science may be able to offer as part of a practical overall contribution. In using the term science I do not wish to overlook the social, political and economic factors involved in the environment. I merely wish to focus attention on a vital aspect of environmental affairs, one that will increasingly involve the engineer, and one whose contribution to human progress and welfare will surely assume greater importance in the years ahead.

It must indeed be perplexing, particularly to the layman, when he hears that there are more scientists working now than in all of human history up to this time, that we are living in the midst of a science and technology explosion, and that governments have accepted science as one of the legitimate goals of society, yet we are continually being presented with environmental problems to which there appear to be no known solutions. This is particularly the case where the impact of man on the environment is considered.

The 'sixties saw a massive awakening in our awareness of the environment. Up to that time our attack on environmental problems was highly fractionated — we distinguished between air and water pollution, between mercury in the food chain and radiation hazards, between thermal and noise pollution, and so on. Only in recent years have we begun to understand the social, economic and technological relationships between all types of environmental degradation and the necessary remedial actions. We now see nature as a *system* in terms of the relationships and interactions between its various parts. We look at all their interactions with each other and with man. The realization of this interrelationship, although it seems obvious, marked a milestone in the development of environmental science. In fact it distinguishes it from all other science, and offers great potential to the engineer, with his familiarity with systems engineering.

Although I use the term 'science' throughout, I believe that the approach of the engineer is necessary if our approach to problem solving is not to become

193

meaningless through the adoption of vague generalities. Whilst the outlook of the concerned citizen is a necessary part of the environmental action, the training and experience of the engineer is also a vital part of the process. If you review the latest environmental protection procedures that are coming into being in most States and the Commonwealth, you find that large development projects must now be accompanied by studies of the environmental impact of those developments. One of the most interesting facts emerging is that most of these environmental impact studies are being done by engineers. Some are being well done, others not so well done, but one cannot help speculating that it is something in the training of the engineer that is directing him towards these studies. My own experience in education in both engineering and the pure sciences convinces me that the engineer's training is directed to problem solving, whereas that of the pure scientist is more towards highlighting and defining problems, and I take great encouragement from this fact as we try to chart the next quarter century of our profession. In fact, I would go further, and say that unless we react to some of the great global problems as a profession, we will embark on a period of sterility where we tend to pursue arid and remote theoretical ideas which are quite unrelated to the world needs. I believe that if we were to direct our energies away from the endless pursuit of technology to a concern for the environment and a desire to serve the developing countries of the world we would usher in a new era in engineering.

Environmental Technology

Modern technology has placed at our disposal the means for extending our knowledge of the physical extent of the environment and the interrelationships between complex, large scale phenomena. We are all familiar with new types of equipment for data collection, communication, and data analysis, and these have given environmentalists the ability to put things together in a way never previously possible. Consider the great variety of instruments that have been developed which have made it possible to expand our sensitivity to the environment in identifying, tracing, and evaluating a great variety of phenomena. We think of lasers, X-ray diffraction apparatus, radioactivity counters, chromatographs, electron-microscopes, gas analysers, and the like.

Orbiting and synchronous satellites are now in operation in the fields of global meteorology, goedesy, and resources inventory. These are being integrated with a wide range of communication devices and automatic data handling equipment to provide complete environmental information on all aspects of our planet and the life forms it supports. It is no longer strictly necessary to have physical contact and presence in an area in order to carry out environmental assessments and pollution monitoring. Remote sensing techniques using radars, lasers and various types of photographic sensors provide means of studying vegetation, terrain, the atmosphere and the oceans.

The advent of computers is making it possible to handle all this information and present it in a form suitable for our use. If these new advances can be incorporated into engineering education, the way ahead would seem almost limitless as we set about to manage constructively the new ecological systems created by technology.

Action

Our own living standards have risen beyond the wildest expectations of our forefathers, but unfortunately each increase in material living standards seems to leave a new environmental problem in its wake, and we cannot solve any of the problems without forsaking some of the standards. What then are we to use as a basis for action? In reviewing the engineer's role in environmental affairs, Lt General Clarke, Chief of Engineers of the U.S. Army, posed three vital questions: *What to believe? What to want? What to do?* [2].

First, we must know what to *believe*. Today the flood of written and spoken material on environmental matters has reached climactic proportions. Plausible statements pass for fact, and experts, always in abundant supply, vie with one another for the seeming purpose of disagreeing in the media about the imminence of ecological collapse, the population explosion, or the depletion of resources. What am I to add to this? As a scientist I must admit to you that the application of environmental science today can rarely meet the needs of society for information and predictive capability, and that the interim answer must lie in your maintaining an enlightened scepticism in the face of this flood of information as we progressively develop the capability of separating fact from fiction. I do not believe that we can afford the luxury of regarding any environmental involvement of man as all good or all bad. As our scientific knowledge increases, we should be able to develop an environmental management philosophy in terms of enlightened human welfare based on maintenance of our own standards and a concern for posterity. This is the message we should be getting across in the engineering schools to counter the doomsters.

This assumes of course that we know what we *want*. It is becoming increasingly harder to formulate a legitimate set of goals of what society needs and wants, particularly in an era when the quality of modern life is under assault from all sides. When you look at our comforts, our air conditioners, our victories over disease and pain, our extended mobility, and the expanded intellectual horizons opened up to the masses by technology, one must ask 'Is it really so bad?', allowing of course that these gains have been purchased at the costs to the natural environment which were not foreseen.

The young express wide disenchantment with our standards, and are continually seeking a return to the simple life, but there does not seem to be any widespread desire to return to the life of the wilderness where the physically strong survive at the expense of the weak, and forms of life are sacrificed and prey upon one another. Of course, the question of goals and standards does not present itself to us as a simple issue. What is to be forsaken, when and by whom? Who is going to decide what we want? It seems to me quite wrong that people living in cities, who have used up most of their natural environment to provide creature comforts, should decide for people who have expressed the desire to build and grow in other areas of the nation. I think we will find, as the Americans have done, that we would benefit from having some broadly stated national goals on resource and environmental matters, but with plenty of room for regional autonomy and self-determination. What it boils down to I suppose, is that in determining what we want, each of us must also give reasonable consideration to what the other fellow wants. I cannot help feeling that we need to get back to a concept of education which would encourage us to live in tolerance and understanding of others rather than the polarity favoured today by professional pressure groups.

This is leading us into what we should *do*. I do not claim to be able to answer this one for you, but can only suggest that we temper our ideals with good sense on the basis that we cannot anticipate any spectacular technological breakthrough to solve the problems for us — there are no heavies waiting in the wings. A flexible response is needed, based on facts, persistence, and strategy, rather than on drama, within the framework of a rational set of national objectives. This is where the commonsense of the engineer should come to the fore.

Many of our environmental conflicts are associated with the exploitation of natural resources, and with growth. Let us take a look at the role of resources in the modern world. It is only being realistic to realize that industrial power is the prerequisite to both political and military power, and industrial power depends upon minerals and fuels which can be converted into heat and mechanical energy, and most importantly, into steel. Any nation which aspires to prominence in world affairs must have adequate and reliable supply of these resources as a basis for a strong industry. Although these elements are to some degree universal, they are not found everywhere in sufficient quantities, so no nation is fully self sufficient. This unequal distribution of mineral resources creates an interdependence among nations, and in times of crisis the industrial powers are vulnerable to a blockade of minerals, the lifeblood of their industrial strength. Thus the very survival of a nation may depend upon its realization of the stake that it has in the mineral resources in foreign lands, in the sea, and lately in 'international' territories like Antarctica, and in the mutual and orderly worldwide development and conservation of these irreplaceable sinews of power.

Preservation or Management?

It is becoming increasingly difficult and unreal to imagine that any country can simply decide to lock-up all its minerals in the ground without causing concern around the world. The great danger of this spirit of unreality is that the seeds for future conflicts are sown, and that the end results may prove more disastrous than what was originally proposed.

It seems difficult to justify public environmental policies based simply on preservation considerations alone. I believe that as engineers we should be developing wise philosophies of stewardship and environmental management embracing a range of approaches from locking resources up in the ground to careful exploitation. As understanding and predictive capability increase, there will be constantly increasing pressures to manage resources and the environment for the benefit of man, to modify and control weather and natural disasters, and to mitigate many of the more subtle effects of man's interference.

I believe that, if a careful assessment of the situation is made, it is possible to demonstrate that an overwhelming majority of the well-informed environmental opinion throughout the world is by no means marshalled against development. For example, it is useful to look at what the International Council of Scientific Unions' Scientific Committee on Problems of the Environment had to say at a workshop co-sponsored by the U.N. Environmental Program, Environment Canada, and UNESCO [3]. All sides of the spectrum were represented. The workshop was to look at environment impact assessment procedures, and to see how they could be integrated with the programs of developing and developed countries. Some quotations are interesting. Under the heading of Environmental Impacts in the Developing Countries, for example, they say

> Although in what follows we emphasise the undesirable environmental effects of human intervention, we recognise that development is necessary to improve social and economic well-being. The quality of life cannot be enhanced without economic progress, ensuring the provision of food and essential services with generally high rates of population growth.

It is further interesting to consider the statement by this international committee when it discussed the general applicability of environmental impact assessments. The Committee is very careful to point out, and I quote,

> In the developing countries particularly, the process of elaborating environmental impact assessments must in no way be viewed as a brake or obstacle to economic development, but rather as a means for assisting decision makers in planning the rational use of their country's natural resources. This is because the economic development of all nations is tied to the successful long term management of their environmental resources.

The International Council also makes some important statements on national environmental planning as the basis for wise resource use, and we see the policy of environmental management being recommended over and above a policy of mere preservation.

Red Herrings

We seem to be submerged today in a philosophy of hopelessness and zero growth. It is difficult to be reassured about living in a community dedicated to

197

zero growth. I for one would not like to live in a community where the percentage of young people progressively decreased, where society became static, where elites became entrenched, and where we essentially became selfish in our attitude to less deserving countries of the world, lost in the smugness of our own comfort. I believe we have an obligation to the less fortunate people of the world, and this can only be met in a vibrant, living, developing nation, which can quite easily, at the same time, be concerned with its quality of life, and with posterity. *This could provide the great impetus which I believe our profession needs to usher it into the next quarter century.*

Some of us with concern for the environment and the quality of life also view with some dismay the emergence of the environment into the streets as a political issue. In fact there is considerable evidence that environmental issues are being used politically on a worldwide basis. Major powers use participation in international environmental conferences as a means of obtaining recognition for their own satellites, and some in fact boycotted the Stockholm Conference for this reason. We find political goals being advanced through linking environmental issues with anti-colonialism and anti-imperialism. Strategically important regions of the world such as straits must be neutralized 'to minimize the risk of massive oil spills'. In Australia today we are in the midst of the uranium debate where it is difficult to separate fact from fiction, and the polarity which is starting to characterize our community seems to be becoming entrenched.

Engineering Education

This, then, is the background against which 'Engineering Education' policies must be formulated. Where are we today as far as environmental education is concerned in engineering schools? Unhappily, there seem to be only injections of environmental education in most courses, largely brought about by re-naming some of the traditional courses in water treatment and industrial pollution. The broad approach of the environmentalist is neglected. I think we would be well advised to address this aspect of engineering training, even to the extent of producing a special engineer called an environmental engineer. Experience in the United States has shown that when environmental protection policies are to be implemented, manpower is the critical resource. Manpower shortages initially develop amongst those needed to extend the scientific base and conduct environmental research and generate the environmental systems understanding. As the science base becomes established a need arises for engineers, administrators and technicians to implement policy. Those concerned with implementing policy must be sufficiently trained in science to be perceptive of the nature of environmental systems, and of what may be gained from research. They must be sufficiently perceptive of the political and sociological factors within government because most of the action takes place within these arenas. This tempts one to look, for the moment, at organizations available for producing people trained in

198

environmental science. A useful start is being made at the tertiary level in Australia, particularly in the newer universities, but on most traditional campuses it is poorly organized, and, in fact, hardly organized at all. Duplication of effort tends to occur in rigidly separated departments and schools even on the same campus, and inter-campus co-operation and accreditation is almost entirely lacking. The various disciplines exist in water-tight compartments.

There are still not enough attempts in universities to foster management organizations for research in environmental science to facilitate teamwork and to optimize the use of the resources available. Why is this, particularly since we are now living in an era where all institutions are funded from the same central source? It reflects, in part, the priorities given by society to environmental science and environmental affairs in the past, and we are inheriting the legacy of our neglect. We have also been sitting on the sidelines expecting technology to bring us the answer. In fact, we have used technology as a substitute for thought. We are now faced with the problem of placing the forces of technology under our conscious control. I also detect in universities remnants of the attitudes of independence which existed when institutions were not funded by the government. I believe there is a serious obligation on us to rationalize programmes within institutions and between institutions to avoid costly overlap and duplication and get the most effective return for public expenditure. The scope of engineering education must be broadened. Usually we need the spur of some sort of government intervention or legislation to bring the point home.

Government and Public Action

All the states of Australia now have government departments concerned with environmental protection. There is an Australian Government department of the Environment, Housing and Community Development.

All these departments are suitably reinforced with legislation to implement their ideas. But of course we, as engineers, know that trying to come to grips with a problem via the law only is not always effective. Law is essentially a coercive, abstract concept, whereas environmental degradation is a reality which requires for its solution a systematic application of engineering knowledge within a broadly developed framework of human values. Although we have certainly focused attention on these problems today through environmental legislation, legislation in one form or another has been on the books for many decades, yet many of the pollution problems that we have today arose in spite of the presence of these laws. So legislation is not enough. We need informed professions and an informed public. This is where engineering educators have a vital role to fulfil in the process of establishing the appreciation of environmental quality and what it entails into our professional lives.

For our sociological response to environmental problems to be effective, we must first of all have a broad national basis of comprehensive planning which should in turn be strongly based on environmental planning. This would lead us to the process of making environmental assessments as a normal component of any development project. We have gone to great pains to develop the environmental impact procedures without any of the other planning elements being present. This may sound trivial, but in my opinion, the most complicated and extensive environmental impact procedures will not achieve anything if the planning background and motivation are not present, and if we as a people are not really concerned with enhancing the quality of our lives in relation to the environment.

We are still at the stage where the great majority of our people do not really appreciate beauty in their lives, and where most environmental actions come from very small sections of the community. Whilst the energies and values of these small groups are to be admired and encouraged, they do not actually provide a firm foundation at this stage for the general implementation of environmental protection procedures at a policy level. We should be planning in response to widespread public demand. We need capable engineers to contribute to this work. We need the techniques and knowledge to complete the assessments, and the procedures for formalizing these assessments in environmental impact statements. There will be unlimited scope for engineers in the years ahead if they choose to move into this challenging field.

Environmental Science

We are at a very early stage of our attempts to rationalize our approach to growth and development in relation to the environment. It seems obvious that the engineer must adopt a broad view of the environment based on all the social, biological, physical and chemical factors which compose the surroundings of man. It is very broad, and goes beyond the normal ideas of pollution and resource exploitation customarily of interest to the engineer. The broader definition highlights the necessity for interdisciplinary contact at all stages of environmental studies, and could lead to the emergence of an environmental engineer as in the United States. No programme of study has any validity unless it embraces as an irreducible minimum the life sciences, physical sciences, socio-economics, and engineering. The synthesis of these disciplines has led to the emergence of environmental science as a discipline in its own right, and this should be of great interest to engineers. The newly emerging discipline of environmental science includes the natural processes, and their interactions with each other and with man. These processes *together* form the systems of air, land, water, energy and life. It is this emphasis on systems and sub-systems which distinguishes environmental science from narrow individual disciplines in science. It is concerned with putting it all together — all the myriad elements of the physical world. It will draw upon such disciplines as physics, meteorology, sociology, geophysics, oceanography, economics, ecology, biology, history, chemistry, mathematics and engineering.

The need for an interdisciplinary approach to environmental problems is daily becoming more evident as we find individual disciplines endeavouring to carve out a place for themselves within environmental science. In addition to the classical disciplines, we need versatile generalists to guide our efforts towards the solution of environmental problems. This seems to be a great weakness in our education programmes, even engineering programmes, where, as in many other fields, educators are tending to reproduce their own kind with emphasis on research training and laboratory experimentation, with a reluctance to go outside the university where the action is. With few exceptions, it is evident to even the most casual observer that there is a lack of any significant inter- or intra-institutional effort. There is a decline in the emphasis on field studies, and this surely must be correlated with our appalling lack of knowledge of the natural environment of our own country, its climate, fauna, flora and resources.

What then, can environmental science, with its multi-disciplinary approach, offer to the engineering profession? It is unfortunately true to say that today it is rarely able to provide all the quantitative information, interpretation, and predictions needed by society to solve its problems.

Progress

Whilst we have a long way to go in extending our knowledge of environmental science, we have brought it to a stage where it is daily being used in the service of mankind. For example, weather is being forecast, however well or poorly these forecasts are sometimes regarded; our knowledge of the earth has increased to the extent where mineral exploration is being expedited and new crops are being grown; we are getting to know sufficient about ecological systems to talk about environmental management; we know enough about the earth and its gravity field to go to the moon and back with great accuracy; and we are becoming aware of the effects of chemicals in the food-chain.

Although the environment is diverse and complex, we are moving towards the stage where we can look at large-scale environmental problems and partition and simplify them so that the parts may be studied as the basis for understanding the larger systems.

Unfortunately, we have not yet started to integrate this knowledge into urban development programmes so as to maintain and enhance environmental quality in the life of everyman, nor have we formally introduced it into our education systems on a widespread basis. All the environmental concern in the world will not enable us to save our wetlands, protect our coastal mangroves, and monitor the global spread of pollutants unless we revamp our education systems to produce the sophisticated skills required.

As our environmental consciousness increases, we are likely to be faced with an unprecedented demand for environmental information from planners in all fields, and it is difficult to see how our current approach to the problem can continue into the next decade. We will have to consider replacing current fragmented practice with a data bank of environmental information, stored in a form suitable for rapid retrieval and fast reproduction for display in a wide variety of formats, ranging from cathode-ray tube displays, through computer generated maps, to simple printouts of information. This vast store of environmental information would be directly addressed and exploited by a wide range of users for general environmental, economic, sociological and industrial planning at all levels of government.

Reliable information on the earth's natural, technological and social resources is very largely lacking for the greater part of the earth's surface, even for our own country, yet at the same time we are faced with an ever-increasing demand for these resources, and an unprecedented population explosion. We need techniques to measure the factors that influence our environment rapidly, globally and accurately and to monitor natural and manmade disasters. This was highlighted at the Stockholm Conference. Unfortunately, the development of the technology is even now outstripping our ability to arrive at sufficient mutual understanding and communication to apply this technology to the interpretation of the world's environment. How often are we presented with a *fait accompli* in some development project because adequate environmental information is not available as a basis for planning?

Of course, in the midst of all this gadgetry, we must not see it as an end in itself. Sensitivity to ecological interrelationships must predominate. Ecology needs to be seen as a separate discipline, and not as an appendage of the life sciences. How many engineers carrying out environmental impact assessments are well grounded in ecology? The proper development of systems ecology may help here, because it is the recognition of the systems nature of ecology that properly places it within the range of subjects included in environmental science.

But we must not lose sight of applied ecology — the branch that will help us to develop sound management strategies for the environment. Here we need to ensure the level of education input is appropriate to the desired output — and to recognize that some 'high-technology' aspects of ecology developed in the northern hemisphere may well be inappropriate in coping with Australian ecosystems. I touch on these problems because I consider that they highlight the complex field of environmental science and the present inability of our education system to cope with it. Despite complexity, I remain optimistic and sometimes wonder why we become so concerned with the doomsday philosophies of remote and improbable happenings, rather than with the immediate problems of our own day. Sometimes I think that we, as educators, tend to become preoccupied with the bigger intractable problems because they can be endlessly debated, yet call for no immediate action. This preoccupation with debate and inaction seems to characterize our response to crises today.

Whither Engineering?

The successful introduction of environmental awareness into the education system should start at school level. Only then will a generation grow up which regards it as important. Environmental studies will also find a regular place at tertiary level. However, for this to be successful, Australians will have to radically alter their approach to university education. With the opening up of university education to all, a complete reappraisal of value of a university degree will have to be made. It can be expected that more and more people will take degrees, and these will, in many cases, cease to be regarded as a training for a job. They will simply round off a person's education. I often wonder if we would be well advised to return to the generalist degree in engineering with depth penetration being addressed at postgraduate level. It is becoming a matter for lively discussion whether environmental science should be offered at undergraduate or graduate level, so the time is ripe for similar discussions in engineering schools.

This is a great challenge to educators, because before environmental concern flowers in our society, we are the ones who have to implant the seed. We should try to impart a balanced view of the relationship between man and nature with a perspective on growth which acknowledges our concern for our immediate environment, yet is sensitive to the hungry and sick of the world. By the turn of the century I can foresee Australia producing vast quantities of food, and creating and distributing wealth to the world's poor.

All human behaviour is directed towards growth, and we should endeavour to create new balances in the ecosystems created by technology and growth. One wonders if there has ever been any such thing as a balance in nature. Humans have always been transformers of their environment. Perhaps overzealous attempts to protect the so-called balance of nature through the zero-growth philosophy could precipitate an evolutionary crisis by thwarting the natural desire to grow.

Conservation should include recognition of the fact that man is a proper part of the environment, that he has as much right to live on the surface of the earth as other species, and that the built environment has its place in the scheme of things. We should not condone wanton destruction of other species, but the total environment and all the material substance of the earth must be used by all species. Economics should also be included in our concept of conservation.

We will have to cultivate our concern for posterity without feeling that we know best for posterity. We do not know whether posterity will or will not welcome our concern. Would any generation have viewed with pleasure the environment of say 100 years ahead?

I am afraid that I have come to the end without saying anything very specific. I have been trying to look ahead for an idea, a challenge, which would put our profession where it was when John Roderick came — on the threshold

203

of a remarkable quarter century. There is no doubt that the engineer is in transition, but there can be no conflict between the goals of engineering and environmental quality if we have an approach to a thorough understanding of the natural forces we are trying to harness. I see the engineer's role as General Clarke saw it when he sought answers to his three questions:

> People tend to think of the engineer as a sort of glorified mechanic; a man who knows only slide-rules and formulas, stresses and strains, and the properties of materials. But engineering in its broader aspects is becoming, if it is not already, a major field of intellectual endeavour. It involves the delicate and difficult task of translating scientific abstractions into the practical language of earthly living; and this is perhaps the most completely demanding task in the world. For it requires an understanding of *both* spheres — the pure ether in which the scientist lives, and also the goals and drives and aspirations of human society in all its complexity. The Engineer must be at once philosopher, humanist and hard-headed, hard-handed workman. He must be a philosopher enough to know what to *believe*, humanist enough to know what to *desire*, and a workman enough to know what to *do*.

References

1. Black, J., *The Domination of Man*, Edinburgh University Press, 1970.
2. Clarke, F. J., 'The Engineer Looks at the Environment', Address to D.C. Professional Engineers, 24 May 1971.
3. SCOPE, *Report No. 5*, Toronto 1975.

H. B. HARRISON

Structural Computation, 1951–78

Introduction

When Dr J. W. Roderick arrived at Sydney in 1951 as Challis Professor of Civil Engineering, the computing equipment within the Department of Civil Engineering could hardly be described as extensive. A manually cranked Brunsvega of indeterminate age supplemented the personal slide rules of staff and students. An electrically driven Marchant calculator was quickly acquired and at least three and possibly more of the authors of chapters in the present volume were encouraged to speed up their thesis computations on this late model calculator. The Marchant has long since suffered the fate of obsolete equipment and it is with mixed feelings that we now see the slide rule regarded as an object of curiosity by the incoming undergraduates, all armed with pocket calculators of annually increasing sophistication. In retiring from his position as Head of the School, John Roderick leaves a computing laboratory so well equipped as to have few peers among modern civil engineering schools.

Today, there would be no area in the whole array of physical sciences where the digital computer has not made some significant impact in the past twenty-five years. In civil engineering it was in the field of structural analysis that the first signals about the approaching computer revolution were becoming loud and clear by the early 'fifties. It is the present intention to describe the gradually changing emphasis in the teaching of structural analysis and design that have accompanied the arrival of the computer era.

The age of effective digital computing probably dates from 1946 when a machine called ENIAC (Electronic Numerical Integrator and Computer) was commissioned at the School of Electrical Engineering at the University of Pennsylvania. It was built for the U.S. Army primarily for use in the preparation of ballistic tables. It was a decimal machine, rather unique and primitive and most of the underlying design concepts were abandoned after its completion. It weighed about 30 tonnes and its 1800 relays and 18000 valves and other components required 140 kW of power [1]. The first British machine was called EDSAC (Electronic Delay Storage Automatic Computer) and it began operation in the Mathematical Laboratory at Cambridge in 1949. It is credited with being the first machine to utilize program storage but of interest to structural engineers is the fact that it is most likely that the first

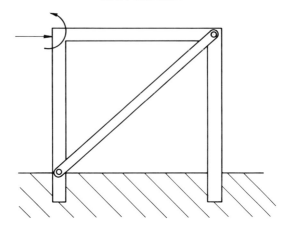

FIG. 1   Southwell's frame analysed on EDSAC by J. M. Bennett in 1950

matrix structural calculations ever done by computer were carried out on EDSAC in 1950. J. M. Bennett analysed the plane frame shown in Fig. 1 [2].

Computer Oriented Methods

The simple, braced portal in Fig. 1 is certainly not large but the significance of Bennett's work lay in his appreciation that to take real advantage of the digital computer as it was then developing, it was necessary to develop and program matrix and tensor methods of analysis and not merely to program existing techniques of manual calculation. Engineers and particularly structural engineers have always faced taxing computational problems and it is natural to expect a concentration of analytical methods at the expense perhaps of conceptual design in any undergraduate syllabus. The great development in the 'thirties was the introduction of relaxation methods. Certainly, the moment-distribution method seemed to occupy pride of place in the problem solving equipment of this author's generation. It is interesting to see, then, that the frame in Fig. 1 was an example taken quite naturally by Bennett from Sir Richard Southwell's classic text on Relaxation Methods [3].

Bennett based his approach on methods developed by Kron [4], an electrical engineer who saw the analogy between electrical networks and structural frameworks and who used matrix algebra to provide a systematic description of structural topology. Two quite separate systems of equations define the properties of a structure, the first describing the behaviour of elements while the second system is concerned with the connection of the elements to form the complete structure. Kron appreciated this distinction which was what Argyris [5] had in mind when he emphasized that matrix structural analysis would have achieved very little if matrix methods had been confined merely to the solution of linear equations. The aim rather has been the consistent development in matrix language of the complete structural theory beginning with the most elementary data and ending with the required deformations and stress-resultants.

It has taken a considerable time for the generality of these methods of structural analysis to be recognized and appreciated by educators. If a beam or frame is analysed numerically by a suitable manual technique (such as moment distribution), the result clearly is not applicable to a different beam or frame. If an algebraic analysis is carried out and formulas obtained for stress resultants and deformations, the result will be useful for all structures of a similar class. The particular numeric data would be substituted into the formulas and useful results obtained while the need for new analyses from first principles in each case would be bypassed. However, algebraic formulas produced, for example, by analysing generally a three-span continuous beam are clearly of no use if the structure under study is a triangulated space frame. The benefit of matrix analysis is that the derived formulas can be applied to all structures; however, the necessary data for use in matrix expressions are not comprised of simple numerical values for lengths and section properties but rather consist of arrays of numerical data.

As computers increased in capacity and efficiency, the data arrays themselves could be generated internally from more elementary topological information. When this happened by the mid 'sixties, the 'black-box' era of structural analysis really had arrived. Learning to accommodate to the 'black-box' phenomenon has been a problem for teachers of structural analysis ever since.

Computer Hardware Development

The CSIRO constructed CSIRAC, the first Australian digital computer and reputedly the world's fifth, in Sydney in 1951. About that time Professor H. Messel and his colleagues in the School of Physics at Sydney University saw the need for a fast digital computer within their School and in 1953 they negotiated to secure circuit diagrams for the ILLIAC which was then operational at the University of Illinois. Work had started in 1949 on the construction of ILLIAC and its sister machine ORDVAC in the Digital Computer Laboratory at the University of Illinois and it was operational in 1952. SILLIAC was working by 1956 in what has become well-known as the Basser Computing Laboratory of the School of Physics. Nowadays one can obtain portable computers with power exceeding SILLIAC's when first installed. But, with its high speed memory of 1024 words of 40 bits, it was to prove very reliable and successful for ten years. The Civil Engineering Department's first venture into the area of computer hardware occurred in 1961 when a Creed paper tape punch was acquired. This set was useful in the preparation and interpretation of the narrow, 5-hole paper tape that comprised the input and output media for SILLIAC. In 1964, the Basser

Department began to operate additionally an English Electric KDF9 and the service was augmented with an IBM 7040 in 1967. SILLIAC was decommissioned in 1968.

By 1970, a remote terminal to a CDC 6600 was acquired by the Basser Department. This terminal, the KDF9 and the IBM 7040 between them carried out a large part of Sydney University's computing until 1974 when the present CYBER 72 system was installed.

The Basser Department's facilities have been extensively used by civil engineering staff and graduate students as also, until 1971, was the CSIRO computing service in the National Standards Laboratory within the University grounds. University staff had access there to a CDC 3200 machine backed at that time by a larger CDC 3600 located at Canberra. The closeness of NSL to the civil engineering school, coupled with the provision of card punches began to attract structures researchers in 1966 at a time when the Basser Department's machines were still geared to paper tape. By 1971, the 6600 terminal within the Basser Department had recaptured the civil engineering researchers — with a little encouragement from the University's administration.

All of this computing activity among staff and graduate students had little immediate impact upon the majority of the graduating class. The facilities were remote, the card and tape punching equipment within the civil engineering precinct was restricted and little could be done with final year classes of 50–70 students apart from merely talk about machine analysis of structures. The occasional honours student with an interest in computing was dealt with satisfactorily but there was a complete lack of an in-house computing facility for teaching purposes. In August 1968 this situation was eased when a terminal was hired to provide access to the commercial time-sharing service pioneered by General Electric. In almost every respect, the initial service provided by the teletype was inferior to that provided to the researcher by the Basser Department and the CSIRO service. It was slow and costly and the computing capacity was limited but the decisive advantage lay in the ability to have immediate running of programs for undergraduates within the School of Civil Engineering.

Strictly speaking, the teletype purchased to access the GE Mark 1 system over the telephone was not the School's first venture into time-sharing. The Basser Department planned to have the KDF9 machine operate in a time-sharing mode for several hours a day and, late in 1967, the School purchased a teletype for use with the university's, then, main machine. This experiment in time-sharing was not really successful, but it is remarkable that the original teletype, a decade later, now acts as the standby monitor controlling the School's own, eleven terminal, minicomputer system.

Today's undergraduate would be amused at the notion that the provision of one, slow teletype to provide experience of on-line computation to classes of 70–100 final year students constituted an advance of some significance. Funds to purchase and maintain the terminals were provided by the Post Graduate Foundation as was also the case when the dial-up computer facility was duplicated late in 1973. By that time the General Electric GE265 call-up system at Waterloo in Sydney was being phased out and replaced by the Honeywell Mark III system in which the on-line computation was carried out in Cleveland, USA, accessed via satellite. Commercial, time-sharing computing had really arrived by the early 'seventies with at least four systems in Sydney competing for the available business. For some months in 1971 the School accessed the IBM Call 360 system with a processor located first at Sydney, then at Canberra and finally at Melbourne.

The individual undergraduate in the late 'sixties and early 'seventies may not have had 'hands-on' experience with interactive computing but at the very least, the process was demonstrated to him. None of the firms offering a time-sharing service added any inducements in the way of concessions for education and so it was never possible to offer students the free, unrestricted access to computation that is the ideal in an educational environment. However, the experience gained with on-line computation via the Honeywell and IBM systems convinced Professor Roderick that the only way to get a satisfactory solution to this educational problem was to provide a small, multi-terminal, time-sharing system within the School for use by the senior undergraduates.

The initiation of the Teaching Computer Project in 1971 by Professor Roderick and Mr P. R. Pettit has been described elsewhere in this volume. When the PRIME 300 system was installed in September 1975 in the C. A. Hawkins Computing Laboratory, some eleven high speed terminals backed by a line printer were available right where the senior undergraduate needed them — namely next door to the design office. The laboratory occupies the space set aside initially for experimental stress-analysis and for structural models. The first card punch in the School (in fact, the first in the Faculty of Engineering) was purchased with ARGC funds in 1966. Further punches were hired later after the Basser Department obtained an IBM 7040 in 1967 and the insidious occupation of the models laboratory by computing equipment commenced about 1968, an encroachment accepted with great forebearance by Mr O. S. Potter. Before the School's teaching computer was installed in 1975, the university had acquired its present main computer and the department was successful in acquiring three terminals to the CYBER 72 system. These were installed in the models laboratory in 1974. The structural models were moved to the extended mezzanine floor in the Materials and Structures Laboratory and the necessary structural and electrical alterations were made by May 1975, so that the C. A. Hawkins Laboratory came into existence.

In completing this account of hardware availability for undergraduate computing, a complete inventory at the time of Professor Roderick's retirement would show that the senior and senior advanced undergraduate has access to an impressive array of six card punches, 3 tape punches, 11 video display terminals and 4 typewriter terminals in the room immediately adjacent to his design office and common room. The 11 video units include one graphics terminal with hard copy unit and these peripherals to the PRIME 300 are available to the undergraduate and graduate student for effectively 24 hours each day. The four typewriter terminals access the University's CYBER and the dial-up teletype, initially installed in 1968 to provide our first real experience with time-sharing, is still in use. One can dial-up the CYBER from this unit and it is often used to transfer programs between the department's teaching computer and the university's central computer. If the need were to arise, commercial bureaux can still be accessed and files transferred to and received from other departments and organizations.

The Development of Computer Software

The advent of the computer has been accompanied by an unprecedented avalanche of jargon. Everyone would know what is meant by the term 'hardware' but the term 'software' conjures up many visions ranging through computer programs, operating systems to the staff who write the programs and tend the machines. Civil engineering software can be considered as a generic phrase describing all those computer programs written over the past decades most often by engineers with specific problems in mind. Within the School of Civil Engineering, software has been developed by staff and research students to solve problems arising from research and teaching interests and so it is of interest in the discussion of civil engineering software, to trace briefly the trend in research interests of the structures group within the school since John Roderick's arrival from Cambridge in 1951.

At Cambridge, he had played an important role in the steel structures research programme which was directed by Professor J. F. Baker (now Lord Baker of Windrush), Head of the Engineering Department. Baker's objective was the development of the plastic methods of structural analysis. The incentive behind this drive to develop non-linear methods of frame analysis was Baker's realization, based on field measurement of strains as well as wartime damage assessments, that the linear-elastic structural model provided a poor estimate of the ultimate load carrying capacity for steel frameworks. Cambridge certainly lived up to its reputation for leadership in the physical sciences in those years. While Bennett and Livesley in the Mathematical Laboratory were adopting Kron's tensor methods for network and linear structural analysis so that advantage could be taken of the new digital computer's calculating power, Baker's team was developing more sophisticated models of behaviour that more closely reflected the observed response to load of real structures. At the same time, another study, coincidentally also referred to as 'structural analysis', was nearing completion in the Cavendish Laboratory under Sir Laurence Bragg. Watson and Crick [6] were busy there unravelling the helical structure of the DNA molecule.

210

Having worked as a computer specialist for Ferranti Limited at Manchester, J. M. Bennett arrived at Sydney in 1956 to take charge of SILLIAC which was then operational in the Physics Department. At Professor Roderick's invitation, he spoke to the staff of the Civil Engineering Department early in 1957, advocating the possibilities of automatic computation especially in structural analysis. Not all of those present were seized by Bennett's enthusiasm for digital computation and its civil engineering applications. In fact, the discussion afterwards centred more on the somewhat derisory discrepancy in relative sizes between the rooms of expensive electrical equipment represented by SILLIAC and the modest proportions of Bennett's plane frame as in Fig. 1. Clearly a lot of progress would have to be made in the areas of speed and memory capacity of digital computers before their use by civil engineers would become general.

Prior to the addition of magnetic tape drives, SILLIAC's storage limitations did not encourage research into areas of structural theory where matrix manipulations were required. Nevertheless staff and research students in civil engineering began to spend more and more time operating SILLIAC directly and coding those problems of plastic and non-linear elastic analysis that could be handled without iterative matrix operations. In the natural course of events, papers began to appear in journals by 1960 which described the solution of various structural problems by computer methods. A short graduate course of lectures was jointly organized by the Basser Department and the Civil Engineering School in 1960. Some fifteen lectures presented by staff and visiting lecturers reflected growing expertise in the use of computers. The titles are interesting and have been summarized in Table 1. Most of the lecturers described how SILLIAC had been used to solve specific problems but it is significant that only two lectures set out the theory in matrix form of the stiffness and flexibility methods of linear frame analysis. This excellent pair of lectures was delivered by B. Rawlings but there were no programs to demonstrate the use of these methods for, with only a few hundred storage locations available for data in the Williams tube memory of SILLIAC, the programming of matrix methods in general was hardly feasible. Needless to say, civil engineering undergraduate contact with either computer or computer oriented structural analysis was practically non-existent at this stage.

In 1959 SILLIAC was programmed to perform elastic analyses of the main frames for the new Materials and Structures Laboratory which was the first building erected on the Darlington site for the engineering faculty. The relocation of the entire faculty, initiated by Professor Roderick as Dean, was completed by 1974. It is quite likely that the steel frames shown in Fig. 2 were the first real structures to be computer analysed in Australia. However, the method adopted for these frames did not use general matrix concepts. The problems were solved by firstly obtaining from slope-deflection analysis a complete algebraic solution even to the extent of solving four simultaneous

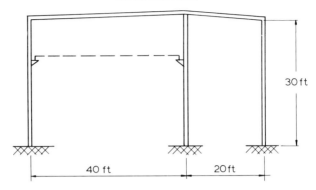

FIG. 2   Frames for the Darlington N.S.W. laboratory, School of Civil Engineering, analysed on Silliac in 1959

TABLE 1   The University of Sydney Department of Civil Engineering in conjunction with the Adolph Basser Computing Laboratory
Automatic Computers and Civil Engineering, September 1960

Title	Lecturer
An Outline of Civil Engineering Problems solved by Automatic Computers	J. M. Bennett
The Experience of the Snowy Mountains Authority in the Use of SILLIAC	K. Johnson
Plastic Design and Analysis of Steel Structures	H. B. Harrison
Survey Reductions, Routine Designs and Cost Calculations — the treatment of multiple calculations	J. M Bennett
Elements of Matrix Algebra	M. W. Low
Application of Matrices to Analysis of Structures	B. Rawlings
Flow in Pipe Networks — a problem involving non-linear equations	J. M. Bennett
Earth Bank Stability and Slip-Circle Analysis	P. T. Brown
Design for Least Weight and Minimum Cost — an application of linear programming	J. M. Bennett
Stresses in Plates and Slabs	D. Campbell-Allen
Plate-Stresses — the solution of the Biharmonic Equation	D. Campbell-Allen
The Economics of Earth Moving	R. O'Connor

equations algebraically. It was then possible to directly encode the solution and solve for successive loading cases without exceeding the few hundred storage locations available in SILLIAC's memory.

Under Roderick's direction, the research effort of the School of Civil Engineering gained momentum during the sixties and extensive use of SILLIAC was acknowledged in the resulting publications. Graduate students and research minded staff gained expertise and were made especially welcome in the computing laboratory by J. M. Bennett who had been appointed a Professor of Physics (Electronic Computing) in 1961. While Bennett and his staff had developed a general frame analysis program which was commercially available to structural engineers using the English Electric KDF9, it was not made use of for undergraduate instruction in the School of Civil Engineering, for, by late 1965, card deck programs for linear and plastic analysis of plane systems were being developed within the School using the CSIRO computer system.

Two things are necessary if the aim is to instruct undergraduates in the general matrix methods of linear analysis. One needs both a computer and a program, in other words, hardware and software. By 1966 a general plane frame program was available and could be serviced and explained by its author — which is always an advantage. The in-house computer was not available for two more years. It was the provision by the Civil Engineering Post Graduate Foundation of a terminal to a commercial time-sharing system that meant that the matrix methods could be demonstrated by 1968 in the presence of the student. The School's first finite element program was not very efficient and the memory available on the General Electric Mark 1 system permitted the analysis of frames of only modest size. But the experience for a student was sufficient to demonstrate the problems that can arise in the 'black-box' age of structural analysis.

The Teaching of Structural Analysis

It is generally agreed that structural analysis comprises an essential component in the education of a civil engineer. Its purpose is the mathematical and numerical simulation of structural response so that a proposed design can be tested for safety prior to construction. Its methods comprise the combination of the sciences of applied mechanics and strength of materials and lead characteristically to sets of simultaneous equations with unknowns ranging from a few to many thousands. The effort in structural analysis has always involved three distinct operations — namely the establishment of the equation sets, their solution and subsequent calculations involving the roots to the equations. It is of course a distortion to separate design and analysis. Structural forms frequently have been determined and governed by the designer's fore-knowledge of the analytical tools available to him. At the same time, new analytical techniques have rarely been developed for reasons other

213

than an urgent need to study a new structural arrangement that may be proposed or may be causing distress and sometimes may have already collapsed.

In the context of framed structures, design as a conceptual activity and analysis as a mental discipline have usually been closely associated. But analysis as a classical as well as useful discipline needed a unifying theme and in the hundred years of development from 1850–1950 a strong central theme never really appeared. By contrast, the dominance of the idea of economic value in design was clearly established by 1873 when Robert Bow in the foreword to his book *Economics of Construction* quoted from Professor W. J. M. Rankine:

> 'In too many cases we see the strength and the stability which ought to be given by the skilful arrangement of the parts of a structure, supplied by means of clumsy massiveness, and of lavish expenditure of material, labour and money: and the evil is increased by a perversion of the public taste, which causes works to be admired, not in proportion to their fitness for their purposes, or to the skill evinced in attaining that fitness, but in proportion to their size and cost'.

The achievement of economy in design presupposes the availability of appropriate mathematical model and analytical methods. Textbooks on structural analysis, published as late as 1950, explain a vast variety of methods each appropriate to a restricted class of structure. Difficulties for the undergraduate in grasping the concepts of structural theory have been amplified by the bewildering array of manual methods — each with its specific application. For example, moment distribution is applicable to rigid frames when axial and shear strains are insignificant. Energy and virtual-work methods are acceptable for portal frames and arches and for computing deformations in trusses. The distinction between determinate and indeterminate structures is of prime importance in the latter methods but not so significant in the slope-deflection technique, which, nevertheless, is of limited application when the order of the equations to be solved becomes large. Static analysis of trusses by tension coefficients and of continuous beams by the three-moment theorem or by formal integration, using the Macaulay technique, appear to be isolated manual methods with seemingly little in common. Odd schemes for calculation, such as the conjugate beam or column analogy methods, have always been difficult to classify. Yet, all these manual techniques have the same objectives — to predict the stress condition in a structure under a given set of loads.

It would be fair to state that the objective of educators concerned with structural analysis has been to transmit to their students an appreciation of the origin and purpose of all these methods and to hope that upon graduation, techniques would be selected and used with an appropriate level of sophistication. The ability to select the best method of analysis for a given structural problem was and is a measure of this sophistication.

It has often been maintained that the development of a 'feeling' for structural behaviour and response is a most important component in the education of students. This clearly desirable feeling is as hard to define as it is to impart. Perhaps it amounts essentially to an awareness and appreciation of the age-old principles of statics. It does not take long to state these principles and, however well expressed, a lecture on them will rarely be recalled by a student as constituting a high point in his undergraduate career. Nevertheless structures can collapse if their designer's grasp of statics is faulty whereas errors in compatibility assessment are often safely accommodated, particularly in ductile frameworks.

The traditional junior courses in Structures, with emphasis on determinate beam systems and simple trusses, initiate the student's appreciation of the behaviour of structures using the tutorial and laboratory as the vehicle with apparently endless problems involving bending moment and shear force diagrams. Influence line concepts also are a particularly powerful educational tool in the development of a feeling for behaviour and should be covered in junior and intermediate courses whether or not the techniques may be outdated in so far as modern design office procedures are concerned. In the senior years of a course in structures, there has traditionally been a heavy emphasis on statically indeterminate structures.

Until quite recently, the teaching of a wide variety of analytical methods served two distinct purposes. The methods were in common use in design offices and, in the process of learning how to use them, the development in the student of an appreciation of structural behaviour was furthered. To-day, this latter purpose is perhaps the sole justification for the retention of practically all methods of analysis other than the computer methods. The problem of a designer inspecting a thick accumulation of computer printout hopefully representing the analysis of his current design is simple to state. He needs assurance that the results are valid — at least within the limitations on validity accepted for a linear-elastic model of behaviour. He needs this assurance before contemplating the adjustment of member sizes following on local stress calculations. The ability to assess the validity of computer printout from a program written by someone else is a central problem of nearly all computer users. In no other field is the problem so acute as it is in structural engineering where computer analysis for all except the simplest of structural arrangements is now the rule rather than the exception.

The Verification of Machine Analyses

Obviously the modern structures syllabus must contain a considerable amount on the subject of matrix analysis and computer methods with emphasis on equation solving techniques. But the verification of a computed solution to a structures problem need not entail a complete, cross-checking re-analysis by a similar method. A great advantage of studying the matrix methods is a more acute appreciation of the basis of all methods of analysis.

. B. Harrison

We say of a valid elastic analysis that it is one satisfying simultaneously the requirements of equilibrium and compatibility.

A manual solution of a plane frame problem by, say, the moment-distribution method is not exempt from the need to satisfy both static and compatibility principles but it may be more difficult to check than a computer solution to the same problem for the reason that joint displacements are not usually calculated in the process of distribution. Consequently, the independent checking of one moment-distribution solution usually had to involve another such solution. Engineers to whom this situation was familiar naturally thought that the verification of one computer solution to a frame analysis problem would necessarily involve a second, independent solution, by another program, perhaps on another machine. Suggestions were offered to code drafting committees in the late 'sixties that acceptable programs might well have to be named in appropriate code appendices. While in principle, such an idea may be no more absurd than the laying down of any other set of acceptable formulae in a code, it is now better appreciated that it is the solution to the frame problem in hand that needs to be valid — irrespective of the program and the machine that produced it.

The validity of a computer solution to a structural problem is assessed by finding if the results satisfy equilibrium and compatibility requirements. However, the fact that a solution satisfies statics may be encouraging but the number of statically admissible solutions to a statically indeterminate problem is infinite. End rotations and member extensions may need to be calculated from stress-resultants and member properties to see whether they are compatible with the joint displacements predicted by the computer. This, after all, is what is meant by 'compatibility'. Battery powered calculators carrying a large number of significant figures speed up the verification process for the student of the late 'seventies.

In the course of laboratory work in their final year, students prepare data for the linear elastic analysis of frameworks using the School's programs loaded on both the PRIME minicomputer and the university's CYBER. The experience to be gained here is how to make effective use of a 'black-box' method of analysis. For the bulk of the final year class, an explanation of how such programs work and an understanding of the matrix operations and theory will come after they have learnt to use them. In punching his data in a free format mode but in an obviously specific sequence, the student quite unaided will incorporate many errors in data; he will also learn to distinguish between the I's and the 1's and to note the difference between an alphabetic and a numeric zero. He will usually check his data by drawing his frame from node co-ordinates and member incidences sent back to the terminal by the computer. The visual display, graphics terminal in the C. A. Hawkins Laboratory is obviously ideal for this purpose as is seen in Fig. 3. But the important lesson that is learnt is that a nicely formatted solution with data printed and verified and with reasonable looking answers — all of these things

216

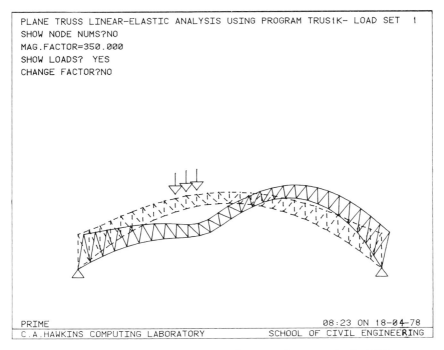

```
PLANE TRUSS LINEAR-ELASTIC ANALYSIS USING PROGRAM TRUSIK- LOAD SET  1
SHOW NODE NUMS?NO
MAG.FACTOR=350.000
SHOW LOADS?  YES
CHANGE FACTOR?NO
```

```
PRIME                                              08:23 ON 18-04-78
C.A.HAWKINS COMPUTING LABORATORY        SCHOOL OF CIVIL ENGINEERING
```

FIG. 3   A Sydney structure treated as a student exercise in 1978

do not remove the need to check that the solution satisfies both equilibrium and compatibility.

Such experiences are of considerable benefit to a student without requiring him to understand computer programming or the matrix theory of structural analysis. They demonstrate to him firstly, the need to input the correct data in the correct sequence. More importantly, they emphasize that a correctly reproduced set of data followed by an impressively tabulated set of answers that both look reasonable and also satisfy many spot checks on joint and overall equilibrium — that all these things are no guarantee of validity. Finally, such experiences have been found most helpful to the student in his grasping quickly the concepts of matrix analysis of structures when he meets these later in his course.

Conclusion

Some problems associated with the teaching of structural analysis in the 'seventies have been discussed. It is clear that a modern undergraduate course in structures must equip each graduating student with enough understanding and expertise to be able at least to make competent use of service bureau programs for linear analysis. No longer can the relevant matrix theory either

217

be taught to a select few honours students or else omitted altogether from an undergraduate syllabus. In showing how these problems have been dealt with at Sydney University over the past twenty years, it was necessary to outline the progressive and rapid updating of the computing equipment that was available to the Civil Engineering School. For students to obtain an easy familiarity with computing methods, both hardware and software are needed and for dealing effectively with classes of 80–100 final year students, immediate machine access is very important. In the maintenance of student interest and enthusiasm, turn-around times of days or even hours are disastrous.

There is, of course, much more to structural analysis than linear-elastic theory. Plastic and stability analysis programs as well as second-order methods are becoming available at computer bureaux so that even more sophistication will be required of the modern graduate in his use of such powerful tools. Vibration predictions and the study of continua by finite element programs are becoming routine in modern design offices. Since the machine has relieved the structural engineer of much of his numerical work, he has time to think more about the assumptions behind his mathematical models and not, for example, think that the most expensive linear elastic analysis of the most complex space structure will yield any direct data about the elastic stability of that structure. The computer is no substitute for that 'feeling' for structural behaviour.

There are difficulties in conveying certain aspects of the computer methods to students. But some concepts that frequently confuse the student when dealing with manual methods may present little or no difficulties in the matrix treatment. For example, the manual slope-deflection and moment-distribution methods entail some conceptual problems when initial strain effects and complicated sway modes may be involved. The general matrix treatment of these effects is quite straightforward. While the flexibility or force method of analysis may have little application at modern computer bureaux, the more general matrix analysis can shed considerable light on some puzzling aspects of certain manual methods of force analysis. Conditioning of the compatibility equations is not always an optimum and the student can see how Clapeyron's Theorem for continuous beams and the elastic-centre methods for arches have automatically ensured well-conditioned equations. The methods of the column analogy for arches and beams can be seen to not only involve equations of the best possible conditioning but also the concept of mixed releases. The student in command of the matrix methods begins to see the manual methods of the past 100 years in a clear perspective — he does not dismiss them but rather tends to develop a mature appreciation of the expertise and tenacity of his structural predecessors.

Matrix methods of linear analysis of frame-works and continua are now commonplace in any civil engineering design environment. Yet few structural engineers would have been impressed by Bennett's frame analysis on EDSAC had they known about it in 1950. Students graduating in the late 'seventies not only will be using computers for analysing the behaviour of trial designs. They will also have to live with new families of partially or fully automatic, design programs. They will need training to be comfortable in a world of operations research techniques, minicomputers, interactive computer graphics and microprocessors. Future graduates of the School of Civil Engineering will be indebted to John Roderick for his perception in anticipating the impact of the computer in civil engineering and his drive and organizing capacity which has ensured that the C. A. Hawkins Computing Laboratory is equipped to handle the task.

References

1. Goldstine, H. H., *The Computer from Pascal to von Neumann*, Princeton University Press, 1972.
2. Livesley, R. K., 'The Pattern of Structural Computing; 1946–1966', *The Structural Engineer* (London), 46, 6, June 1968, 177–82.
3. Southwell, R. V., *Relaxation Methods in Engineering Science*, Oxford University Press, London 1940.
4. Kron, G., 'Tensorial Analysis and Equivalent Circuits of Elastic Structures', *Jnl. Franklin Inst.*, 238, 6, 1944.
5. Argyris, J. H., 'On the Analysis of Complex Elastic Structures', *App. Mech. Rev.*, II, 7, 1958.
6. Watson, J. D., *The Double Helix*. Weidenfeld and Nicholson, London 1968.

CONTRIBUTORS

D. CAMPBELL-ALLEN

E. H. DAVIS

B. G. HUTCHINSON

Dr Hutchinson graduated in civil engineering from the University of Sydney in 1956 and before leaving Australia in 1957 worked for the N.S.W. Public Works Department at Eucumbene Dam. He holds postgraduate degrees in civil engineering from Queen's University at Kingston, Ontario and the University of Waterloo. During his professional life in Canada he has worked for the Alberta Research Council and served as a consultant in transport planning to a number of federal, provincial, municipal and private agencies. He joined the Department of Civil Engineering at the University of Waterloo in 1962 and was appointed a full professor in 1968. He has published a number of technical papers in the areas of highway engineering, transport planning, benefit-cost analysis and urban systems modelling, and is the author of a textbook in urban transport systems planning. In 1975–6 he served as a visiting professor in the School of Highways and Transport at the University of New South Wales.

W. G. RYAN

W. G. Ryan graduated in 1955 and spent that year in the N.S.W. Department of Main Roads Bridge Design Section. He then joined Monaro Shire as Assistant (late Deputy) Shire Engineer. In May 1958, he joined the Snowy Mountains Hydro Electric Authority as Concrete Control Engineer initially in the Materials Laboratory Scientific Services Division, and later on Tumut 2 Project in the Major Contracts Division. In 1960 he accepted the position of Concrete Engineer with Ready Mixed Concrete Ltd and carried out assignments in Melbourne and Hobart before appointment as Production Manager, Victoria at the end of that year. He transferred to Sydney late in 1962 as Area Engineer, was appointed Chief Concrete Engineer in Sydney in 1964, then for Australia in 1965. He established Central Research Laboratory for Ready Mixed Concrete Ltd and Blue Metal Industries Ltd in 1966, and in July 1975 was appointed General Manager, Concrete Division, Blue Metal Industries Ltd.

Mr Ryan was awarded Master of Engineering in Highway Engineering, University of New South Wales for research into use of fine ground granulated blast furnace slag in concrete, 1973, and is the author of many papers on concrete materials technology presented or published both in Australia and overseas. He is the Immediate Past Federal President, Concrete Institute of Australia; Immediate Past Chairman Institution of Engineers Australia National Committee on Concrete Research and Engineering; Member of Federal Council National Association of Testing Authorities; Past Chairman Standards Association of Australia Committee on Methods of Testing Concrete; and Member of American Concrete Institute Committee 548, Polymer Concretes. In October 1977 he was elected a Fellow of American Concrete Institute for services to concrete and concrete construction, the first Australian to have been so recognized.

B. J. VICKERY

Barry Vickery graduated from the University of Sydney with the degrees of BE (1957), MEngSc (1960) and PhD (1968). Between the years 1959 and 1966, except for a period when he was Guest Worker and then Senior Scientific Officer, Aerodynamics Division, National Physical Laboratory, U.K., Barry Vickery held the position of Lecturer in the Department of Civil Engineering, the University of Sydney. For the years 1971–6 he held the position of Associate Professor and from 1966–71 he was Assistant and then Associate Professor in the Faculty of Engineering Science, the University of Western Ontario, Canada, and in 1976 he returned from Sydney to accept a Professorial position, which he holds to-day.

He is the author of twenty-seven papers and more than thirty reports. He is also co-author of a book, *Architectural Aerodynamics* and his research activities have been in the fields of theory of structures, fluid mechanics, industrial aerodynamics and applied statistics. Professor Vickery is the Regional Editor (Canada) of *International Journal of Industrial Aerodynamics*, a Member of the ASCE Task Committee on Wind Forces and a Member of the Committee on Wind and Earthquake Forces, joint ASCE/IABSE Tall Building Committee. He is a Member of the Institution of Engineers, Australia and in 1971 received from that Institution two Awards: The Chapman Medal for contributions to the Art and Science of Structural Engineering, and the J.J.C. Bradfield Prize for contributions to Civil Engineering.

R. P. R. CHADWICK

Dick Chadwick graduated in 1956. His first job was with the Water Conservation & Irrigation Commission of N.S.W. After eight months with the W.C. & I.C. he secured a position as a technical sales representative with a small private company in the building industry. Then, after four years he left to commence his own consulting practice as a Structural Engineer. This unfortunately coincided with the recession of 1961, and — in common with many professionals connected with the building industry — he found things very difficult. He returned to specialized contracting, this time on his own behalf.

He now heads (and owns) twenty-one businesses in the five Eastern States of Australia, with a staff of about 500 people. The businesses are quite diverse. Sixteen are involved in a variety of supply and/or contracting activities associated with the construction industry. There are two manufacturing companies — in Sydney and Melbourne — producing a wide range of goods in sheet metal. Another business imports, assembles and sells safety cabins for farm tractors. His most recent activity is the manufacture and/or importation of golf clubs and other golf equipment.

N. S. TRAHAIR

Nick Trahair received from the University of Sydney the degrees of BSc (1954), BE in Civil Engineering with 1st class honours (1956), and MEngSc (1959). He worked with the Department of Works in Canberra for two-and-a-half years before returning in 1960 to the University of Sydney where he became an Associate Professor. His PhD was awarded in 1968. His research interests are in the field of structural stability, with particular emphasis on the lateral buckling of steel beams. His teaching efforts are concentrated in this area and on the behaviour and design of steel structures and has been active in the development of Australian design codes for steel structures. He has taught and carried out research work in the U.S. (1968) and the U.K. (1974–5), and has given lectures on his speciality in the U.S., the U.K., and in Europe. At the beginning of 1979 he was appointed Professor of Civil Engineering.

A. J. W. POWELL

Anthony Powell graduated from the University of Sydney in 1953 with a BE in Civil Egnineering; in 1965 he was awarded his Diploma of Town and Country Planning, and then three years later, awarded Master of Town and Country Planning. He is now a certified Town Planner and a Member of the Royal Australian Planning

Institute. Following graduation Mr Powell was engaged as Investigation Engineer by the Snowy Mountains Hydro-Electric Authority. Then in 1960–3 he worked as a Research Engineer in the United Kingdom.

After returning to Australia his major interests have been with Town Planning. While working as Principal Planner for the State Planning Authority of New South Wales, he also served as External Lecturer in Public Administration and Planning Law with the Department of Town and Country Planning, University of Sydney (1969–73). He has served as Councillor with the National Roads and Motorists' Association (1970–4), as Director for Westlakes Ltd and is now a Principal of Liberman, Powell and Associates, Consulting Town Planners. In February 1974 Anthony Powell was appointed as Commissioner for the National Capital Development Commission, a position he has held to date, while also acting as Chairman for the Darwin Reconstruction Commission in 1975.

P. B. JONES

Phil Jones graduated BE in 1954, MEngSc in 1960 and PhD in 1972 and is an Associate Professor in the School of Civil Engineering, University of Sydney. His current research interests are in the design of simple surveys by statistical analysis.

Another research field in which Phil has been active is the examination of personal and instrumental errors especially in connection with automatic levels.

C. R. LONGWORTH

Charles Longworth, BE, DIC, FICE, FIEAust., MAus.IMM is Executive Chairman of Longworth & McKenzie Pty Ltd. After graduating in Civil Engineering from The University of Sydney in 1955 he worked for R. Crooks Michell and Peacock, Consulting Engineers, in Sydney, Newcastle and Adelaide. He was a founding partner of Longworth & McKenzie in 1957 and has subsequently been active in establishing this company in the geotechnical, mining, port engineering and environmental fields. In 1961 he undertook post-graduate training at Imperial College, London in soil and rock mechanics. For the past twelve years his work has been associated with the Australian coal industry and in 1977 his company received an Award of Merit from the Association of Consulting Engineers Australia for work in the coke manufacturing industry. Over the years he has visited many mining projects in Australia and overseas. He is a past National Chairman of the Australian Geomechanics Society and was foundation Chairman of the Australian Tunnelling Association. He is currently a member of the visiting committee on Applied Geology to the University of New South Wales.

H. G. POULOS

Harry Poulos received his BE degree in 1961, PhD in 1965 and DScEng in 1976, all from the University of Sydney. After working for a consulting firm for a year, he joined the School of Civil Engineering at the University of Sydney in 1965, where he is now a Reader. His main research interests are concerned with problems relating to the settlement of foundations and the behaviour of pile foundations. He has spent two periods of study leave at M.I.T. in Boston in 1969–70 and in 1976. He has also been a visiting professor at the University of Western Ontario and a special consultant to McClelland Engineers Inc. in Houston, Texas. He was the recipient of the 1972 Warren Prize of the Institution of Engineers Australia (jointly with E. H. Davis) and the 1973 J. James R. Croes Medal of the American Society of Civil Engineers (jointly with D. J. D'Appolonia and C. C. Ladd).

M. S. NICKLIN

Malcolm Nicklin graduated from the University of Sydney early in 1953 with the degrees of BSc and BE in Civil Engineering with first class honours. He is a Fellow of the

American Society of Civil Engineers, Fellow of the Institution of Engineers, Australia and a Member of the Association of Consulting Engineers, Australia. He joined the Consulting firm of Macdonald Wagner & Priddle as a graduand and, apart from the year 1957 when he took a year's leave of absence to work with a consulting engineer in London, has remained with the firm ever since. He was appointed an Associate Partner in 1960 and a Partner in 1964. Upon the incorporation of Macdonald Wagner & Priddle Pty Ltd he was appointed the firm's Managing Director, the position he presently holds.

He has been involved in many major projects in Australia including port and harbour works, particularly for bulk sugar storage and handling and tanker berths, optical and radio telescopes, grain storages, petroleum product pipelines and industrial complexes and has participated in many feasibility studies for mineral developments. His close association with the sugar industry has involved him in projects in South America, Fiji, Indonesia and currently a major bulk sugar terminal in Mauritius.

N. M. HAWKINS

Neil Hawkins is Professor of Civil Engineering and Adjunct Professor of Architecture at the University of Washington, Seattle. He obtained his BSc and BE degrees from the University of Sydney in 1955 and 1957 and his MS and PhD degrees from the University of Illinois in 1959 and 1961. He served on the staff of the School of Civil Engineering, University of Sydney from 1961 until he transferred to the University of Washington in 1968. He is active in the American Concrete Institute, the American Society of Civil Engineers, the Earthquake Engineering Research Institute, and the Post-Tensioning Institute. From 1971 to 1978 he served as chairman of ACI-ASCE's Committee on Shear and Diagonal Tension. He received the Edward Noyes Prize of the Institution of Engineers, (Aust.), in 1965, ACI's Wason Medal in 1970, ASCE's State-of-the Art Award in 1974, ASCE's Raymond C. Reese Award in 1976 and ACI's Raymond C. Reese Award in 1978.

Contributors

B. RAWLINGS

Barry Rawlings graduated in the University of Sydney, where he was awarded the degrees of BSc, BE, with first class honours in Civil Engineering, and subsequently the research degrees of MEngSc and PhD. He is a Fellow of the Institution of Civil Engineers, the Institution of Structural Engineers and the Institution of Engineers, Australia.

Dr Rawlings was a Lecturer, subsequently Senior Lecturer and Reader, in the Department of Civil Engineering at the University of Sydney over the period 1953 to 1967, when he accepted appointment as Professor of Civil and Structural Engineering at the University of Sheffield in the United Kingdom. He held appointments as Professor and Head of Department during the period 1967 to 1975, and was a member of the University Council. He was External Examiner for courses in Civil Engineering of the Universities of London, Manchester and Dundee, and for the Council for National Academic Awards course at Sheffield Polytechnic.

In 1975 Dr Rawlings returned to Australia to take up his present appointment as Chief of the CSIRO Division of Mechanical Engineering. Since returning he has also been involved in a number of other activities, and he is a member of the Institution o Engineers, Australia's Board of Examiners, a member of its Task Force on Energy and a member of its National Committee on Coastal and Ocean Engineering. He also holds the appointment of Honorary Visiting Professor at the University of Wollongong, New South Wales.

D. C. O'CONNOR

Desmond O'Connor commenced study at the University of Sydney in 1950 after serving articles as a Surveyor. He graduated in Civil Engineering in 1954, and immediately joined the University of New South Wales, where he was Lecturer, and later Senior Lecturer, in Civil Engineering until 1963. During this period he was awarded the degrees of ME(N.S.W) and MSc, International Centre for Aerial Survey and Earth Sciences, Delft. He went to the U.S.A. in 1963 as a Research Engineer with the U.S. Army Corps of Engineers, and later became Director of the Research Institute and Scientific Advisor to the Engineer Topographic Laboratories. He was awarded his PhD in Civil Engineering from the University of Illinois in 1967. From 1971–3 he served with the U.S. Army Staff in the Pentagon as Chief of the Environmental Sciences office, and was a member of the Army Research Council.

In 1973 he returned to Australia as Foundation Professor of Environmental Studies at Murdoch University in Perth, and is now Dean of Environmental and Life Sciences. He is an Environmental Consultant to the mining industry, and a commercial pilot, combining this with his research interests in remote sensing and air pollution meteorology.

H. B. HARRISON

Howard Harrison is a graduate of Sydney University, receiving the BSc in 1951, the BE in 1953, the MEngSc in 1957 and the PhD in 1965. After graduation he joined the staff of the Building Surveyors Department of the City Council of Sydney but left in 1954 to join the School of Civil Engineering where he is now an Associate Professor. Teaching and research interest have been in the area of structural theory and analysis and the application of computer methods. In 1964–5 he was awarded a Fulbright Grant and spent a year as Visiting Professor at Lehigh University. In 1972 he joined the staff of Manchester University and taught in the Simon Engineering Laboratory. He has received two awards of the Institution of Engineers, Australia for outstanding publications: the R. W. Chapman Medal was awarded in 1960 and the Institution Award in 1967.